PRAEGER INTRODUCTORY GEOGRAPHIES

East-Central Europe

Praeger Introductory Geographies

FRANCE
E. Estyn Evans

ITALY
J. P. Cole

SPAIN
W. B. Fisher and H. Bowen-Jones

HUMAN GEOGRAPHY
Emrys Jones

EAST-CENTRAL EUROPE

An Introductory Geography

R.H. OSBORNE

FREDERICK A. PRAEGER, *Publishers*

New York · Washington

BOOKS THAT MATTER

Published in the United States of America
in 1967 by Frederick A. Praeger, Inc., Publishers
111 Fourth Avenue, New York, N.Y. 10003

Issued by Chatto & Windus, London, as
*East-Central Europe: A Geographical
Introduction to Seven Socialist States*

Library of Congress Catalog Card Number: 67-21456

Printed in the United States of America

FOREWORD

To the west of the Soviet Union over 120 million people live in eight
Socialist states that stretch from the Baltic Sea in the north to the
Adriatic and Black Seas in the south and whose destiny since the Second
World War has to a large extent been decided, directly or indirectly, by
the Soviet Union. One is here excluded from consideration: East Germany
(the 'German Democratic Republic') has already been dealt with in the
volume on 'Germany' in this series. The other seven countries, with a
total population of about 104 millions (1965), are Albania, Bulgaria,
Czechoslovakia, Hungary, Jugoslavia, Poland and Rumania.

This book has been written for those whose knowledge of these
countries is only very slight. Throughout I have tried to restrict myself to
essentials, yet at the same time to present an adequate range of facts.
I have written primarily for teachers and students of geography, but I
hope at the same time that this book may be of use to others, including
businessmen and enquiring tourists.

No apology is made for giving attention to the historical and political
background of each country: geographers often tend to forget that there
is more to the 'personality' of a country than the sum-total of the landscape manifestations of its natural phenomena and human activities.
Apart from the two introductory chapters, which range over a number
of general topics, I have thought it best to deal with each country as a
separate entity. Despite a considerable degree of integration with each
other and with the Soviet Union (Albania and Jugoslavia excepted) these
seven sovereign states still remain very distinct economic and social
organisms that continue to carry the stamp of their own history and
culture.

Within each chapter I have followed the same sequence of topics and,
I trust, have treated them in more or less the same depth for each country.
At times this proved a tedious discipline, but it is hoped that this
standardized approach may be of value. In general my emphasis has been
on the human geography of each country, rather than the physical. As
regards the latter I have been concerned less with processes than with
the factual details of the physiographic 'layout'–the theatrical stage and
its 'props', within the context of which the human drama takes place.
At times, of course, the latter bears no relationship to the physical

setting. On the other hand, I hope that where environment and man do interact that I have made this clear.

In considering the physiography of each country I have tried to arrive at a system of regions that is acceptable, as a first approximation, to the physical geographer, and one that is, at the same time, not too detailed for the human geographer. This proved one of the more difficult tasks that confronted me. In certain instances I have taken the liberty of introducing my own ideas of regional sub-divisions, but more usually what is presented is an adaptation from several sources. In the interests of greater simplicity I have often translated geographical names where appropriate, but the precise renderings are open to discussion in some instances. The maps of land-use regions also presented some difficulty and they must be regarded as no more than highly-generalized versions of much more complex patterns of surface-cover. Needless to say, a good library atlas should be consulted throughout by the reader.

This book would never have been possible had I not received some financial assistance at various times from the Universities of Edinburgh and Nottingham towards the cost of visiting the countries concerned. I am particularly grateful to the University of Edinburgh for giving me a term's leave of absence and a generous travel grant in the autumn of 1958 and to Professor J. Wreford Watson for his support. On that occasion I also remember with special gratitude the hospitality of the Geographical Institutes of the Polish Academy of Sciences and of the Rumanian Academy. I am also indebted to the British Council for sponsoring a four-week visit in 1962 and to the corresponding authorities who were my hosts.

It would be impossible for me to try to list all the many academic colleagues who made me welcome during visits of varying length and character and who offered their time to accompany me in the field or to discuss the geography of their countries with me. For all of them, of whatever rank, I shall always retain feelings of gratitude and friendship. My special thanks are due to those who agreed to give me their comments on the geographical section of my chapter dealing with their own country. Since some of them prefer to remain anonymous I have decided to mention no names. It must be stressed that the account of the historical background of each country is entirely my own. In addition I must place on record my debt to the many Esperanto speakers, whose help with mundane details of travel and accommodation eased my path on a number of occasions in several of the countries concerned. Their ready companionship also enlivened many hours and, coming from all walks of life, they greatly deepened my understanding of their homelands.

During the preparation of this book I have received encouragement from Professor K. C. Edwards and generous advice from a number of Nottingham colleagues, both in the Department of Geography and in several other Departments. Dr C. A. M. King, in particular, kindly read through all the sections on physical geography and drew attention to some slips and obscurities. Mr E. M. Bridges of University College, Swansea, commented on soils. Several friends and acquaintances from the countries concerned helped with the pronunciation of place-names. Stephen de Winter assisted with Albanian. I am also indebted to the United Nations Organization for providing translations of the Universal Declaration of Human Rights, to the Meteorological Office for supplying climatic data on Hungary and to Mr P. Geelan of the Permanent Committee on Geographical Names for advice on several points. Finally I wish to thank those who helped in the physical preparation of maps and text—Mr K. Bowler, of the Department of Geography of the University of Nottingham, for patient cartographical assistance, and Mrs E. O. Wigginton and my sister, Mrs Constance West, for typing a succession of drafts that bristled with unfamiliar names.

In a broadcast to the nation in September 1938, Mr Neville Chamberlain, the British Prime Minister, referred to the Sudetenland dispute in Czechoslovakia as 'a quarrel between people of whom we know nothing'. I hope that this book may do something to help English-speaking readers to achieve a greater knowledge not only of Czechoslovakia but also of the other Socialist countries of East-Central Europe. If a dedication is needed let it be to all these 'people of whom we know nothing'—and about whom and their countries we ought to know so very much more.

Nottingham   R. H. O.

CONTENTS

Foreword   *page* 5

Chapter

1 THE PEOPLES
The Three Europes   17
The Cultural Background   20
Language and Religion   24
The Road to Socialism   30

2 THE GEOGRAPHICAL BACKGROUND
Modern Changes in Political Geography   38
Physical Geography   51
Economic Geography   56
Population and Urbanization   63
Transport and Trade   67

3 ALBANIA
Introduction   71
Historical Background   73
The Land   77
Climate and Soils   80
Land-Use and Farming   82
Industry and Mining   84
Distribution of Population and Chief Cities   86
Transport and Trade   88

4 BULGARIA
Introduction   91
Historical Background   93
The Land   98
Climate and Soils   103
Land-Use and Farming   104
Industry and Mining   107
Distribution of Population and Chief Cities   111
Transport and Trade   115

5 CZECHOSLOVAKIA

Introduction   *page* 118
Historical Background   120
The Land   129
Climate and Soils   137
Land-Use and Farming   139
Industry and Mining   143
Distribution of Population and Chief Cities   150
Transport and Trade   154

6 HUNGARY

Introduction   157
Historical Background   159
The Land   164
Climate and Soils   168
Land-Use and Farming   170
Industry and Mining   172
Distribution of Population and Chief Cities   177
Transport and Trade   182

7 JUGOSLAVIA

Introduction   184
Historical Background   189
The Land   197
Climate and Soils   205
Land-Use and Farming   207
Industry and Mining   210
Distribution of Population and Chief Cities   216
Transport and Trade   223

8 POLAND

Introduction   227
Historical Background   230
The Land   238
Climate and Soils   244
Land-Use and Farming   246
Industry and Mining   249
Distribution of Population and Chief Cities   263
Transport and Trade   278

9 RUMANIA

Introduction	*page* 283
Historical Background	288
The Land	294
Climate and Soils	300
Land-Use and Farming	302
Industry and Mining	305
Distribution of Population and Chief Cities	310
Transport and Trade	317

Appendices

1 *The Languages of East-Central Europe*	322
2 *Guide to the Pronunciation of Geographical Names*	325
3 *Statistical Tables*	345
4 *Bibliography*	366

Index	380

MAPS

Chapter 2 THE GEOGRAPHICAL BACKGROUND

1 International boundaries in East-Central Europe, 1914 (*a*)
and 1938 (*b*)   *page* 39

2 International boundaries in East-Central Europe, 1941/2 (*a*)   46
and post-1945 (*b*)

Chapter 3 ALBANIA

3 Relief of Albania   78

4 Generalized physiographic regions (A) and drainage (B) of
Albania   79

5 Generalized land-use regions (A), mineral exploitation (B),
and distribution of chief cities and towns (C) in Albania   83

Chapter 4 BULGARIA

6 Relief of Bulgaria   99

7 Generalized physiographic regions of Bulgaria   100

8 Drainage of Bulgaria   100

9 Generalized land-use regions of Bulgaria   105

10 Mineral exploitation in Bulgaria   109

11 Distribution of chief cities and towns in Bulgaria   112

12 Sofia   113

Chapter 5 CZECHOSLOVAKIA

13 Dissolution of Czechoslovakia, 1938–9   126

14 Relief of Czechoslovakia   130

15 Generalized physiographic regions of Czechoslovakia   132

16 Drainage of Czechoslovakia   134

17 Generalized land-use regions of Czechoslovakia   140

18 Mineral exploitation in Czechoslovakia   143

19 Distribution of chief cities and towns in Czechoslovakia   151

20 Prague   152

Chapter 6 HUNGARY

21 Hungary before and after the First World War   158

22 Relief of Hungary *page* 165
23 Generalized physiographic regions of Hungary 165
24 Drainage of Hungary 166
25 Generalized land-use regions of Hungary 170
26 Mineral exploitation in Hungary 173
27 Distribution of chief cities and towns in Hungary 178
28 Budapest 179

Chapter 7 JUGOSLAVIA

29 Constituent republics of Jugoslavia (*a*) and territorial growth
of Serbia, Montenegro and Jugoslavia (*b*) 187
30 Relief of Jugoslavia 198
31 Generalized physiographic regions of Jugoslavia 200
32 Drainage of Jugoslavia 202
33 Generalized land-use regions of Jugoslavia 208
34 Mineral exploitation in Jugoslavia 212
35 Distribution of chief cities and towns in Jugoslavia 218
36 Belgrade 219

Chapter 8 POLAND

37 Changes in the boundaries of Poland–the Partitions, 1772–
1795 (*a*) and the 'Congress' Kingdom, 1815 (*b*) 228
38 Changes in the boundaries of Poland–after First World War
(*a*) and after Second World War (*b*) 229
39 Relief of Poland 239
40 Generalized physiographic regions of Poland (and regional
names) 240
41 Drainage of Poland 241
42 Generalized land-use regions of Poland 246
43 Mineral exploitation in Poland 251
44 The Upper Silesian–Ostrava coal-basin (geological structure) 252
45 The Upper Silesian industrial district: Pre-Tertiary geology,
settlement and communications 253
46 Distribution of chief cities and towns in Poland 265
47 Warsaw 266

Chapter 9 RUMANIA

48 Changes in the boundaries of Rumania since 1913 284
49 Relief of Rumania 294
50 Generalized physiographic regions of Rumania 295

51 Drainage of Rumania   *page* 296
52 Generalized land-use regions of Rumania   302
53 Mineral exploitation in Rumania   306
54 Distribution of chief cities and towns in Rumania   311
55 Bucharest   312

TABLES

1 The Three Europes   19
2 Languages and religions in East-Central Europe   25
3 Climatic statistics–Albania   81
4 Climatic statistics–Bulgaria   104
5 Climatic statistics–Czechoslovakia   138
6 Climatic statistics–Hungary   169
7 Climatic statistics–Jugoslavia   207
8 Climatic statistics–Poland   245
9 Polish coal output   257
10 Foreign trade of Poland, 1964   281
11 Climatic statistics–Rumania   300

Chapter 1

THE PEOPLES

The Three Europes

Since 1917, the year of the 'Bolshevik' or 'Great October' Revolution in Russia, Europe has been divided ideologically into Communist and non-Communist zones that are basically antipathetic to each other. The Communist zone increased territorially in the years 1944–8, largely as a result of the victory of the Union of Soviet Socialist Republics over Nazi Germany. This led to the establishment of regimes favourable to the Soviet Union in the countries of East-Central Europe, which had all either been occupied by, or allied with, Germany. The way was then open for the rapid conversion of their economic and political systems to the Soviet model. Today, however, it is increasingly realistic to speak of *three* Europes rather than two, in view of the gradual reassertion of national identity exhibited in varying ways and in varying degrees by the countries in question. They thus constitute a distinctive group lying between the Soviet Union and the rest of Europe.

In the east of the continent is the European part of the Soviet Union, populated chiefly by Russians. Between the Russians and the western boundary of the Soviet Union there are other national groups, however, including the Estonians, Latvians, Lithuanians, Byelorussians, Ukrainians and Moldavians (basically Rumanians). Of these the Ukrainians are by far the most numerous. In area the European part of the Soviet Union accounts for more than half of Europe, but in terms of population for under 30% (see Table 1). From the Soviet point of view the conventional European boundary of the Urals is, admittedly, of little significance. This is because for over three centuries Russian settlement has been expanding eastwards into Siberia. Indeed, the colonization of Soviet Asia is still proceeding. The Ural range is, in any case, scarcely a formidable physical barrier and the richness of its mineral resources has made it an important north–south zone of urban and industrial development that straddles the two continents.

To the west of the minority peoples of the European Soviet Union, each with their own constituent republics, are the eight states that may conveniently be termed Communist or Socialist East-Central Europe. These are Albania, Bulgaria, Czechoslovakia, East Germany (the 'German Democratic Republic', corresponding to the post-war Soviet zone

17

of occupation), Hungary, Jugoslavia,* Poland and Rumania.† They exhibit important differences in language, culture and level of economic development and there are also variations in climate and terrain. They also differ in geographical extent and population size: Poland has well over 30 million inhabitants, while Albania has under 2. In spite of basic similarities in their Socialist systems many pre-existing differences remain in their human and economic geography and, moreover, the Russian prototype of Socialism that each set out to imitate (usually with inadequate regard for local conditions) has subsequently undergone modification. Jugoslavia was expelled from the Soviet bloc as early as 1948 and thereafter the country developed its own form of Socialism that in many respects differed greatly from practice in the Soviet Union. At the same time a 'non-aligned' path was followed in foreign affairs. The small state of Albania, a Jugoslav protégé between 1944 and 1948, after the withdrawal of the occupying Italian and German forces, remained loyal to Moscow in 1948, but by the early 1960s had again changed protectors and had become a European mouthpiece of China in her growing ideological differences with the Soviet Union.

After 1956 Poland was allowed by the Soviet Union to follow a 'Polish road to Socialism', and Hungary eventually achieved certain beneficial changes despite a disastrous national rising in the same year. Changes have appeared more recently in other countries, partly owing to a resurgence of national feeling and partly owing to the influence of developments in the Soviet Union itself. The use of the term 'satellites' for these states has thus become rather less appropriate than formerly. The six states other than Albania and Jugoslavia nevertheless retain close ties, both military and economic, with the Soviet Union. The Warsaw Treaty of 1955 is the formal expression of their military alliance, while the Council for Mutual Economic Assistance or Aid ('Comecon' or 'CMEA'), set up in 1949, co-ordinates economic relationships. Taken together the eight states account for nearly an eighth of Europe's area and for a fifth of its population (Table 1).

The rest of Europe, often referred to as 'Western Europe' (although it includes countries like Greece and Finland, which both lie well to the

* The government of the country uses the name 'Yugoslavia' in its English-language publications, as also does the United Nations Organization. The present author (in common with many others) prefers the form 'Jugoslavia', which is closer to the country's own name for itself.

† Until 1965 the government of the country used the name 'Rumania' in its English-language publications. Since then it has favoured the form 'Romania', which is the spelling used in the country itself (although 'Rominia' was previously used for a time). The change in practice occurred too late for alteration in this book. It may be noted that 'Romania' was, in any case, already in use by the United Nations and many authors.

TABLE 1

THE THREE EUROPES

Area and population (1963)

	Population (in millions)	Percentage	Area (thousand square km)	Area (thousand square miles)	Percentage
Socialist East-Central Europe	119·6	20	1,274	492	12
European Soviet Union	171·8	28	5,571	2,151	53
Rest of Europe	319·3	52	3,679	1,420	35
Europe	*610·7*	*100*	*10,524*	*4,063*	*100*

east), consists of twenty-four states (including eight very small ones) and Turkey-in-Europe. Their combined area is over one-third of that of Europe, but they contain over one-half of the continent's population. These countries also exhibit some important differences. There are great variations in their density of population and degree of industrialization, for instance. There are also significant variations in their economic and political systems and social structures, despite the unqualified epithet of 'capitalist' that is conferred on them by the Soviet Union and the other Socialist states. However, parliamentary democracy, related to a multi-party system, is the usual form of government, and from the economic point of view private enterprise is dominant, although there are varying degrees of government planning. Some countries have large state-owned sectors of the economy and some have well-developed co-operative movements.

Militarily most of the states of 'Western Europe' belong to the North Atlantic Treaty Organization, set up in 1949. Spain is linked to it indirectly, and a few countries are officially neutral, such as Austria, Finland, Sweden and Switzerland. Economically the West European countries have an association for economic collaboration in the Organization for Economic Co-operation and Development (OECD),* the fore-runner of which was the Organization for European Economic Co-operation, initially set up to administer post-war American aid. Also important, however, are the two trading associations–the 'Common Market' (European Economic Community, i.e. EEC) and 'EFTA' (European Free Trade Association), which are both working towards the gradual elimination of tariff barriers and other hindrances to international trade amongst their member-states. Within the countries of the Common Market, where eventual economic integration is the goal, the European Coal and Steel Community (ECSC) plays an important role.

* Canada, Japan and the U.S.A. are also members.

At this point it is perhaps necessary to defend the use of the term 'East-Central Europe' for the eight states mentioned above. The use of the term 'Eastern Europe', which is often popularly used for this whole group, has the unfortunate effect of implicitly excluding the Russians (and other associated national groups) from Europe. Although the Soviet Union extends into Asia, where millions of Russians are now resident, it is nevertheless true that the Russians are a European people and that over 90 millions of them, together with some 35 million Ukrainians, as well as other smaller nationalities, live within the conventional boundaries of Europe. The term 'Eastern Europe' ought thus to include the European part of the Soviet Union, but perhaps not all of the eight states, however.

'Central Europe' or 'Middle Europe' was more useful as a geographical term before the Second World War. There were then less profound differences in economic and political philosophy between these eight countries and the rest of Europe outside the Soviet Union. It was then appropriate to place Austria, Switzerland and perhaps the whole of Germany in the same group as, say, Czechoslovakia and Hungary, even though the term 'Central Europe' might be rather imprecise in geographical terms. Today the term 'East-Central Europe' may be taken as defining those more easterly countries of Central Europe and those of the Balkans that came under Soviet influence at the end of the Second World War and where an essentially Russian type of Socialism has been installed. The addition of the adjective 'Socialist' lends further precision to this admittedly makeshift geographical definition. It is realized, of course, that the type of Socialism adopted, even in its much modified Jugoslav form, has features that are repugnant to many Socialists elsewhere in the world.

The Cultural Background

The fact that Europe is ideologically divided should not blind us to the fact that, broadly speaking, a common European civilization, with a common cultural heritage, stretches from the Atlantic to beyond the Urals. European civilization may be said to have drawn its inspiration from the Classical world of Greece and Rome – an influence which was to be powerfully re-emphasized by the Renaissance – from the Christian Churches, and from the West European political revolutions of the 17th, 18th and 19th centuries. These latter were chiefly concerned with the liberties of the person and with parliamentary constitutionalism. Admittedly Russia never experienced the direct impact of the Renaissance, largely owing to her geographical remoteness, nor did Rumania and the Balkans (conventionally defined as the area south of the Kupa–Sava–Danube line), owing to the Turkish occupation. But in all these areas the

Orthodox Church and its Byzantine culture were civilizing influences that were successful in withstanding periods of infidel rule by the Mongols (Tatars) in Russia and by the Turks in the Balkans. Nor did West European democracy have a chance to take root in Russia, owing to the resistance of the Tsarist regime. On the other hand she eagerly absorbed western culture and technology from the time of Peter the Great onwards, and by the 19th century was making her own contributions in these fields.

The Balkans at the time of the Turkish invasion, in the latter part of the 14th century, do not seem to have been substantially inferior to Western Europe as regards their general level of cultural and economic development: the 'backwardness' of the Balkans is, in fact, a relatively new phenomenon in their long history. French cultural and revolutionary influences were felt in Rumania early in the 19th century, before the final overthrow of Turkish suzerainty. Serbia and Bulgaria were also receptive to Western influences and, like Rumania, were eager, after their liberation, to make up for centuries of isolation from the rest of Europe. In some respects the constitutional monarchies acquired by these three countries were surprisingly advanced for their time–on paper, if not always in practice.

The cultural development of the Poles and of the peoples of the Habsburg Empire followed rather different paths from those of the nations of south-east Europe. Poland and Hungary were two of the most important states of medieval Europe. Both were bastions of the Roman Catholic Church and acted as barriers against intruders from the east; indeed the West European countries owe much to the shield that they provided. Both Hungary and Poland were devastated by Tatar invasions in the 13th century. Hungary disintegrated after an unsuccessful attempt to hold back the Turks in the 16th century, though the Poles, under King John Sobieski, were instrumental in saving Vienna from the Turks in 1683–a defeat that heralded the beginning of the Turkish withdrawal from Central Europe. In Poland a form of parliamentary government, based on the large class of 'gentry', became strongly entrenched, and it may be claimed that it was the almost anarchic liberalism of late 18th-century Poland that paved the way for its downfall at the hands of its three better-organized, but autocratic neighbours of Austria, Prussia and Russia. Hungary, although liberated from the Turks by Habsburg forces at the end of the 17th century, did not regain its freedom from ensuing Austrian rule until 1867. Thereafter the assertion of Magyar nationalism over the minorities in Hungary encouraged their secession in 1918. Independent Poland, re-emerging in 1918, was also unwise in the handling of her minorities, particularly the Ukrainians, in the inter-war period. The tragedy of both countries was that they regained their independence at a time when their own minorities were themselves anxious for political rights.

The Czech Lands, constituting the Kingdom of Bohemia, lost their independence to the Habsburgs in 1620. Like Poland and Hungary, Bohemia had played a significant part in the cultural development of medieval Europe. It had also been noted for the emergence of an early form of Protestantism, as expressed in the Hussite movement. The consolidation of Habsburg rule robbed Bohemia of her native aristocracy and stifled her Protestantism. To the south of Austria and Hungary were Slovenia and Croatia. The Slovene lands early became marcher territories of the Holy Roman Empire, while Croatia eventually became an appendage of the Hungarian Kingdom, although never losing its identity. Both Slovenia and Croatia were deeply affected by the setting up by Napoleon of his Illyrian Provinces, which had the result of stimulating the South Slav movement. Despite its suppression of nationalism the positive aspects of the Habsburg Empire should not be overlooked. Stretching from Lwów and Kraków in the north to the Adriatic coast in the south, and from Prague in the west to Braşov in the east, it undoubtedly provided a framework within which very considerable economic and cultural progress was made. Moreover, representative government had, by 1914, made great headway despite a failure to acknowledge the rights to full national expression of certain of the minorities, particularly those of Hungary.

In all countries of East-Central Europe the 19th and early 20th centuries were not only an era of struggle for the recovery of national independence in the political sense, whether from the Turk, the Habsburg Empire or, as in the case of Poland, from three rulers, but also of a rediscovery and renewal of submerged or stagnant national cultures. Increasing literacy, rising living standards and improved means of transport and communications aided these trends, which expressed themselves in scholarly historical research, the standardization of the various languages and creative efforts in the arts that often drew inspiration from national themes. While literary achievements often had a rather limited national appeal, musical endeavour frequently found a wider public, even when coloured by national sentiment or based on national source-material. The names of Chopin, Dvořák, Smetana and Liszt immediately spring to mind in this context. In the 20th century further contributions have been made (e.g. Bartók and Kodály in Hungary or Enescu in Rumania).

The gaining of independence was in some instances marred by excessive nationalism and the abuse of constitutional government. Later, in the 1930s, Fascist movements gained some measure of favour even before Nazi Germany obtained physical control of the countries of East-Central Europe in the years 1938–41. Scarcely had these influences been vanquished than Marxism insinuated itself with the active encouragement of its chief protagonist, the victorious Soviet Union, and with varying degrees of internal support. In addition to the carrying out of a radical transformation of economy and society a new philosophy was thus imposed upon East-Central Europe.

In spite of the great changes in economic, political and social life resulting from the Russian Revolution of 1917 and from the introduction in East-Central Europe of new regimes modelled on those of the Soviet Union in the years 1944–8, it is important to remember that the cultural unity of Europe has not been shattered, even though certain barriers have been erected against the free flow of ideas from abroad and the internal spreading of views that do not meet with official approval. Needless to say, censorship is not peculiar to Socialist regimes, nor are such features as political indoctrination and the re-writing of history that so often accompany it. The development of mass education in the Soviet Union since the Revolution and the broadening of educational opportunity in East-Central Europe since the Second World War have, indeed, tended to lead to a reinforcing, rather than the reverse, of the sense of a common European heritage.

Undoubtedly one of the most serious cultural impacts of Marxism is on religion. As a state-sponsored atheistic philosophy it has reduced the liberties of the often once powerful Churches and deliberately sought to undermine their influence, especially in educational and social matters. Some prominent Church leaders were imprisoned for refusing to submit to the government. On the other hand, the State, having confiscated Church property, has usually taken over some responsibility for the salaries of priests and for the upkeep of the fabric of many churches (in their capacity as 'national monuments'). The building of new churches is often impossible, however. In some countries splinter groups of the clergy have collaborated actively with the government, in spite of the fact that the long-term elimination of religious activities is, in effect, official policy.

In view of the many vicissitudes experienced by the countries of East-Central Europe it is difficult not to be struck by their resilience. After a period of suppression by Stalin and his local imitators in the late 1940s and early 1950s national feeling has slowly and sometimes painfully found ways of reasserting itself, although the pace and character of change have differed widely from country to country. At the same time contacts have been cautiously re-established with the rest of the European family.

Language and Religion

The gradual recovery of national identity in East-Central Europe since the late 1950s makes it more than ever necessary to appreciate the distinctive characteristics of each of the nations concerned. Thus linguistic and religious differences (Table 2 and Appendix A) are still of great importance. Seven of the eight countries are considered in this book, East Germany being excluded. Of the seven countries four (Bulgaria, Czechoslovakia, Jugoslavia and Poland) speak languages belonging to the Slavonic group (which also includes Russian, Ukrainian and Byelorussian), while one (Rumania) speaks a Romance (Latin) tongue and one (Hungary) a language of the Finno-Ugrian group. Albanian is apparently descended from the ancient Illyrian tongue. Polish, Czech and Slovak belong to the western branch of the Slavonic languages. Czech and Slovak are very closely related languages that are mutually intelligible, while both have strong affinities with Polish. All three languages are written in the Roman alphabet, although diacritical marks abound.

South Slavonic languages are spoken in Jugoslavia and Bulgaria. In Jugoslavia over 70% of the population speak Serbo-Croat, the common language of the two most numerous peoples. Despite 19th-century standardization there still remain certain differences of pronunciation and vocabulary, as well as a number of distinct dialects, but the most important difference is that the language is written in the Roman alphabet by the Croats and in the Cyrillic by the Serbs. There are two other Slavonic languages spoken in Jugoslavia—Macedonian and Slovene—both of which are intelligible, with some effort, to Serbs and Croats. Macedonian, regarded until recently as a dialect of either Serb or Bulgarian (to which it is closer), is now considered to be a separate language. Bulgarian, like Serb and Macedonian, is also written in the Cyrillic script and, although purified since the 19th century, it still exhibits some Turkish influences. Bulgarian and Macedonian are interesting among the Slavonic languages in that, unlike the others, they do not have case-endings for nouns and also possess a definite article (which, however, is joined on at the end of the noun or its qualifying adjective).

Rumanian, as its name implies, is, like French, Italian, Spanish or Portuguese, a language based on the Latin of the Roman Empire, and the precise circumstances of its survival in what was one of the frontier districts still excites the interest of scholars. Through time it has been greatly affected by Slavonic and other influences, however. Although a large part of the vocabulary of Rumanian has some resemblance to Italian the vowels are less 'pure' and include many diphthongs and triphthongs. (For this reason Rumanians have less difficulty than many

TABLE 2

LANGUAGES AND RELIGIONS IN EAST-CENTRAL EUROPE

Country	Dominant language	Alphabet	Dominant traditional religion	More important minorities (N.B. All countries have Gypsies in addition)
Albania	Albanian, i.e. Shqip	Roman	Mohammedan. Also Orthodox and R.C.	—
Bulgaria	Bulgarian (Slavonic)	Cyrillic	Orthodox	Turks (Mohammedan)
Czecho-slovakia	Czech and Slovak (Slavonic)	Roman	Roman Catholic	Hungarians, Germans. Also Poles, Ukrainians
Hungary	Hungarian, i.e. Magyar (Finno-Ugrian)	Roman	Roman Catholic	Germans
Jugoslavia	(a) Serbo-Croat ⎫ (b) Slovene ⎬ (Slavonic) (c) Macedonian ⎭	Roman (NW. half) Cyrillic (SE. half)	(a) Orthodox (Serbia proper, Montenegro, Macedonia) (b) Catholic (Slovenia, Croatia) (c) Catholic and Orthodox (Vojvodina area of Serbia) (d) Mohammedan (Kosmet area of Serbia) (e) Mohammedan, Catholic, Orthodox (Bosnia–Hercegovina)	Albanians (chiefly Mohammedan), Hungarians, Turks (Mohammedan). Also Slovaks, Bulgarians, Rumanians
Poland	Polish (Slavonic)	Roman	Roman Catholic	Byelorussians, Ukrainians
Rumania	Rumanian (Romance, with Slavonic influences)	Roman	Orthodox	Hungarians, Germans. Also Jews, Ukrainians

Europeans in reproducing English vowel sounds.) Rumanian is written in the Roman alphabet, but a Cyrillic script was also used until the middle of the 19th century.

Shqip, the language of the Albanians, is a much-modified descendant of the Indo-European tongues spoken in the Balkans before the Roman invasion, probably Illyrian. It shows Latin, Slavonic, Greek and Turkish influences and uses a Roman alphabet.

Magyar, the language of Hungary, is a member of the Finno-Ugrian group, which also includes, but at a very great remove, Finnish and Estonian. It is therefore quite different in vocabulary and structure from the Germanic, Romance and Slavonic languages, which all form part of the Indo-European family. Like Finnish it is characterized by a great frequency of lengthy agglutinative (compound) words. This feature, combined with a stress on the first syllable, gives it a ponderous rhythm. The Roman alphabet is used.

Mention must also be made of the larger of the minority languages. Tens of thousands of German speakers still live in Czechoslovakia and Hungary, despite the emigration and evictions occurring at the end of the last war, while in Rumania the figure approaches half a million. In Jugoslavia several thousand Italian speakers live in those areas annexed from Italy at the end of the last war. In Bulgaria and Macedonia there are several hundred thousand Turks, whose language, now written in the Roman alphabet, lies outside the Indo-European family. Finally, there are the gypsies of East-Central Europe, whose numbers may possibly approach one million and whose rate of natural increase is high. Some are nomadic, but most are sedentary. Even where this is the case they tend to maintain a self-imposed segregation in spite of government efforts to improve their conditions. They have often preserved their own dialects, which are basically Indo-European, in view of the presumed migration of their ancestors centuries ago from the northern part of the Indian sub-continent.

While language may be the most important factor in national consciousness, religious allegiance is also of significance. Poland, Czechoslovakia, Hungary, and Slovenia and Croatia in Jugoslavia, are, at least nominally, predominantly Roman Catholic. Even before the onslaught of Marxism in the last twenty years the degree of fervour tended to vary, however, being least in Bohemia, possibly owing to greater industrialization and possibly owing to the fact that the Roman Catholic Church had in the past been the ally of the Habsburgs in suppressing Protestantism, which had been deeply rooted in the 17th century before the country lost its independence. In Hungary Calvinism flourished in the north-east and in Transylvania when these areas enjoyed autonomy under the Turks in the 16th and 17th centuries. Even after the expulsion of the Turks the Habsburg Counter-Reformation could not extinguish these Protestant strongholds in the heart of Central Europe.

In Bulgaria, Rumania, and Serbia and Macedonia in Jugoslavia the Byzantine version of Christianity is dominant in the form of the 'Orthodox' Churches. During the middle ages there were occasions when Rome attempted their absorption. Later, in the 16th and 17th centuries, especially in areas under Polish and Austrian rule, special arrangements were made for Orthodox Churches, chiefly in the Ukraine and Transylvania, to acknowledge the supremacy of the Pope while retaining their own rite. In this way the 'Greek Catholic' or 'Uniate' Churches came into being. Since 1945 they have been reabsorbed by their national Orthodox Churches. In general the Orthodox Churches have been less successful than the Catholic Church in holding the allegiance of the educated classes in modern times. The Orthodox Churches often seem to outsiders to lack a positive evangelical function and to be content with a narrow ritualism. At the same time they traditionally adopt a passive attitude towards the State. Nevertheless in the 19th century the lesser clergy particularly were often active in the cause of national liberation. On the other hand Catholicism has never been willing to surrender its sovereignty to temporal authorities and has associated itself much more actively with the political, social and even scientific life of the nations concerned. Indeed, in some of them it can be argued that Catholic interests were too much involved in politics. As a result the anti-religious efforts of Marxism have met much tougher resistance in the Catholic countries than in the Orthodox ones. The Protestant communities have usually been too small to effect much resistance and in some instances pre-existing radical and anti-Catholic sentiments have made them more amenable to acceptance of the post-war regimes. In the Balkans Mohammedanism survives amongst the Albanians (including those of Serbia), the Turkish minorities of Bulgaria and Macedonia and also amongst some of the Jugoslavs of Bosnia–Hercegovina.

Common ties of language or religion have not always promoted automatic friendship between the peoples of East-Central Europe. Relations between Poles and Czechs have never been particularly cordial and have at times been acrimonious, especially in relation to their dispute over the Cieszyn (Těšín) area. There are also psychological differences. An extreme Czech view of the Poles would be to describe them as a nation of reckless cavaliers who have been imbued with the ethos of their now vanished aristocratic and military elite. The Pole may often scorn the Czech as materialistic and spineless. The Czech reaction to distasteful authority is less overt, however, than that of the Pole. The calculated ingenuousness

of Hašek's very astute 'Good Soldier Schweik' (a Czech in the Habsburg
Army at the time of the First World War) is a trait that is not yet dead.
Moreover, events since 1939 have taught the Poles a sense of caution and
realism that was sometimes lacking in the past. Between the Czechs and
the Slovaks there often exists a mutual antipathy. The Slovaks broke
away in 1939 after only twenty years of union and although they
have been reunited since 1945 relationships between the two have not
always been easy. The Czechs are a mature nation with a long history,
while the national consciousness of the Slovaks has ripened only in
modern times after their release from a thousand years of Hungarian
rule.

The Hungarians present some points of similarity to the Poles despite
a difference in language. Both countries were great states in the middle
ages, periodically sharing the same ruler or dynasty, both defended
Europe against the Tatars and the Turks, both saw their independence
crushed at various times by the Russians, both once held sway over large
areas inhabited by other peoples, and both are proud nations that have
been humbled in modern times after a brief, and admittedly unrealistic,
attempt to relive their former grandeur. Such a long-standing friendship
between two countries is, in fact, rather an unusual phenomenon for
East-Central Europe, and it was further sealed by feelings of solidarity
in the autumn of 1956 when both nations challenged the regimes in
power. For the Slovaks, Rumanians, Croats and Serbs the Hungarians
appear in a different light, however, as a master-race which formerly
exercised rule over non-Magyar lands fringing the Pannonian (Hungarian)
Basin. The understandable resistance of Magyar minorities to incorporation in break-away territories after 1918 exacerbated bad feeling. For
their part the Rumanians of Transylvania were only too eager after 1918
to exert authority over the former ruling Hungarian minority, and the
temporary retrocession of northern Transylvania to Hungary in 1941–4
revived a hostility that has not yet been entirely extinguished.

Between the two World Wars Rumania enjoyed fairly close relationships with Poland, if only because both contained territories in the east
to which the Soviet Union had some claim. The Rumanians formerly had
a rather dubious reputation in the eyes of other countries, their ruling
classes being regarded as effete and corrupt, not without some justification. There is little evidence that these characteristics were also typical
of the nation as a whole, however. Since the gaining of Rumanian independence a hundred years ago Rumanian nationalism has leaned for
some of its inspiration on the Roman antecedents of the people and this
feature, combined with the linguistic differences between the Rumanians
and the Magyars to the west and the Slavs to the north and the south,

has led at times to spurious claims of cultural superiority. Like their old enemies, the Magyars, the Rumanians have no sentimental ties of language with Russia and the Slavonic world, although it is true that they belong historically to Byzantine Christendom.

Within Jugoslavia linguistic affinities do not always transcend religious and other cultural differences. The Slovenes, in the far north-west, despite having thrown in their lot with the Croats and the Serbs in 1918, are in temperament more akin to their former rulers, the neighbouring Austrians, than to their fellow South Slavs in, say, Bosnia or Macedonia. Between the Catholic Croats and the Orthodox Serbs, with their quite separate historical experience, tensions are still sometimes discernible, while in Bosnia–Hercegovina the Mohammedan Jugoslavs still regard themselves as separate from their Christian compatriots. Such feelings have been partially mollified by the present federal structure of the country, but a further cause of internal friction arises from the sacrifices required from the more-developed north to pay for economic progress in the less-developed south.

Between the Serbs and the Bulgars, until recently both largely peasant societies who also had much in common as regards their culture, there has been much enmity in the past, especially over the title to Macedonia. The Bulgars thus fought the Serbs in 1913, and also in both World Wars. In Albania, Bulgaria and the southern parts of Jugoslavia Turkish cultural influences were formerly strong, but have been largely eliminated, although certain residual effects are evident in such matters as food and music.

It will thus be seen that although the countries of East-Central Europe have been remoulded to a considerable extent in the image of the Soviet Union there remains a wide range of cultural and psychological differences. In many respects the closest affinities of the Poles, the Czechs, the Hungarians and the Slovenes lie with Western Europe rather than with either the Soviet Union or south-eastern Europe. Attitudes to the Soviet Union also vary. The Bulgarians and the Czechs have traditional feelings of friendship towards her. The Hungarians, Poles and Rumanians have painful memories of Russian interference and at times of armed suppression. Jugoslavia cannot easily forget the 'war of nerves' carried out against her after 1948. Albania has been hostile to her former protector, the Soviet Union, since the break between the two countries in 1961 (and strained relationships with neighbouring Greece and Jugoslavia have persisted for many years). In living standards there are also wide variations within East-Central Europe, although gaps are probably narrowing, both between countries and between urban and rural areas. Nevertheless, the Czech worker, while distinctly less well off than his north-west

European counterpart, probably enjoys a real income about twice as high as that of his opposite number in south-east Europe.

The Road to Socialism

Although the human organization of a country is not the immediate concern of the geographer it is, nevertheless, of considerable significance to him, not least because it affects certain aspects of economic and social geography, including geographical aspects of relationships with other countries. It is, therefore, necessary to know in outline how the countries of East-Central Europe came to have their present systems and what the characteristics of these systems are. As a preliminary it is also necessary to recapitulate in brief the development of European Socialism and especially its role in Russia.

Socialist philosophy in its modern form goes back to the early 19th century, where, in England at least, some of its exponents regarded Socialism as applied Christianity. This association is, however, a feature that is chiefly confined to Protestant countries of north-west Europe. More usually Socialism is regarded as inherently incompatible with religious belief. Most modern Socialists have been influenced to a varying degree by the writings of Karl Marx (d. 1883), who, with Friedrich Engels, issued the 'Communist Manifesto' in 1848. In 1864 Marx helped to form the International Workingmen's Association ('First International') and in 1867 he published the first volume of his great treatise, *Das Kapital*.

Inspired by the philosopher Hegel, Marx viewed the whole course of historical development as a 'dialectic', i.e. a series of contradictions and their resolution. In this context he considered that the organizational mode of production and exchange (particularly property relationships) determined the whole nature of society ('dialectical materialism'). The history of man is seen as the history of class struggles, in which feudalism gives way to capitalism (organized by, and in the interests of, the capitalists or 'bourgeoisie'), and this, in turn, is destined to be followed by the victory of the working class ('proletariat'). The prediction of such an outcome hinged to a large extent on Marx's economic theories, particularly the theory of 'surplus value', whereby the excess value of a commodity over and above the cost of labour expended on its production accrues not to the worker but to his exploiter, the capitalist. (For Marx, as for some other 19th-century economists, only human labour could create value.) In time the number of capitalists diminishes, but those remaining become increasingly powerful, while the proletariat grows in number and becomes increasingly impoverished. Finally the system breaks down owing to its inherent contradictions (including its tendency towards violent boom-and-slump fluctuations). Having seized power the proletariat will then socialize the means of production and exercise a 'dictatorship of the proletariat' in its own interests. Ultimately Socialism will be succeeded by Communism, when the State will 'wither away' and rewards will be 'from each according to his abilities, to each according to his need'.

Marx's analysis and his predictions were based largely on his study of industrial society in early and mid-Victorian Britain. In no mature industrial nation have Marx's predictions about a working-class revolution come to pass, however. The only instance that merits consideration at all is the consolidation of power by the Communists in February 1948, in Czechoslovakia, the most industrialized country of East-Central Europe, and even here special factors have to be taken into account. Where a Socialist or quasi-Socialist revolution has occurred in the world (whether spontaneous or externally induced) it has been in societies where capitalism was only feebly developed, and where, in fact, vestiges of feudalism sometimes survived, the leading examples being Imperial Russia in 1917 and China in the late 1940s.

The First International was eventually succeeded by the Second, which collapsed in 1914: nationalism amongst the working-class parties of the European countries proved stronger than international class solidarity. Before the First World War a distinction had already arisen between Socialist leaders as to what methods they considered the most appropriate for achieving their goal. Some believed in the gradual transformaion of society through constitutional means, while others, notably the *Bolshevik* wing of the Russian Socialists, led by 'Lenin' (Ulyanov), were in favour of violent revolutionary change. The term 'revisionist' came to be applied to the former by the latter, who obviously tended to be more important in those countries where constitutional avenues to change did not exist. Marxism as a doctrine was embellished by Lenin, who popularized the notion of 'Imperialism' as the last stage of capitalism, i.e. when it reaches out to exploit other less-developed countries.

In February 1917, the Tsar was forced to abdicate and for a few months war-weary Russia, with her mounting casualties, briefly experienced her only period of 'bourgeois democracy', until the new government of Kerensky was overthrown by the 'October' Revolution (November 7th New Style), engineered by Lenin and the Bolsheviks. Their immediate aims were peace, land-reform and bread, and Russia therefore withdrew from the war with Germany in the winter of 1917–18. There followed three years of civil war and foreign intervention by Western armies, from which the new regime emerged successfully. Lenin died in 1924. By 1929 'Stalin' (Dzhugashvili) had consolidated his power and exiled his rival

'Trotsky' (Bronstein), second only to Lenin as leader of the revolutionary struggle. The Union of Soviet Socialist Republics, into which most of the territories of the old Russian Empire had been formally converted in 1923, was now reconciled, at least temporarily, to the fact that similar revolutions were not imminent in other countries. Certainly for a time, just after the end of the First World War, there had been revolutionary activity of varying importance in a number of European countries, especially defeated Germany, and in Hungary a revolutionary regime under Béla Kun was in power for several months in 1919. But by the late 1920s Europe was relatively stable once more and was enjoying renewed prosperity, although this proved to be short-lived.

Using a system of iron control Stalin thus pursued a policy of 'Socialism in one country'. In the 1930s heavy industry was expanded at great sacrifice through a series of five-year plans and agriculture was ruthlessly collectivized. Numerous leading figures were executed in purges starting in the mid-1930s. Externally there was reciprocal enmity between the Soviet Union and Nazi Germany. In 1936 Germany and Japan (and Italy a year later) signed the 'Anti-Comintern Pact'. The Comintern was the 'Third International', sponsored by the Soviet Union in 1919 and adhered to by other Communist parties in the world. The Russian Bolsheviks had formally adopted the title 'Communist' after the Revolution, and sympathetic Socialist elements had formed Communist parties in other countries. It was therefore surprising when the Soviet Union suddenly made an expedient treaty of non-aggression with Germany in August 1939, only days before Hitler's invasion of Poland, which both countries partitioned shortly afterwards. The Soviet Union was herself invaded by Germany in June 1941.

Even before the successful conclusion of the war the Soviet Union was clearly determined to have friendly regimes in those countries lying between herself and Germany. These countries not only contained territories (eastern Poland and Bessarabia) to which Russia had claims, but their inter-war governments (except in Czechoslovakia) had suppressed Communist parties or their equivalents, and, moreover, they had succumbed to Germany only too easily in most instances, after either diplomatic pressure or military attack. Great Britain and France, the guarantors of some of these countries, had, in Soviet eyes, not only used them after the Revolution as a *cordon sanitaire* against the Soviet Union, but had later been unwilling, in the late 1930s, to ally themselves with the Soviet Union for the purpose of halting the eastward expansionism of Nazi Germany. The Western Powers, for their part, were suspicious of a state that openly favoured the eventual overthrow of their economic and political institutions and they viewed with distaste the arbitrary violence of Stalin's rule. Finally the countries of East-Central Europe had been used as a springboard for the unprovoked German attack of 1941, which had caused such immense devastation and the loss of about 20 million Soviet lives.

Provisional Hungarian and Polish governments sponsored by the Soviet Union were set up in Debrecen and Lublin in 1944, as soon as the eastern districts of Hungary and Poland were freed from the Germans. In Bulgaria the Fatherland Front, which had seized control, was backed by the presence of the newly-arrived Red Army. In Jugoslavia Tito's Communist-led partisans already commanded large areas of the country. The Czech government-in-exile arrived in liberated Košice in 1945 with an admixture of Communists who had spent the war years in the Soviet Union, while in occupied Rumania the Soviet Union helped into power the Communist-dominated National Democratic Front. To a certain extent the initial, reformist aims of the new governments were acceptable to large sections of the population, such as land redistribution, the nationalization of some key industries and the bringing to justice of wartime collaborators.

Nevertheless, the Soviet Union was not content until power had been firmly consolidated by trusted Communists or reliable sympathizers. The precise stages by which all anti-Communist forces were deprived of power and influence in less than three or four years cannot be gone into here. Post-war economic difficulties, the relative dearth in some countries of able politicians with liberal convictions and unsullied wartime records, the trauma of the German occupation, and the physical presence or proximity of the Red Army, were obviously facilitating factors, but also important was the sheer determination of the relatively small number of Communist leaders, many of whom had suffered imprisonment before or during the war, or who had spent years of exile in Moscow. By early 1948, after the dethronement of the King of Rumania and what may be described as a 'constitutional coup' in Czechoslovakia, power had passed completely into the hands of the Communist parties (or analogous parties with other names). These often absorbed pliable elements of other left-wing parties. Those opposition leaders who did not escape were often imprisoned, and some were executed. The Western Powers, although alarmed at trends in East-Central Europe, including elections that were considered to be 'managed', proved unable to alter the course of events, even in the ex-enemy countries. Virtually all normal contacts with the countries concerned eventually broke down: the so-called 'Iron Curtain' had fallen. Scarcely had this happened, however, when Jugoslavia was expelled from the *Cominform* (in effect the post-war successor of the *Comintern*) in the summer of 1948, because of Tito's resistance to

Moscow's demands. The Jugoslav régime, originating in a genuine revolutionary movement that had actively fought the Germans and that owed little to the Soviet Union, proved unshakeable. The incident had unfortunate repercussions in the other countries, however, where several leading Communists were tried or disgraced for alleged 'nationalist deviationism'. Some were executed – and later posthumously rehabilitated from the mid-1950s onwards.

The growing hostility between the Western Powers and the Soviet Union – the 'Cold War' – was intensified by the long Soviet blockade of the access routes of the Western Powers to their sectors of Berlin in 1948–9. The North Atlantic Treaty Organization was formed as a defensive measure in 1949, and later in the year the split became sharper with the setting up of the two rival German states corresponding to the Western and Soviet Zones of occupation ('German Federal Republic' and 'German Democratic Republic'). The outbreak of the Korean War (1950–3) led to a further worsening of relationships.

Within East-Central Europe rapid and far-reaching changes took place between 1944 and the early 1950s. The nationalization was carried out of industry, mining, transport, financial institutions and services of all kinds, usually on the basis of confiscation or only nominal compensation, and the private sector was thus reduced to negligible proportions. Despite the only recent redistribution of the land taken from estates and large farms, measures for agricultural collectivization were embarked upon, although at a relatively slow pace and with less upheaval than had occurred in the Soviet Union twenty years previously. The process was not fully completed until the early 1960s and in two instances the programme of collectivization was even abandoned – in Jugoslavia in 1953 and in Poland in 1956. New constitutions were introduced setting up 'People's Republics' as a transitional stage on the way towards full Socialism. A few tame vestiges of other parties were still allowed to survive in some instances, but in practice emphasis was put on a single, dominant, 'monolithic' party, as in the Soviet Union, within which little freedom of discussion was allowed. In parliamentary elections there was no contesting of seats, merely approval of a candidate or a list. Marxism–Leninism became the official philosophy of the State; indeed, it might be called a secular religion that arrogantly insists on its own infallibility. The whole social structure underwent a great change. The middle classes were not only largely expropriated in material terms, but were sometimes relegated to menial work. On the other hand many successfully, if reluctantly, came to terms with the new social order. Formerly underprivileged sections of the community undoubtedly benefited by the provision of new opportunities. Economically there was much hardship as a result either of the payment of reparations to the Soviet Union or disadvantageous trading agreements with her. In some countries, such as ex-enemy Rumania, joint enterprises controlled vital sectors of the economy, largely for the benefit of the Soviet Union. Moreover, the drive for increased industrialization meant heavy sacrifices, especially as some of the projects were ill-conceived and grandiose (the error later to be known as 'gigantomania'). The new régimes were also infected by the Stalinist excesses of the Soviet Union; imitators of Stalin's arbitrary methods held down cowed populations with the aid of an all-pervading secret police.

The death of Stalin in 1953 and the end of the Korean War in the same year led to gradual changes within the Soviet Union and East-Central Europe and to a general, if fluctuating, improvement in East–West relations. In 1956, at the 20th Congress of the Communist Party of the Soviet Union, Khrushchev denounced certain aspects of Stalin's rule and thereafter a slow process of 'de-Stalinization' set in, culminating in further attacks at the 22nd Congress of 1961. The slight relaxation after 1953 made possible a wave of disaffection in Poland in 1956 that led to a liberalization of the régime. In Hungary in the same year an open revolt was crushed by the Red Army.

Stalin's methods and views are now referred to retrospectively as the 'cult of personality' or 'dogmatism'. While the official party line in all the countries concerned is now to criticize these it is equally important not to fall into the opposite error of 'revisionism', which can lead to a betrayal of the revolutionary essence of Marxism–Leninism. The ultimate inevitability of war between the Communist and capitalist worlds, once an article of faith, is now no longer held and 'peaceful co-existence' is the official policy. But this does not extend to the ideological field, where Marxism–Leninism must never surrender its claim to have a monopoly of truth regarding the economic and social aspects of man. It is still asserted that all countries are inevitably moving towards Socialism, although it is now agreed that not only may the paths differ, but also the detailed organization of the new society itself. However, no one in East-Central Europe is permitted to opt out of 'building Socialism' and fundamental criticism of the régime is not allowed.

Much greater flexibility and realism were being introduced into the running of the socialized economies of East-Central Europe by the mid-1960s. Russian bureaucratic methods related to the Stalinist era of coercion and shortage had hitherto been blindly applied, such as the centralization of detailed control by Ministries, the fixing of prices with little regard to costs, the absence of adequate incentives in the wage system and a bilateralism in foreign trade that almost amounted to barter. Such rigidities had been discarded by Jugoslavia in the 1950s, with considerable success, although this had the effect of turning the country into an experimental Socialist laboratory. The great achievement of the Jugoslavs was to allow a high degree of autonomy to nationalized enterprises, in which workers' councils had real powers, to allow demand and supply considerable play and to link wage-bonuses directly with factory profits. Such innovations were heretical at the time in the Soviet Union. However, both here and in the countries of East-Central Europe ideas of 'profitability' and 'market relations' as guides to economic efficiency were gaining ground by the mid-1960s and foreign trading arrangements were also becoming more flexible. What has been called the 'command' type of Socialist economy is thus undergoing transformation.

At the same time a more realistic attitude is being taken towards contemporary capitalism. Obsession with the classical writings of Marx and Lenin and the sterile teachings of Stalin had led to a wilful self-deception about the real nature of the capitalist world in the 1950s. Here there had by now been an acceptance of various forms of economic planning, in which private interests are deliberately guided or penalized, and government intervention to iron out economic fluctuations had become commonplace as a result of the recognition of new theories of employment and money enunciated by Keynes and other Western economists in the 1930s. In the advanced countries of Western Europe the idea of the 'Welfare State' had taken root; large sectors of industry had been nationalized; workers' living standards were quite obviously rising; colonial possessions had been given up. The prophecies of Marx and Lenin about mature capitalist societies had not come about.

The social structure of East-Central Europe now differs greatly from that on the eve of the Second World War. Landowners, independent businessmen and most shop-owners have long since been dispossessed. In certain countries private craftsmen selling their own goods are still tolerated, as are some other strictly limited forms of small-scale private enterprise. Except in Jugoslavia and Poland independent peasant farmers have become collective farmers. Social classes have not been entirely eliminated, although economic differentiation between them is usually small. Political life centres on one party or a Communist-dominated 'front', which permeates all activities and whose edicts must be observed. Membership of the Party is usually large and includes a broad spectrum of persons, including both dedicated Marxists and opportunists from all walks of life. Educational facilities and social-welfare provisions are certainly very much wider than ever before, and it may be said that to a large extent a 'meritocracy' is coming into being, in which rewards tend to be broadly related to ability, training and efficiency, although Party membership also counts for much. Religious observance can be a handicap to personal advancement, as also can 'bourgeois' or aristocratic antecedents, although less so now than formerly. In Catholic countries the Church has slowly achieved a some-what precarious *modus vivendi* with the State, but the anti-religious prejudices of Marxism remain. In spite of the stress on collective and state ownership the yearning for personal material possessions is still very much alive; indeed, there are now gradually increasing possibilities for the private ownership of houses and cars, although these tend to be very expensive. The new generation that has grown up since the war is often out of sympathy with those in authority. Their indoctrination has, in fact, tended to make them apathetic towards politics and impatient of the former revolutionaries and agitators who often still cling to power—and to increasingly irrelevant slogans and clichés.

Chapter 2

THE GEOGRAPHICAL BACKGROUND

Modern Changes in Political Geography

In 1914 large parts of East-Central Europe lay within the three Empires of Austria–Hungary, Germany and Russia (Fig. 1a). To the south of Austria–Hungary the frontiers of the Turkish Empire had been in retreat for a hundred years, after a period of stability since 1739 along the Sava–Danube–Carpathian line. At the height of its power, in the 16th and 17th centuries, Turkey had also held most of Hungary.

Parts of Serbia and Greece liberated themselves from Turkey in the first half of the 19th century, and the vassal Rumanian Principalities of Moldavia and Wallachia were united in 1859 after having achieved, by stages, full internal autonomy with the help of Russia and the Western Powers. After the Russo–Turkish War of 1877–8 the Treaty of Berlin recognized the autonomy of the northern part of Bulgaria and permitted the enlargement of Serbia and the small mountain state of Montenegro, the latter having always remained free of Turkish control. However, in Bosnia–Hercegovina and the adjoining Sanjak of Novi Pazar the Turkish withdrawal was followed by Austrian encroachment. Greece obtained more territory from Turkey in 1881, and the southern part of Bulgaria was united with the north in 1885. The two Balkan Wars (1912–13) resulted in the further enlargement of Bulgaria, Greece, Montenegro and Serbia at Turkey's expense and the restriction of Turkey-in-Europe to approximately its present limits. At the same time Albania gained its independence from Turkey, although a large Albanian-speaking area came under Serbian rule. Within the space of about a hundred years the Balkan peoples and the Rumanians had thus finally freed themselves from the Turk after centuries of occupation and vassalage respectively. The new pattern of independent states was broadly similar to that existing in the latter part of the 14th century before the Turkish invasion. Their re-emergence was often followed by a strident nationalism that involved both territorial disputes amongst themselves (particularly between Bulgaria and Serbia, who each had historical claims to Macedonia) and agitation on behalf of brethren within the Austro–Hungarian Empire (South Slavs and Rumanians).

The Austro–Hungarian Empire was the outcome of territorial accumulation by the Habsburg dynasty that had taken place since the

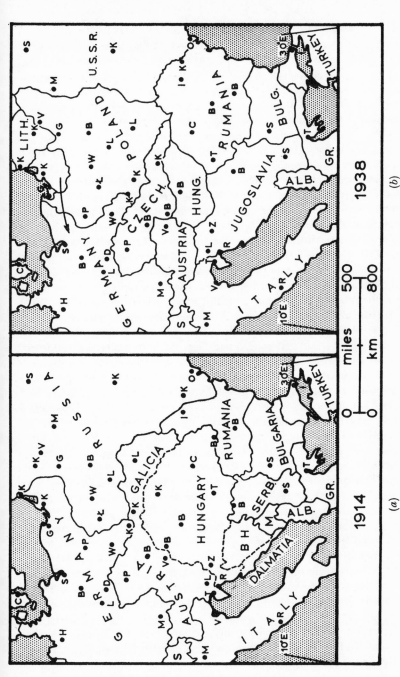

Fig. 1. International boundaries in East-Central Europe, 1914 (*a*) and 1938 (*b*)

14th century, the most recent acquisition having been Bosnia–Herce-govina, formally annexed in 1908. There had also been important losses at various times, such as the seizure of Silesia by Prussia in 1741 and the loss of the provinces of Lombardy and Venetia to independent Italy in 1859–66. In 1848–9 the Empire had been racked by revolutions, in which demands for political democracy were complicated by nationalist movements on the part of the non-German minorities, especially the Magyars, liberated from Turkish rule by Habsburg forces a century and a half earlier, but not allowed to regain their independence. However, the intolerance of the revolutionary Magyars towards their own minorities within Hungary turned the minorities against them and made it possible for Vienna to retrieve control. A delayed effect of the Magyar insurrec-tion was the *Ausgleich* or 'Compromise' of 1867, whereby the ancient Hungarian territories, under Magyar rule, were granted a separate government for internal matters. A parallel administration governed the remaining Austrian territories, and joint ministries were responsible for the foreign affairs and defence of this 'Dual Monarchy'. This concession satisfied the Magyars but not the other minorities, whether under Magyar rule (Croats, Rumanians, Serbs, Slovaks) or Austrian rule (Czechs, Poles, Slovenes, Dalmatian Croats).

By 1914 certain concessions had been made to minorities within the Austrian territories, but within Hungary only the Croats enjoyed any national privileges. Agitation from Serbia for South Slav unity was now a serious nuisance and the possibility of the creation of a third, Slav state within the Empire was suggested by some as a means of countering this influence, although the Magyars were opposed to such a 'Trialist' solution. Taken together the Slavs in the Empire were more numerous than the combined total of German speakers and Magyars. Perhaps a dynastic empire was already doomed in an age of increasing national consciousness on the part of linguistic minorities, especially when these could look with envy beyond the frontiers to independent states like Serbia and Rumania who were ready to embrace their kindred.

The assassination of the heir to the Imperial throne, the Archduke Francis Ferdinand, by a young revolutionary in the streets of Sarajevo in Bosnia, in June 1914, was the immediate cause of the First World War, the effects of which were to shatter the Empire. Ironically the Archduke had been accused by his detractors of favouring a Trialist scheme. Austria–Hungary, suspecting the complicity of Serbia, sent her an ultimatum in July and, despite a conciliatory reply, declared war. Germany, Austria–Hungary's ally, declared war on Russia, who had mobilized in support of Serbia, and also, shortly afterwards, on France, Russia's ally. Great Britain then declared war on Germany because of her violation of the neutrality of Belgium. Austria–Hungary and Germany were eventually supported by Bulgaria and Turkey, and the Western Allies, Russia and Serbia by Italy, Rumania and Greece (who were promised territorial gains).

In Russia the Tsar was forced to abdicate after the first ('February') Revolution of 1917. After the second ('October') Revolution of the same year the new Bolshevik government sought peace with Germany (Treaty of Brest-Litovsk, 1918). In October 1918, Austria–Hungary sued for peace with the Western Allies, but rapidly disintegrated. The Emperor Charles, the last of the Habsburgs, withdrew from the political scene. Early in November Germany obtained an armistice, after the abdication of the Kaiser. The Hohenzollern leadership, first of Prussia and then of its creation, the German Empire, was thus brought to an end. The power vacuum that resulted from the collapse of the three Empires meant that the way was open for their subject peoples to gain independence or attach themselves to already independent kindred states. Such developments were, moreover, favoured by the Western Allies, whose war aims in this respect had been embodied in the famous Fourteen Points of President Wilson earlier in the year. The territorial changes (Fig. 1b) were eventually included in the various Peace Treaties of the ensuing years.

The changes affecting the former Austro–Hungarian Empire were as follows. Austrian Poland (known to the Empire as 'Galicia') was re-united, after 150 years of separation, with the German and Russian parts of Poland. The Czech Lands of Bohemia and Moravia, which had lost their independence at Austrian hands three centuries previously, joined with Hungary's province of Slovakia, which the Magyars had occupied a thousand years previously, to form Czechoslovakia. Austrian-held Slovenia and Dalmatia became part of a South Slav kingdom, later to be called Jugoslavia. This also included Croatia and the Vojvodina (both formerly Hungarian), Bosnia–Hercegovina, and the already independent states of Serbia and Montenegro. The Serbian king became King of the Serbs, Croats and Slovenes. Rumania obtained the Hungarian province of Transylvania, lying within the Carpathians, and adjoining areas in the Pannonian Plain; in addition to Rumanians large numbers of Hungarians were thereby included. Rumania also regained the Bucovina, taken by Austria from Turkey in the 1770s. Italy obtained the South Tyrol, Trieste (Austria's seaport), and the adjoining Istrian peninsula, with a considerable South Slav population. Geographically Austria was now restricted to the German-speaking provinces, including the city of Vienna, which subsequently languished owing to the loss of its functions as capital of a large state inhabited by over 50 million persons. Union with Germany, desired by many, was forbidden by the Allies. Hungary was restricted to the inner part of the Pannonian Plain, populated almost exclusively by Magyars, but large numbers found themselves on the wrong side of the generous boundaries of the new states of Czechoslovakia and Jugoslavia and the enlarged Rumania. With the collapse of the Empire one of the world's Great Powers thus disappeared from the stage of history after playing a prominent role for several centuries. Its passing was regretted by few at the time; but there are still elderly people in certain countries of East-Central Europe who look back with nostalgia to an era when *personal*, if not *national*, liberty enjoyed stronger guarantees than were sometimes later to be the rule.

North and east of the Habsburg Empire territorial losses were suffered by both Russia and Germany. By the wartime Treaty of Brest–Litovsk revolutionary Russia lost a broad zone of territory, including Finland, the three Baltic states of Estonia, Latvia and Lithuania, Russian Poland and the Ukraine. Bessarabia, Russia's largely Rumanian-speaking province, taken from Turkey in 1812, broke away and was united with Rumania. In this way Russia was forced to shed her non-Russian western territories, which passed under German control until the end of the war. By the end of 1918 the defeat of Germany by the Western Allies allowed these areas to establish their claims to full independence. The Ukraine was absorbed by the Soviet Union, however, after the failure of an armed intervention by Western forces. Germany's losses included the cession of territory to Poland. With the collapse of the three Empires conditions were favourable to the re-emergence of an independent Poland, which had disappeared from the map as a result of the three partitions of 1772, 1793 and 1795, carried out by Austria, Prussia and Russia. Germany also gave up the port of Danzig and district, which became a Free City.

In the inter-war period the countries of East-Central Europe were faced with numerous problems. All had suffered serious war casualties, and there had been devastation in certain areas. In four of the seven countries there was the task of welding together territories that often differed widely in terms of economic and cultural levels and sometimes as regards their legal system. Poland had not been united for 150 years and many disparate changes had taken place in the Austrian, Prussian and Russian-held areas since then. The Czechs had not been united with the Slovaks since the collapse of the 'Great Moravian Empire' of the 9th century. The Serbs and the Croats had never formed part of one organized state, nor had the Rumanians of Moldavia and Wallachia and the Rumanians of Transylvania. The Serbs and Croats also differed in religion, the former belonging to the Orthodox and the latter to the Roman Catholic form of Christianity. In Hungary the problem was one of adaptation to territorial truncation. This was also true, but to a much smaller extent, of Bulgaria, which, as another defeated power, had to give up her recently-acquired access to the Aegean Sea. Often the new frontiers caused economic difficulties. The 'common market' of the Habsburg Empire had disappeared, and the difficulties resulting from new tariff barriers and new, unstable national currencies hindered the free flow of commodities along pre-existing pathways. In Poland there were some difficulties in the marketing of textiles and coal now that former outlets in Russia and Germany respectively were either closed or greatly diminished.

Smouldering international animosities relating to frontier grievances and minority questions were rife in the post-war years. Germany did not willingly accept the partitioning of the Upper Silesian coal-basin with Poland. A plebiscite of 1921 had here produced a complicated geographical mosaic of voting. In southern East Prussia a plebiscite had gone in Germany's favour despite the existence of a substantial Polish minority. The separation of East Prussia from the body of Germany by the Free City of Danzig (Polish *Gdańsk*) and the adjoining 'Polish Corridor' was a grievance that Hitler was later to exploit in 1939 as a pretext for his attack on Poland. Poland and the Soviet Union remained estranged after a war between them in 1920–1. This had been precipitated by Poland, who wished to regain her old frontier of 1772 rather than adhere to the so-called Curzon Line, based largely on linguistic grounds and lying much further to the west, which the Western Allies had recommended. In the event Poland obtained from the Soviet Union a frontier that lay between these two limits, but which included large numbers of Byelorussians and Ukrainians. In the north-east Poland occupied the admittedly largely Polish city of Wilno (Lith. *Vilnius*), but which was also the historical capital of newly-independent Lithuania. Poland also disputed with Czechoslovakia the future of the Cieszyn (Czech *Těšín*) area of Silesia. A partition by the Western Allies placed a substantial Polish population under Czechoslovak rule, as well as a number of coal mines.

Hungary, although an ex-enemy, felt herself to have been harshly treated. The new boundaries, imposed without plebiscite, left large numbers of Hungarians outside the homeland. Her agitation to have the humiliating Treaty of Trianon amended in her favour led to a defensive alliance of Czechoslovakia, Jugoslavia and Rumania, known as the 'Little Entente'. Rumania was not only faced with a recalcitrant Hungarian minority in Transylvania, but her absorption of Bessarabia led to poor relations with the Soviet Union, who never recognized this transfer. Bulgaria nursed territorial grievances against her neighbours. In the Second Balkan War (1913) Rumania had taken the southern Dobrudzha from her and Serbia had taken some of her newly-acquired territorial gains from Turkey. Moreover, after the First World War Greece had been given the stretch of the Aegean coast that Bulgaria had retained from her Turkish spoils in 1913. The question of Fiume (Croat *Rijeka*), formerly the port of Hungary, embittered relationships between the new state of Jugoslavia and Italy. Finally in 1924 it was incorporated in Italy by mutual agreement.

In 1933 the rise to power of Adolf Hitler and his 'Nazi' Party in a Germany suffering severely from the Great Depression was ultimately to be as important in its long-term implications for East-Central Europe as the Sarajevo assassination. In 1936 Hitler came to an understanding ('Rome–Berlin Axis') with Mussolini, Fascist dictator of Italy since 1922, who had recently conquered Ethiopia and who, like Hitler, was now beginning to help the insurgents in the Spanish Civil War. Thereafter Europe witnessed a series of international crises fomented by Germany, with the concurrence of Italy. A leading aim was the extension of their influence over East-Central Europe. In the spring of 1938 Austria, which had become economically weak and politically unstable, readily submitted to German pressure and accepted union ('Anschluss') with Germany. The undermining of Czechoslovakia was the next aim of Hitler. This was an industrialized, relatively prosperous country where constitutional parliamentary government had survived at a time when its neighbours, after periods of democratic practice in the 1920s, had succumbed to more or less authoritarian systems with 'managed' parliaments. This development partly resulted from the need to ovecome debilitating internal dissensions and partly reflected a desire to emulate the seeming success of the régimes in Italy and Germany. In Hungary and Poland military–aristocratic régimes were in power, while in Bulgaria, Jugoslavia and Rumania there were royal dictatorships.

The 'Achilles heel' of Czechoslovakia was its large German-speaking minority, compactly located in the 'Sudetenland' just within the mountainous periphery of the western provinces of Bohemia and Moravia and thus immediately adjacent to Germany (now including Austria). Theoretically it might have been argued that these Sudeten Germans should have been granted the right of 'self-determination', which, in the conditions of 1938, would almost certainly have led to union with Germany. However, it has to be remembered that the existing frontier was one of the few really effective 'natural' ones in Central Europe, and that the German minority already enjoyed adequate rights. It was also clear that Hitler was interested not so much in the welfare of the Sudeten

Germans as in the subversion of the Czechoslovak state. The Nazi-inspired Sudeten German Party was thus deliberately encouraged to make increasingly far-reaching demands. Britain and France, her friend and ally respectively, were placed in a cruel dilemma. Would they be justified in going to war with Germany in order to defend the territorial integrity—and ethnic complexity—of Czechoslovakia? In the end, by the Munich Agreement of September 1938, made jointly by Britain and France with Germany and Italy, the Czech government was called on to cede the German-speaking areas. The remainder of the country was thereby placed in an extremely vulnerable economic and strategic position, especially as Hungary and Poland also demanded the areas populated by their minorities. Critics of the agreement maintained that this 'appeasement' of German aims only encouraged German ambitions and that advantage might have been taken of the supposed readiness of the Soviet Union to collaborate in resisting the German threat. Certainly the Czech nation has never forgiven the action of Britain and France. In March 1939, the remaining areas of the Czech Lands were suddenly occupied by Germany and converted into a 'Protectorate', Slovakia became a puppet state, and Carpathian Ukraine, the eastern extremity of the country, was seized by Hungary, who had held it before 1918. Shortly afterwards Italy occupied Albania, over which she already exercised strong economic control, and thus obtained a military foothold in the Balkans.

Relations were now deteriorating between Germany and Poland over the Free City of Danzig, largely German in population, but for which Poland had responsibility as regards foreign relations. Hitler proposed the union of Danzig with Germany and extra-territorial rights of passage through the adjoining Polish Corridor. These proposals were rejected by Poland and finally, on September 1st, 1939, Germany invaded her. Britain and France declared war on the 3rd, but considered it impossible to give military assistance, despite guarantees made to Poland earlier in the year in the hope of deflecting Germany from her purpose. As soon as it was clear that Poland had been defeated she was invaded from the east by the Soviet Union. An unexpected German–Soviet Pact, made a few days before Germany's attack, had paved the way for this eventuality. This pact had been made at a time when protracted negotiations were taking place for an alliance between Britain and France and the Soviet Union. Eastern Poland, with its large Byelorussian and Ukrainian populations, was incorporated into the corresponding republics of the Soviet Union. Parts of western and northern Poland were annexed by Germany and the remainder became the 'General Gouvernement' occupied territory (Fig. 2a).

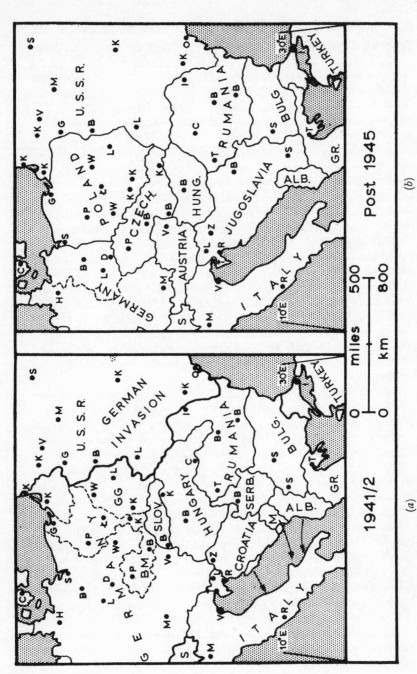

Fig. 2. International boundaries in East-Central Europe, 1941/2 (a) and post 1945 (b)

In the spring and early summer of 1940 Hitler succeeded in occupying Denmark, Norway and the Low Countries, and also defeated France after a few weeks of fighting. Italy now felt that the time was opportune to declare war on Great Britain, who stood alone after the fall of France. Italy invaded Greece later in the year, but was temporarily repulsed. By the spring of 1941 Bulgaria, Hungary and Rumania had joined the German–Italian coalition. The previous year Rumania had not only been forced by the Soviet Union to return Bessarabia and to cede the northern Bucovina, but Germany had also forced her to yield territory to her neighbours, Bulgaria (southern Dobrudzha) and Hungary (northern Transylvania). A Franco–British guarantee to Rumania of 1939 was of no avail in the circumstances. Jugoslavia's adherence to the alliance was frustrated at the last moment by the overthrow of the government, and Germany thus had to take the country by force in April 1941. Germany and Italy occupied certain areas, while Bulgaria, Hungary and Italian-held Albania obtained long-deferred territorial revenge. Puppet states were established in an enlarged Croatia and a diminished Serbia.

In June 1941 Hitler invaded the Soviet Union, and by the end of the year had advanced to a line running approximately from the outskirts of Leningrad and Moscow to Rostov-on-Don, although only the latter was ever taken. At this time Germany and her allies controlled virtually the whole of the European mainland (Fig. 2a), except the neutral states of Spain, Portugal, Sweden and Switzerland, and even the two latter were encircled. Turkey was also neutral. It was at this juncture that Japan, the non-belligerent associate of Germany and Italy (Tripartite Pact of 1940), attacked the United States Pacific Fleet at Pearl Harbor. The resulting involvement of the United States in the war against Germany and the decisive victory of the Red Army at Stalingrad (now Volgograd) in the winter of 1942–3 were vital factors that turned the tide in the European War. Another factor was the defection of Italy from the German alliance after a coup had deposed Mussolini in July 1943. During the summer and autumn of 1944 the Red Army advanced westwards and took eastern Poland, eastern Hungary, Rumania and Bulgaria, and also assisted in the liberation of Jugoslavia, where, however, Tito's partisans already held much of the country. In Albania partisans seized power from the withdrawing enemy forces. British and American forces opened a Second Front by invading Normandy in June 1944 and by the end of the year France and Belgium were free. The following spring the Western and the Soviet Armies continued their advance into Germany itself and on May 8th, 1945, the common enemy made the required unconditional surrender. Hitler had meanwhile committed suicide in the ruins of Berlin.

The territorial settlement after the Second World War (Fig. 2b) inevitably acknowledged the fact that the Soviet Union was now the effective master of East-Central Europe, having occupied the vacuum left by the collapse of Germany. Her troops were stationed in the ex-enemy states of Hungary and Rumania and also in Bulgaria, which, however, had not been at war with the Soviet Union until the latter herself declared war just before crossing the frontier in the summer of 1944. Soviet troops were also stationed in devastated Poland where, it could be claimed, they were necessary to maintain lines of communication with occupied East Germany. Czechoslovakia and Jugoslavia, where Soviet troops did not remain for long, had friendly governments.

It was only to be expected that the Soviet Union would wish to retain those areas that she had acquired in 1939–40, before the German attack on her, and which had, to a large extent, been integral parts of Imperial Russia in 1914. Thus long before the end of the war the Soviet Union was insisting on the eventual reincorporation of eastern Poland. Here she had a case on ethnic grounds and could, embarrassingly, point to the Curzon Line as justification for expecting Western support. Great Britain and the United States did, in fact, give their tacit approval, but the Polish government-in-exile in London could not bring itself to agree. Moreover, there was mutual distrust between the Polish and Soviet governments; indeed, diplomatic relations had been broken off in 1943. At the Yalta conference, early in 1945, Great Britain and the United States agreed to such an eastern boundary and also to the idea of territorial compensation for Poland in the north and west at the expense of 1939 Germany. At the Potsdam conference, held after Germany's defeat, southern East Prussia, Danzig, and pre-war Germany up to the line of the Rivers Oder and Neisse were all placed under Polish 'administration', pending the final delimitation of the frontier by a German peace settlement. This is still the formal legal position, as far as the West is concerned, over twenty years later. The Soviet Union annexed the northern half of East Prussia. The Polish state was thus shifted westwards and its new limits were, in fact, similar to those of the 12th century. The newly-acquired areas in the north and west thus became known as the 'Regained' or 'Recovered Territories'.

To the south of Poland, Czechoslovakia was restored to her 1937 boundaries, except that she ceded the extreme east of the country, Carpathian Ukraine, to the Soviet Union. This had never been part of Russia before, having been in Hungarian hands prior to 1918 and again since 1939. Hungary was deprived of her wartime gains and also reverted to her 1937 limits. Rumania thus regained those areas lost to Hungary in 1940, but at the same time the Soviet Union retained Bessarabia and the northern Bucovina, and Bulgaria retained the southern Dobrudzha. A reunited Jugoslavia obtained territory from Italy, including several Adriatic islands, the mainland enclave of Zadar, the Istrian peninsula, and the greater part of the Soča valley. Trieste became a Free Territory, the city itself (Zone A) being occupied by British and American troops and the rural hinterland to the south (Zone B) by Jugoslav troops. In 1954 Zone A passed to Italy and Zone B to Jugoslavia by mutual agreement.

The territorial settlement was associated with some of the largest population shifts of a political kind in modern history, equalled in scale only by those occurring at the time of the partition of the old Indian Empire in 1947. These movements of population had been preceded by wartime shifts of many kinds, such as the agreed repatriation (1940–1) of long-established German-speaking minorities (*Volksdeutsche*) from the Soviet Union, especially from those areas taken by her in 1940, i.e. the three Baltic states, northern Bucovina and Bessarabia. Many of these persons were settled in German-occupied Poland. Another type of movement was the deportation of large numbers of persons from various occupied countries for forced labour in Germany.

The post-war shifts* were particularly concerned with the flight or eviction to defeated Germany of nearly all the German-speaking minorities of East-Central Europe, as well 'as the large population living in those areas of 1939 Germany itself that were now to be under Polish administration. Many Germans had already fled just before the end of the war, as the Russian front advanced. The transfer of those remaining was authorized by the Potsdam Agreement of the Allies, although in fact the removals were already under way. Precise calculation of the numbers crossing the Oder–Neisse line during 1945 and succeeding years is vitiated by the fact that civilian population losses were considerable in eastern (1939) Germany towards the end of the war and that many men were in the armed forces. Moreover, the Oder–Neisse lands and parts of 1939 Poland contained *Volksdeutsche* settlers, as well as temporary evacuees from other parts of Germany. The total of normally resident Germans who were displaced may have been over 8 millions.

About 3 millions were transferred from Czechoslovakia, about a quarter of a million from Hungary, and smaller numbers from Jugoslavia and Rumania. Certain numbers of Germans were allowed to remain, however, especially in Rumania, which now contains the largest of the residual German minorities in East-Central Europe.

The evacuation of the German population from the recently-acquired

---

* The figures are based largely on L. Kosiński, 'Migrations of population in east-central Europe, 1939–1955', *Geographia Polonica* 2 (Warsaw, 1964), 123–31.

Northern and Western Territories of Poland and the Sudetenland of Czechoslovakia was followed by the resettlement of these areas. About 4 million Poles, including a large part of the 2 million repatriates from those areas of 1939 Poland now lying in the Soviet Union and colonists from other parts of Poland, moved into the Regained Territories. About 1¼ million Czechs and Slovaks moved into the Sudetenland. In addition to these major upheavals there were other shifts, such as the movement to Hungary of many Hungarians formerly living in Czechoslovakia, Jugoslavia and Rumania, of Italians to Italy from areas ceded to Jugoslavia, of Byelorussians, Lithuanians and Ukrainians from Poland to the Soviet Union, and of Serbs and Croats to areas evacuated by Germans and Hungarians in the Vojvodina. Several hundred thousand Jews who had survived the German extermination policy left for Israel or other destinations. Altogether the post-war changes in East-Central Europe led to population movements, chiefly taking place in 1945–8, that probably involved some 20 million persons. Later population shifts included a movement of Turks from Bulgaria to Turkey in the early 1950s, of Hungarians to the West at the time of the 1956 rising, and of most of the remaining Germans from Poland to Germany in the late 1950s. This latter movement coincided with a new wave of Polish repatriation from the Soviet Union.

The effect of these population shifts has been to reduce the size, both absolute and relative, of the minorities in East-Central Europe. In pre-war Czechoslovakia and Poland the minorities had accounted for about one-third of the population. The extermination or emigration (both pre-war and post-war) of the greater part of the formerly large Jewish population (over 3 millions in Poland and 2–3 millions in the other countries) has also had a profound effect. Minorities in Poland are now very small indeed. Czechoslovakia has a very much smaller number of Germans than before, but there is still a large, although reduced, Hungarian minority (0·5 million), as well as some Poles and Ukrainians. Hungary also has a much-reduced German minority. In addition to her considerable minority of Germans (0·4 million) Rumania still has a large number of Hungarians (1·6 million), as well as other much smaller groups. There is also an important Hungarian minority in Jugoslavia (0·5 million), as well as large numbers of Albanians (0·9 million) and Turks (0·2 million) in the south of the country. Bulgaria has a reduced Turkish minority (0·6 million). In relation to the population of their homeland the Hungarians of Czechoslovakia, Jugoslavia and Rumania and the Albanians of Jugoslavia are almost certainly the leading minorities in the whole of Europe. Outside the countries of East-Central Europe the Soviet Union still contains well over 1 million Poles and also more than 2 million Rumanians, if one includes the 'Moldavians' living in the Moldavian Republic across the River Prut in Bessarabia. In addition there are considerable numbers of émigrés living in Western countries, especially Poles. Bulgarians and Rumanians are poorly represented in this respect however.

Physical Geography

Between the Bay of Gdańsk in northern Poland and the Corfu Strait, off southern Albania, there is a distance of some 1,650 km/over 1,000 miles, and between the Istrian peninsula in the west and the Danube delta in the east one of over 1,300 km/800 miles. In the far north there are the predominantly low and sandy shores of Poland with their spits and lagoons. The latter features are also found along parts of the Black Sea coast of Bulgaria and Rumania, but here also there are the vast reed and willow swamps of the Danube delta (greatly exceeding in area that of the Vistula in Poland, which is largely cultivated) and long stretches of cliffs. The Adriatic coast of Jugoslavia is noted for its 'drowned' characteristics; towering limestone heights rise almost sheer from the sea and there are narrow steep-sided inlets and many offshore islands. Further south, however, Albania has deltas, lagoons and coastal plains. There are also wide differences of terrain within the seven countries, in addition to these coastal contrasts. The main physiographic units may be listed as follows.

(a) THE RODOPI (RHODOPE) BLOCK OR MASSIF. This is a great wedge of ancient rocks extending north-westwards from the Aegean Sea into the Balkan peninsula and sinking under later deposits at its 'apex' south of Belgrade. It embraces large areas of southern Bulgaria, Jugoslav Macedonia and Serbia. It was uplifted, fractured and tilted by the Alpine earth movements, at which time volcanic activity also took place. Glaciation has etched the higher summits, which, rising to over 2,500 m/8,200 ft, are found in the Rila and Pirin Mountains of Bulgaria. Elsewhere subdued relief forms are usual.

(b) AREAS OF HERCYNIAN ROCKS, WITH LATER MESOZOIC DEPOSITS PARTLY COVERING THEM OR LYING ON THEIR FLANKS. The Hercynian elements of East-Central Europe, like the Rodopi Block, were uplifted, fractured and tilted by the Alpine earth movements and volcanic activity also took place. The complete or partial removal of later Mesozoic deposits has revealed ancient erosion surfaces, so that here also relief-forms are usually subdued in character. Amongst the Hercynian areas is the 'horst' known as the 'Bohemian Diamond', the raised margins of which locally exceed 1,000 m/3,300 ft in height and give natural frontiers between western Czechoslovakia and Austria, Germany and Poland. Within the northern half of the Diamond there are wide areas of Cretaceous sandstones and marls. A much smaller and lower Hercynian area occurs in southern Poland in the Holy Cross Mountains, which are flanked to the west by a series of Mesozoic scarplands. Several Hercynian elements of varying size appear within or on the margins of the Pannonian Basin (see below). These include the large Bihor Massif of western Rumania and a number of 'islands' within the Basin that are covered by Mesozoic deposits, such as the Mecsek Mountains in southern Hungary and the hills of Slavonia in northern Jugoslavia. The 'Central Range' of Hungary also consists of Mesozoic rocks, within which Hercynian outcrops are sometimes exposed. Finally there are the Hercynian rocks of the northern part of the Rumanian Dobrogea, which form a rampart that is skirted by the lower Danube.

(c) THE TERTIARY ('ALPINE') FOLD-MOUNTAINS. These include the following: (i) The great reversed-S of the *Carpathian* system, which extends from Bratislava in Slovakia, through Rumania, north-east Serbia and Bulgaria (*Stara Planina* range), to reach the Black Sea as Cape Emine between Varna and Burgas. Differing greatly in height and width the various constituent ranges include ancient crystalline rocks caught up in the folding (especially in the Tatras and other ranges in Slovakia and in parts of the Southern Carpathians of Rumania), Mesozoic limestones, and Cretaceous and Tertiary 'flysch'* deposits. Volcanic rocks also occur. In the highest parts of the Carpathians (the High Tatras and the Southern Carpathians of Rumania) there are glaciated peaks with heights exceeding 2,500 m/8,200 ft. Elsewhere relief has a more rounded character. (ii) The *Julian Alps* and the *Karavanke*, two of the most easterly ranges of the Alps themselves, correspond to the frontier districts between Jugoslavia and Italy and Jugoslavia and Austria respectively. Here, too, glaciated peaks rise to over 2,500 m/ 8,200 ft. Foothills of the Alps extend further north-eastwards along the frontier between Hungary and Austria. (iii) Extending from north-west to south-east for almost the whole length of Jugoslavia, and constituting the seaward half of the country, are the parallel *Dinaric* ranges which often have the character of almost flat-topped ridges. In their limestone districts 'karstic' scenery is well developed. Further to the south the Dinaric ranges continue into Albania, but on the borders of Albania and Jugoslav Macedonia they have almost a north–south direction as the Rodopi Block is approached. Many summits in the southern Dinarics rise to over 2,500 m/8,200 ft.

---

* A general word used to describe various deposits of clays, marls, shales and sandstones found on the outer margins of the young fold-mountain system and belonging to the Upper Cretaceous and Lower Tertiary periods.

(d) PLATFORMS OF CRETACEOUS OR TERTIARY ROCKS. These dissected high plains, which in places rise to over 300 m/1,000 ft, include (i) the Moldavian Platform of eastern Rumania and (ii) the Lublin Plateau of south-eastern Poland, both of which may be regarded as extensions of the Russian Platform lying to the east. There is also (iii) the Northern or Danubian Platform of Bulgaria, situated between the Danube and the Stara Planina.

(e) MAJOR TERTIARY LOWLANDS. At the time of the Alpine earth movements many areas, some of great extent, experienced subsidence. Such areas, as might be expected, lie within, or on the margins of, the Tertiary fold-mountain ranges. The largest by far in extent is (i) the Pannonian (Hungarian) Basin, which is encircled by the Carpathians, the Dinaric ranges and the Alps and which is internally split into two unequal portions by the Central Range of Hungary. Other areas of subsidence are (ii) the Wallachian (Danubian) Plain of southern Rumania, between the Carpathians and the Danube; (iii) the Sandomierz Depression of southern Poland, situated to the north of the Carpathians; and (iv) the Plain of Silesia, lying in south-western Poland to the north of the Bohemian Diamond. Its south-eastern extremity in turn rests upon a basin of Carboniferous rocks which provide one of the largest coalfields in Europe. A further large Tertiary depression is (v) the Plain of Thrace, in southern Bulgaria, lying just within the northern mountain margins (*Sredna Gora*) of the Rodopi Block. Within the arc of the Rumanian Carpathians is the Transylvanian Plateau Basin (300–500 m/1,000–1,650 ft), which may also be included in this group.

(f) MINOR TERTIARY LOWLANDS. In addition there are numerous smaller depressions, often faulted in character. They include the elongated West Bohemian basin (noted for its brown-coal deposits), the smaller South Bohemian basins, the routeway of the Moravian Corridor, and many basins and corridors in the Balkans, especially within the Rodopi Block, where they are often of vital importance for routes and settlement. Leading examples are the Sofia basin, the 'Rose valley' of Bulgaria, and the basins situated along the Morava–Vardar route. The coastal plains of Albania are filled-in Tertiary embayments belonging to the Dinaric system.

(g) AREAS OF GLACIAL DEPOSITS. Apart from local deposits of relatively small extent in, or on the margins of, the higher Tertiary fold-mountains and the Rila Mountains, the only large area of glacial deposition is in Poland, where the northern two-thirds of the country, underlain by Mesozoic and Tertiary rocks, is covered by glacial deposits of various kinds, including terminal moraines, glacial till and fluvioglacial material. In the far north of the country the most recent terminal moraines give hills that in a number of places reach heights of well over 225 m/750 ft.

DRAINAGE

The drainage of East-Central Europe flows northwards to the Baltic, south-eastwards to the Black Sea and southwards to the Mediterranean (Adriatic and Aegean Seas). Poland drains towards the Baltic, by means of the Odra (German *Oder*) and Vistula systems, as also does western Czechoslovakia, by means of the Labe (German *Elbe*). The middle part of East-Central Europe is drained towards the Black Sea by the Danube and its great tributaries, such as the Czech Morava and the Váh (Czechoslovakia), Tisza (Hungary), Drava, Sava and Serbian Morava (Jugoslavia), Olt, Siret and Prut (Rumania) and Iskŭr (Bulgaria).

The Danube, having already flowed for some 1,000 km/600 miles through southern Germany and Austria from its source in the Black Forest, enters the countries of East-Central Europe upstream of Bratislava. Here it is nearly 1,900 km/1,200 miles from its outfall into the Black Sea. During its course the river passes through two gorge sections; one is immediately above Budapest, where the river cuts through the Central Range of Hungary, and the other, which is much longer, begins 80 km/50 miles east of Belgrade, where the Danube cuts a passage (including the 'Iron Gates') through the Carpathians as they swing southwards into north-east Serbia from Rumania. For part of its course the Danube marks the international boundary between Czechoslovakia and Hungary, Rumania and Jugoslavia, and Rumania and Bulgaria, while the northern, Chilia, distributary, together with the Prut, form the boundary between Rumania and the Soviet Union. Below Vienna seven cities of over 100,000 inhabitants are situated on the banks of the Danube, including Budapest and Belgrade, the capitals of Hungary and Jugoslavia. The others are Bratislava, Novi Sad, Ruse, Brăila and Galaţi. All are significant river-ports. Apart from the Danube the only other rivers of East-Central Europe reaching the Black Sea are several in Bulgaria, the most important being the Kamchiya.

Despite considerable regulation of the course of the Danube and its major tributaries serious flooding can still occasionally occur in parts of the Pannonian Basin (e.g. in 1965, in Slovakia, Hungary and Jugoslavia). The steady increase in national wealth of the countries concerned and the rapprochement between the Soviet bloc and Jugoslavia have recently made possible a co-ordinated programme of building barrages on the Danube. These will aid flood-control and navigation and will provide hydro-electric power to help meet growing energy demands.

Relatively few rivers drain into the Adriatic from Jugoslavia, largely owing to the karstic conditions of the hinterland; the most important by far is the Neretva. On the other hand the coastal plains of Albania are traversed by eight rivers within a distance of less than 150 km/90 miles, the most important being the Drin. The Aegean rivers are the Vardar (Jugoslavia) and the Struma, Mesta and Maritsa (Bulgaria), all of which pass through Greek territory before reaching the sea.

CLIMATE

Throughout the greater part of East-Central Europe the climate may be said to be Continental, but Oceanic influences from the west are nevertheless of some importance, particularly as regards the raising of winter temperatures. The 'continentality' of the climate increases eastwards, therefore, and the greatest temperature ranges are to be found in Moldavia. The Adriatic coasts of Jugoslavia and Albania have a Mediterranean climate, however, and strong Mediterranean influences are also felt in the Aegean valleys of Macedonia and southern Bulgaria.

Nearly all inland lowland areas have average January temperatures that are at or below freezing-point, down to about −4·0°C/25°F. The coldest conditions are found in Moldavia and the extreme east of Poland. Areas with average temperatures above freezing include certain places on the Black Sea coast of Bulgaria, the Aegean valleys and, very strikingly, the Adriatic coastlands of Jugoslavia and Albania, where temperatures vary from 6°C in the north to 9°C in the south (43°–48°F). All lowland areas have average July temperatures of between 18° and 25°C/64·5° and 77·0°F, the coolest areas being northern and western Poland and the hottest Albania, southern Bulgaria and southern Jugoslavia. In hilly or mountainous districts temperatures tend to be lower at all seasons.

Average annual precipitation in most lowland areas varies between 500 and 650 mm/20 and 25·5 in. There tends to be a maximum in the summer months, but in some areas this is not markedly so. Albania, the Jugoslav coast and the Aegean valleys have a very pronounced winter maximum combined with virtual drought in the summer. A very few areas, notably the Rumanian Dobrogea, have an annual precipitation total of under 450 mm/18 in. In upland areas totals can rise to well over 1,000 mm/40 in. The wettest places by far are in the coastal ranges of Jugoslavia, where wide areas receive more than 1,500 mm/60 in., and where locally the highest rainfall totals in all Europe have been recorded. Highland Albania also receives more than 1,500 mm. Snow-cover in the interior lowland areas of East-Central Europe varies from about one month to about three months.

Economic Geography

INTRODUCTION

Before the present economic characteristics of the countries of East-Central Europe and the geographical patterns of economic activity within them can be fully appreciated it is necessary to consider the pre-war situation. Apart from Czechoslovakia there was a very great dependence on agriculture, which supported between 50 and 80% of the population, partly on a subsistence basis. The figure in Czechoslovakia was about one-third. Generally speaking holdings were small and usually fragmented. Land-reform measures, of varying efficacy, in the 1920s and 1930s, had reduced the area of estates and very large farms where these existed, but in some countries, especially in Hungary, an influential class of large landowners still remained. Increasing population pressure and 'land hunger' in rural areas were often leading to progressive sub-division of holdings.

In the years before the First World War there had been a large volume of emigration to the Americas, especially from the Habsburg Empire, but in the 1920s the United States quota system severely reduced this outlet. Within the countries themselves the growth of non-agricultural employment opportunities was insufficiently rapid to relieve pressure on the land. Rural overpopulation–in the sense that output could have been maintained with a much smaller labour force–was thus a chronic economic and social problem in the inter-war period. The situation was worsened in the early 1930s by the general world depression, in which the prices of foodstuffs and raw materials fell much more than those of manufactures. The indebtedness of peasant farmers increased as a result. Agricultural productivity was low and scarcely rising in many areas. In addition there were certain backward regions in each country, where dependence on agriculture was particularly excessive and where non-agricultural employment was negligible.

Foreign trade rested largely on exports of agricultural produce and raw materials, such as timber and minerals (e.g. oil from Rumania and non-ferrous metals from Jugoslavia). Depressed foreign markets in the early 1930s caused balance-of-payments problems and hampered economic growth, while the servicing and repayment of foreign loans became a millstone. Foreign concerns often had a high degree of participation in mineral exploitation and other sectors of the economy and were sometimes accused of controlling in their own interest the level of output and the extent of domestic processing.

On the other hand it cannot be said that governments were unaware of all these problems. It has to be remembered that the more advanced western countries who were their mentors were also in economic difficulties at this time and that government intervention to induce economic expansion had not yet become as acceptable or customary as it is today. Attempts were, indeed, made by various governments of East-Central Europe to stimulate industrial growth, usually of steel and engineering products, including armaments. Higher-value agricultural exports also grew in importance, such as Polish bacon and Bulgarian fruit and vegetables. The agricultural sector ultimately gained considerable stability as a result of trading agreements with Nazi Germany, whose government-influenced expanding economy was offering a widening market in the late 1930s. Albania had increasingly close economic relations with Fascist Italy. Such peaceful penetration proved to be a preliminary to conditions in the Second World War, when the economies of East-Central Europe were harnessed to the German war-machine and to a lesser extent the Italian. To a limited extent an artificial prosperity was thereby achieved in some of the countries and a number of wartime plants were inherited, except in those areas where devastation or dismantling (by the Soviet Union) took place.

The Soviet capture of much of East-Central Europe in 1944–5, as the Red Army liberated it from German control, gave Communist leaders and other Socialists an opportunity that was not to be missed. Not only would they abolish an economic, political and social system that they considered to be nefarious, but by imitating the methods of the Soviet Union they considered that they would achieve a quicker pace of economic growth and deploy their country's resources to better advantage. Capitalism as it had hitherto been experienced had been found wanting and must be replaced. Socialism on the Soviet model would be a more effective means of catching up with the advanced capitalist countries as regards industry and technology. The fruits of mature capitalism would thus eventually be achieved by Socialist methods.

For several years there were great economic difficulties, partly due to problems of post-war recovery. The offer of American aid to the countries of Europe in 1947 was refused at Soviet insistence, although the Soviet Union was at that time scarcely in a position to offer substantial help, owing to her own recovery problems. In fact for some years she was obtaining supplies of a number of commodities on favourable terms from East-Central Europe. In time, however, much industrial plant was certainly supplied. The rapid decline of normal trading connections with the West also hampered progress and automatically intensified economic ties with the Soviet Union. By the late 1950s the heavy programme of industrial investment was at last beginning to produce tangible benefits and living standards were now beginning to show some improvement. The international *détente* of the late 1950s also led to increasing trade between East and West, involving the purchase of a wide range of plant from western countries, especially for the chemical, metallurgical and engineering industries. By the mid-1960s such trade was even being financed in some instances by western credits. Moreover, certain western firms had begun to enter into joint manufacturing agreements, e.g. for engineering goods, sometimes for export to third countries.

Despite years of hardship there is no doubt that impressive industrial expansion has occurred, although the rate of increase in living standards has been held back in order to permit a high rate of capital investment. A large volume of manpower has been transferred from the agricultural sector. By 1963 about 1¼ million persons in the seven countries were engaged in mining and over 9 millions in manufacturing. In 1963 the volume of industrial production (including mining and energy) was between four and six times that of 1938 in Czechoslovakia, Hungary and Jugoslavia. In Rumania it was over seven times, in Poland over nine, and in Bulgaria seventeen. Even if one questions the basis of calculation of these figures there is no doubt that a very great expansion has been achieved.

On the other hand increases in agricultural output, especially livestock products, have been much less impressive and in some countries the effect of collectivization was detrimental, at least for a time. Morale was undermined as a result of what amounted to virtual confiscation of land and stock, even though, as a transitional measure, various forms of rent for their use might be paid to the peasants. Landless labourers and 'dwarf' small-holders who had so recently benefited by land redistribution measures were thus effectively dispossessed of their gains. As in the Soviet Union remuneration on collective farms is usually on the basis of work-days performed (of differing value according to the skill involved) and is partly given in kind. Small private plots are permitted, together with a limited number of livestock, and surplus production above household needs can usually be sold freely. An important part of national requirements of meat, milk and eggs is supplied by private plots, in fact.

Unemployment and under-employment have been greatly reduced, but not been entirely eliminated, although it is true that particular industries or localities may have labour shortages. Czechoslovakia, however, is similar to industrialized north-west Europe in that labour tends to be generally scarce, except in parts of Slovakia. Only Jugoslavia publishes unemployment figures: the official percentage varied between 5 and 7% of the labour force in the years 1958–62. Serious inter-regional differences in the level of employment and general economic development also still remain, but are gradually being reduced. New industry is being deliberately located in such areas as eastern Slovakia, the eastern half of Hungary, southern Jugoslavia, Moldavia and western Wallachia. Differences in social provision between town and country also persist, although there has certainly been a rapid improvement in rural living conditions. Peasant incomes have risen substantially in Jugoslavia and Poland, while in the other countries the collective farms are active in providing many amenities and the private plots are often lucrative.

AGRICULTURE

Climate, terrain and soil provide advantageous conditions for grain cultivation over wide areas of East-Central Europe, although harvests can fluctuate widely. Only in Bulgaria and Rumania is the production of grain normally more than adequate for human and animal needs so that there is a surplus for export as well. Hungary and Jugoslavia can feed themselves in average to good years and sometimes have export surpluses. In all instances the quantities exported are, however, smaller than in the earlier decades of the present century, when populations were smaller, the diet poorer, and agriculture less diversified.

Wheat is cultivated in suitable areas in all the countries concerned, from the reclaimed marshes of the Vistula delta in the north of Poland to the Albanian lowlands and the Tertiary basins of Macedonia. The most important areas, however, are the loess tracts of southern Poland, Bohemia and Moravia, the Pannonian Basin (extending from Hungary into Slovakia, Rumania and Jugoslavia), the Wallachian Plain, the Moldavian Platform, the North Bulgarian Platform and the Plain of Thrace. In all these areas there are fertile soils, usually derived from loess or other fine deposits, and often having the character of 'black-earths'. In such areas barley is also grown, but only locally does it achieve prominence (e.g. Moravia). Maize is grown in the Pannonian Basin and the other areas of plain to the east and the south mentioned above, but is virtually absent from Bohemia and Poland. Northern and central Poland, with predominantly sandy soils, are noted for a heavy emphasis on the rye–potato combination, which also occurs in the less favoured areas of Bohemia and Hungary and in some upland basins in the Balkans. Oats are grown in the moister parts of Poland and Czechoslovakia. Rice is cultivated under irrigated conditions in a few districts of Hungary (Great Plain), Rumania (Danubian Plain), Bulgaria (Plain of Thrace), coastal Albania and Macedonia.

Sugar beet is grown in broadly the same areas as wheat, provided soil and moisture conditions are adequate and transport is available to sugar mills. Yields can vary greatly from year to year, according to climatic conditions. Highly localized cash crops are tobacco and cotton. Tobacco is grown in certain districts in all the countries from southern Poland to the Balkans, but Bulgaria produces over a third of the total output. Bulgaria is also responsible for most of the cotton. Market gardening occurs in the neighbourhood of many large towns, but Albania, Bulgaria, Hungary and Rumania also have a considerable export trade in fresh or processed fruit and vegetables of various kinds. Czechoslovakia, East Germany and Poland are important markets. Vines are grown in many districts in the Pannonian Basin, Rumania and the Balkans, and there are some localities with well-known quality wines for export. Plums for brandy-making are cultivated in Albania, Bulgaria, Jugoslavia and Rumania, while in Hungary apricot brandy is a speciality. In Czechoslovakia and Poland, especially the former, beer is made from local barley and hops. Poland is also noted for its vodka, made from potatoes or rye.

All the countries carry large numbers of livestock, although until recently the quality was often rather poor. Cattle tend to be predominantly associated with the arable areas and are usually stall-fed; climatic conditions do not favour the development of really good permanent pasture for cattle, except in some upland districts and damp river lowlands. Pigs are also associated with the arable areas and depend chiefly on maize, or on potatoes in the north. Sheep are particularly numerous in the Balkans, where they are associated with both hill grazings and lowland arable districts. Transhumance in the Carpathians and in the ranges of the Balkans was formerly much more important than today. The number of horses tends everywhere to be either almost static or declining, mainly as a result of increasing mechanization. In all the countries great stress is now laid on better methods, improved strains of seeds and livestock, fertilizers, mechanization and greater diversification and intensification. In some areas the drainage of marshes (e.g. Albania, Poland, Rumania) or the irrigation of moisture-deficient districts, with the aid of river-control schemes (e.g. Bulgaria and eastern Hungary) is of importance. In those countries with a collective system the cultural landscape of the countryside has been greatly modified. The small peasant parcels have been merged into large consolidated fields which form the cultivation units of collective farms worked from new centralized farm buildings. Sometimes the land of several neighbouring villages constitutes a single collective farm as a result of a policy of further amalgamation.

In hilly and mountainous districts, or on infertile sandy wastes, there are extensive forests and woods, including plantations. There are thus important lumber industries and associated activities, especially in Czechoslovakia, Jugoslavia, Poland and Rumania. Jugoslavia and

Rumania are particularly active in export markets. Coniferous trees are the more important in Czechoslovakia and Poland and deciduous hardwoods (chiefly beech and oak) in the remaining countries.

MINERAL RESOURCES AND INDUSTRY

Energy resources are very unevenly distributed. Poland possesses one of the greatest bituminous (black) coalfields in Europe in Upper Silesia, but nevertheless the proportion of coking coal available is relatively small. The southern extension of this field lies in Czechoslovakia, where, although output is only one-fifth of that of the Polish portion of the field, the coking-coal proportion is much higher. 80% of East-Central Europe's black coal is derived from these two areas. There are also smaller fields in Lower Silesia (Poland), Bohemia (Kladno particularly), Hungary (Pécs), Jugoslavia (Istria and north-east Serbia), Rumania (the Banat and the upper Jiu valley) and Bulgaria (small coalfields in the Stara Planina). Poland is a large net exporter of coal, but her coking-coal supplies are barely keeping pace with growing needs. With the exception of Czechoslovakia, the remaining countries are net importers, especially of coking coal.

Brown coal and lignite are also exploited. The leading fields in terms of output are in West Bohemia (the largest output by far), the Central Range of Hungary, the extreme south-western corner of Poland and the Konin area in the centre, and the Struma and Maritsa valleys of Bulgaria. There are also fields in Jugoslavia (especially Slovenia, Bosnia and Serbia), and in Albania and Rumania. Only Albania and Rumania have adequate petroleum resources. Indeed, Rumania is the leading producer in Europe, apart from the Soviet Union, and has a large export surplus. She is also richly endowed with natural gas. All the other countries have small petroleum fields and gas fields, and while these yield useful outputs a deficit remains (except in Albania)—hence the recent building of the 'Friendship' oil pipe-line system from the Soviet Union to Czechoslovakia, Hungary and Poland.

In all the countries the building of electricity power-stations, whether thermal or hydro, has been a leading feature of post-war development. The generation of current in 1963 was between seven and ten times that of 1938 in four of the countries; in Jugoslavia it was over twelve times, in Albania and Bulgaria over twenty-five. Thermal means predominate and in Hungary and Poland hydro-generation is proportionately very small indeed. On the other hand, in Jugoslavia, which has one of the biggest hydro potentials in Europe, well over half of the nation's current is generated by water and in Albania two-thirds.

Steel, like electric power, is one of the basic ingredients of industrial growth and here too a very great increase in capacity has taken place. In 1938 about 5 million tons of steel were produced, almost entirely in Czechoslovakia and Poland, but by 1963 the total had almost reached 23. Nearly all the countries nevertheless have a shortage of iron ore. Only Bulgaria can satisfy her own, rather modest, present needs. Albania, lacking an iron industry, exports her ore output. Czechoslovakia and Poland, still the largest steel producers (about 8 million tons each per annum), have particularly large ore deficits, both absolutely and relatively. The Soviet Union and Sweden are the leading suppliers, although countries in other continents are now also regularly sending shipments. The expansion of the steel industry has involved the modernization and extension of plants in existence at the end of the war, such as those in Upper Silesia (Poland), the Ostrava and Kladno areas (Czechoslovakia), Miskolc (Hungary), Hunedoara and Reşiţa (Rumania) and Zenica and Sisak (Jugoslavia), as well as the building of new ones, such as Częstochowa and Nowa Huta (Poland), Kunčice (Czechoslovakia) and Dunaújváros (Hungary). Newer plants not fully completed by 1965 include Košice (Czechoslovakia), Skopje (Jugoslavia), Kremikovtsi (Bulgaria) and Galaţi (Rumania).

East-Central Europe has also expanded its output of other metals. Bulgaria and Jugoslavia both have large export surpluses of copper, lead and zinc, an increasing proportion of which is now refined before export. Hungary and Jugoslavia have export surpluses of bauxite and also produce some aluminium metal themselves. Czechoslovakia and Poland have aluminium industries based on Hungarian bauxite imports. Rumania also mines a number of non-ferrous metal ores and is now developing her bauxite resources for domestic aluminium production. Poland is a leading exporter of zinc, based on home ores and imported concentrates. She also produces some lead, copper and nickel. Large new copper resources are now being developed. Czechoslovakia, where much mining of precious and base metals has taken place in the past, produces only modest quantities of non-ferrous metals and has a growing dependence on foreign supplies. Manganese ores are obtained in several of the countries, Hungary and Rumania being notable exporters. Albania and Jugoslavia are large exporters of chrome ore.

Expansion has also been marked in chemicals. Sulphuric acid is derived from non-ferrous metal smelting in several countries and also from the processing of pyrites. Poland is now exploiting newly-discovered deposits of sulphur and has a considerable export surplus. Both Poland and Rumania have very large deposits of salt. East-Central Europe also has chemical industries based on coal (black, brown and lignite), petroleum and natural gas. Synthetic fibres and synthetic rubber are being produced in increasing quantities and there is also great stress on increasing the supply of chemical fertilizers to raise the level of agricultural productivity.

Engineering industries have also grown in scale and scope, and, moreover, their geographical distribution has widened. Jugoslavia and Poland have both become important shipbuilding countries. The motor-vehicle industry has also grown, but personal car-ownership on the scale of north-west Europe is still a long way off. The ratio of cars to total population is similar to that of north-west Europe in the 1920s. Only Czechoslovakia produces more than 100,000 motor vehicles per annum (1963), while Albania and Bulgaria produce none at all, although the latter will be a producer by 1970. Production is concentrated in capital cities (Budapest, Prague and Warsaw) or in certain specialized towns, such as Braşov (Rumania), Kragujevac (Jugoslavia), Mladá Boleslav (Czechoslovakia) and Starachowice (Poland). The rate of increase in textile production has been less impressive than in some other sectors of industry, reflecting the rather low priority given to consumer goods for a long period. Czechoslovakia and Poland, with large, old-established textile industries, have a considerable export trade. Czechoslovakia has been a large producer and exporter of footwear since before the Second World War.

A further important feature of the economic geography of the countries of East-Central Europe is their system of administrative-economic regions. This development represents an attempt to decentralize detailed supervision in a number of sectors of the economy and at the same time to link economic devolution with conventional local government functions at the provincial level. The precise pattern in each country is the product of special circumstances, including the degree to which the pre-existing system of local government areas could be adapted and the average size of region differs considerably from country to country. In Jugoslavia the constituent republics fulfil similar functions, but have much wider powers.

Population and Urbanization

The seven countries vary considerably in area and population. Poland is the largest in area (312,500 square km/120,700 square miles) and also in population (30·7 millions in 1963). Apart from Albania, Hungary is the smallest in area (93,000 square km/35,900 square miles) and Bulgaria in population (8·1 millions). Differences in overall density are not very great, however. Bulgaria, Jugoslavia and Rumania have similar densities of 73, 75 and 79 persons per square km respectively (189, 194 and 205 persons per square mile), while Albania has 61 per square km

(158 per square mile). Czechoslovakia and Hungary have densities of 109 and 108 per square km (282 and 280 per square mile). Within each country there are, of course, wide differences in density, related chiefly to the natural conditions prevailing for agriculture and the extent of industrial and urban development.

Annual rates of natural increase differ considerably from country to country, largely as a result of differences in the birth-rate. Natural increase is, for instance, low by European standards in Hungary, high in Jugoslavia and Poland, and very high in Albania. With the exception of Albania, birth-rates in 1963 were lower than in 1938, 1948 or 1958 (see Appendix C). Death-rates fell considerably in all countries between 1938 and 1958, but since then there has been little change, except in Poland, where a further decline has brought the rate down to the low figure of 7·5 per thousand. This largely reflects the very youthful age-structure of the population.

It may also be noted that of those born a higher proportion now survive beyond the first year of life. In 1938 the infant mortality rate varied between 121 per 1,000 in Czechoslovakia and 183 in Rumania. In Albania the figure was almost certainly higher. By 1963 these levels had been greatly reduced and varied between 22 in Czechoslovakia (a rate similar to those of north-west Europe) and 78 in Jugoslavia (although in parts of the country, especially Slovenia, much lower rates prevail) and 91 in Albania. While the reduction is partly due to greatly-increased medical care since the establishment of the present régimes it is also true that there was very great improvement between 1938 and 1948. The annual increase of population in the seven countries as a group is about 1 million.

Despite much natural growth since the pre-war years it is nevertheless true that the total population of the states of East-Central Europe did not surpass its 1938 level of over 101 millions until 1963, i.e. 25 years later. Moreover, the individual 1963 populations of Czechoslovakia, Poland and Rumania were then still below the 1938 level, although the population of Bulgaria, on the other hand, had increased by nearly one-third (partly as a result of gaining the southern Dobrudzha from Rumania, but chiefly owing to natural growth) and that of Albania by as much as three-quarters. War deaths, boundary changes and the expulsion of German-speaking minorities all contributed to the situation. The number of war deaths probably approached 10 millions, nearly two-thirds (6 millions) of the persons concerned being Polish citizens. Jugoslavia also suffered high losses (1·7 millions). The Soviet Union annexed eastern Poland, the Carpathian Ukraine (from Czechoslovakia) and the northern Bucovina and Bessarabia (from Rumania), although not necessarily all the associated populations; many Poles were transferred to the new Poland, for instance. Nearly 5 million resident Germans were transferred to Germany from the pre-war territories of the countries of East-Central Europe, including about 3 millions from Czechoslovakia and 1 from Poland. On the other hand there were some gains. Poland incorporated over 1 million Poles living in those areas of 1939 Germany annexed by her in 1945, and Jugoslavia gained several hundred thousand Croats and Slovenes living in the Istrian peninsula and in other districts ceded by Italy.

The rapid expansion of industry and mining in recent decades has inevitably led to an increase in the number of persons living in towns and in the proportion this bears to the total national population. The definition of what constitutes a town differs from country to country, however, so that international comparisons cannot be made precisely. By 1961 some 40 million persons were living in communities of over 5,000 persons, but the numbers living in places considered to be 'urban' were several millions less than this. Thus in Hungary and Rumania populous communities of over 5,000 inhabitants may still remain essentially agricultural and rural in character, whereas in Czechoslovakia many places with smaller populations fulfil industrial and urban functions. Official percentages of urban population vary from about 30% in Albania, Bulgaria, Jugoslavia and Rumania to nearly 50% in Czechoslovakia and Poland. The figure for Hungary is about 40%. It may be noted that the urban population of Poland (over 14 millions) exceeds the individual *total* populations of four of the other countries – Albania, Bulgaria, Czechoslovakia and Hungary. Poland also contains seven of the fourteen large cities or conurbations with about half a million inhabitants or more.

The towns of East-Central Europe vary considerably as regards their history, functions and architecture. Many urban settlements in the Balkans and in parts of Hungary and Rumania have Roman antecedents, including the capital cities of Belgrade, Budapest and Sofia, as well as leading provincial cities, such as Cluj, Constanţa, Craiova, Ljubljana, Niš, Pécs, Plovdiv, Skopje, Split and Varna. In some of them Roman remains are visible. On the other hand the oldest towns of Czechoslovakia and Poland are medieval in origin, since these territories lay outside the limits of the Roman Empire, although in some instances earlier primitive settlements existed.

The capital cities differ in various respects. Bucharest, Budapest, Prague and Warsaw have populations of between 1 and 2 millions, the largest being Budapest (1·9), while Belgrade and Sofia have well under 1 million, even with suburbs. Tirana has just over 150,000. Belgrade,

Budapest and Prague have dramatic sites overlooking rivers, Sofia is situated near the foot of a mountain range within a large upland basin, while Bucharest and Warsaw, lying in the open plains, have rather monotonous sites, relieved nevertheless by a chain of lakes in the former and by the broad Vistula in the latter.

Architecturally Prague is a rich museum of Gothic and Baroque. In Poland an equivalent role is jointly fufilled by Kraków, the capital until the end of the 16th century, and Warsaw, its successor. Owing to immense wartime destruction the old buildings in Warsaw are either greatly restored or are rebuilt versions of the originals. Budapest consists of two portions—historic, royal Buda on the high west bank of the Danube, and 19th- and 20th-century Pest on the low, east bank, with its spider's web of planned boulevards. By comparison with these Belgrade, Bucharest and Sofia are less impressive, although the long north–south boulevard of central Bucharest, dating from the inter-war period, has a spacious dignity. It must be remembered that Belgrade and Sofia were relatively small towns until well into the second half of the 19th century, when they still retained something of an 'Oriental' appearance as a result of centuries of Turkish influence. Tirana was little more than a village until the 1920s.

The relative national importance of the population of the capital city also varies. Budapest contains nearly half the urban population of Hungary and nearly one-fifth of the national total. Bucharest, Sofia and Tirana each contain about a quarter of the urban population of Rumania, Bulgaria and Albania respectively. By contrast, Prague contains only one-sixth of the urban population of Czechoslovakia and the relative importance of Belgrade and Warsaw is even smaller. Moreover, Belgrade has a lesser rival in Zagreb, the Croatian capital, while in Poland the Upper Silesian urban complex exceeds the capital in population. In Hungary the next largest city after Budapest has less than a tenth of the population of the capital and in Rumania the position is similar. As regards geographical situation Belgrade, Budapest and Tirana are more centrally located within their respective countries than are Bucharest, Prague and Sofia. Post-war boundary changes have modified the relative location of Warsaw within Poland, with the result that Łódź is now nearer the centre of the country. The capital cities are not only administrative, cultural and commercial centres, but are also industrial towns in their own right, with well-defined manufacturing quarters in most instances, concerned with a wide range of consumer goods, as well as engineering products. The further growth of the larger capital cities is generally discouraged and restrictions are often placed on taking up residence in them.

The leading provincial cities are, with few exceptions, old-established regional centres of commerce and culture, into which modern factory industry has been introduced only within the last hundred years usually, and sometimes only in the 20th century. Examples of 19th-century industrialization include some of the towns of the Czech Lands and Poland, such as Brno, Plzeň, Poznań and Wrocław, the two former then lying in Austria and the two latter in Germany. Purely industrial towns that grew up in the 19th and early 20th centuries are not numerous and are largely restricted to the Czech Lands and Poland. They include Łódź, the great Polish textile centre, most of the towns of the Polish Upper Silesian coalfield (headed by Katowice) and Ostrava in the extension of the field lying in Czechoslovakia. In south-east Europe a smaller example is the oil town of Ploieşti in Rumania. In the inter-war period the growth of the new Polish port of Gdynia was noteworthy and also that of the Czech footwear town of Zlín (now Gottwaldov). Since the Second World War a number of new towns have come into existence usually in association with the development of mining or of chemical or metallurgical industries. They include Nowa Huta, a morphologically separate suburb of Kraków, Dunaújváros (Hungary), Dimitrovgrad (Bulgaria) and Tychy, the largest of the new residential satellites for the Upper Silesian Industrial District. There are many smaller examples.

Sprawling 'conurbations' or 'urban agglomerations' are not numerous. Even the capital cities are reasonably compact, although the housing shortage has stimulated commuting within a wide radius. In Czechoslovakia and Poland there are two industrial conurbations based on the major coalfields—the Polish Upper Silesian Industrial District ('G.O.P.') and the much smaller Czech conurbation centred on Ostrava. Łódź has a number of neighbouring satellites, and along the shores of the Bay of Gdańsk the twin ports of Gdańsk and Gdynia have fused with the intervening resort of Sopot to form the *Trójmiasto* or 'Tri-town'. On the Black Sea coast resort development has led to some prolongation of the built-up areas of Constanţa and Varna, while on the Adriatic coast both Rijeka and Split have a number of smaller neighbours to which they are tenuously linked.

Transport and Trade

Inland freight transportation, except in Albania, is chiefly by railways, which in many instances are heavily overstrained. The electrification of main lines or the introduction of diesel traction is everywhere enabling more intensive use to be made of the existing system, and in some countries urgently-needed new lines have been built since the Second World War. Road transport lags greatly behind north-west Europe in its scale of development, and the quality of the roads themselves is often inadequate, but improvements are gradually being made, stimulated by the steady growth of freight traffic and of domestic and international passenger traffic, including tourism. Rivers and canals are of importance for navigation in some countries. Traffic on the Danube and its major tributaries, the Tisza and the Sava, has increased greatly since the mid-1950s, after periods of either decline or stagnation resulting from the depression of the 1930s, wartime difficulties and the post-war tension between Jugoslavia and her Socialist neighbours. The joint Jugoslav-Rumanian project for the Iron Gates will greatly assist navigation of this difficult stretch of the Danube and will thereby stimulate traffic on the upstream section. There is some barge traffic on the Labe (German *Elbe*) in Bohemia and also on the Odra and lower Vistula. These two latter rivers are linked to each other across northern Poland, while the Vistula is connected eastwards to the Soviet Union and the Odra westwards to East Germany. The idea of an Odra–Danube water link through the Moravian corridor has been internationally approved on a number of occasions, but the putting into effect of such a project has been repeatedly deferred. A Rhine–Main–Danube canal is in course of construction through Germany and Austria.

Sea traffic is increasing as foreign trade expands. On the Baltic coast of Poland the largest ports by turnover are Szczecin, Gdańsk and Gdynia. Constanţa, Varna and Burgas are important on the Black Sea coast, especially the former, but the lower Danubian river-ports of Ruse, Brăila and Galaţi, also have a considerable trade. On the Adriatic coast the largest port is Rijeka, followed by Split. All these ports also handle traffic for the land-locked states of Czechoslovakia and Hungary. Air traffic, both domestic and foreign, is rapidly increasing.

Foreign trade has expanded greatly since the Second World War and its emphasis has changed as regards both content and trading partners. The formerly high degree of dependence on exports of food-stuffs and raw materials (typical of all countries except Czechoslovakia) has been reduced and, moreover, a higher proportion of such primary commodities is now processed to some extent before dispatch. Exports of manufactured goods are rapidly growing in importance. Key raw materials have to be imported in many instances, however, and also supplementary food supplies, so that increasing export outlets are vital. The degree of dependence of the national economy on foreign trade varies considerably, being greatest in Czechoslovakia and Hungary. About two-thirds to three-quarters of all foreign trade is with the other Socialist countries, headed by the Soviet Union as the leading trading partner, and most of this trade takes place on the basis of long-term agreements. China has supplanted the Soviet Union as Albania's leading partner, however. A high level of trade with the Soviet Union has a geographical as well as a political rationale, since she is well placed to supply raw materials and also has a growing market for manufactured goods. Between the two World Wars, by contrast, trade between East-Central Europe and the Soviet Union was very small indeed, largely owing to political factors.

Despite these close links with the Soviet Union there is also a growing volume of trade with the advanced capitalist countries and also with the less-developed countries of Africa, Asia and Latin America, to whom manufactured goods and capital equipment are now being exported and technical advice made available. Tourism is also being actively encouraged as a source of foreign exchange. West Germany has become the leading non-Socialist trading partner for all the countries of East-Central Europe, except Albania and Jugoslavia (Italy in both instances). Prewar economic associations have thus re-asserted themselves, even though West Germany has not yet restored normal diplomatic relations (1965). East Germany, as might be expected, has a very high level of trade with her Socialist partners. Austria is the non-Socialist country proportionately most dependent on trade with East-Central Europe.

Economic collaboration amongst the countries of East-Central Europe and between these and the Soviet Union takes place within the framework of the *Comecon* (CMEA) organization, a body which, although set up in 1949, did not become really important until the mid-1950s. Its present constitution was drawn up in 1960. It would be wrong to compare Comecon too closely with the European Economic Community or Efta, since these foster spontaneous economic relationships as a result of the reduction of tariff barriers. Comecon is more concerned with formal collaboration at the official level, and individual enterprises have only limited powers of initiative in undertaking foreign trade. Jugoslavia became an associate member of Comecon in 1965. Albania has withdrawn.

There are several important examples of international collaboration within Comecon. There is the 'Friendship' oil pipe-line system, bringing oil from the Volga region, and also an electric-power network (220 and 400 kV) with its headquarters in Prague and a key junction of transmission lines at Mukachevo in the Carpathian Ukraine. There are also agreements as regards industrial specialization, especially in certain fields of engineering, so that competitive duplication does not take place, and so that an 'international socialist division of labour' is encouraged. The less-developed countries, Rumania in particular, have shown some apprehension, however, in case their industrial ambitions should be checked in the interest of the more advanced countries.

Other forms of association include *Intermetall* (headquarters Budapest), set up in 1965 to co-ordinate the steel-finishing industries of Czechoslovakia, Hungary and Poland, and *Sixpool*, an operating partnership of the national airlines of Bulgaria, Czechoslovakia, East Germany, Hungary, Poland and Rumania. There is also a railway rolling-stock pool arrangement. Bilateral arrangements have been made for special purposes between particular countries, such as the joint hydro-power schemes on the Danube (Czechoslovakia and Hungary and Jugoslavia and Rumania), although it is true that such schemes are the outcome of Comecon recommendations. In 1964 an International Bank for Economic Co-operation was set up, using a transferable Soviet rouble for facilitating multilateral trade within the Comecon group. A further important task of Comecon is the co-ordination of each country's 5-year plans for the years 1966–70. In spite of such growing inter-dependence it must be stressed that each country still jealously retains its own separate economy, with its own national currency, national bank and foreign trade regulations.

Chapter 3

ALBANIA · SHQIPERIA

Introduction

Albania, one of the smaller countries of Europe, both in area and in population (1·81 millions in 1964), is located on the eastern shores of the Adriatic Sea. Cape Gjuhëz, in the south, near Vlorë, is only about 75 km/45 miles from the 'heel' of Italy, lying across the Strait of Otranto. Albania stretches from north to south for about 325 km/200 miles. The width of the northern half of the country varies between 80 and 100 km/50 and 60 miles, and the southern half widens to about 145 km/90 miles in the neighbourhood of Lake Prespa, but then gradually tapers southwards. In the far south the large Greek island of Kérkira (Corfu) lies little more than 2 km off the Albanian coast. Greece adjoins the country on the south-east and Jugoslavia on the north and east.

The land frontiers pass, in general, though mountainous country and, with some important exceptions, broadly follow watersheds. However, to the south-east the Vjosë rises in Greece and the Southern Drin on the Greek border, while to the east both the Black and the White Drin rise in Jugoslavia. Their valleys provide passage-ways leading across the frontiers. The White Drin (Drin i bardhë), with its numerous tributaries, drains the extensive area of high plains and encircling mountains known as the *Metohija* before entering Albania. The Black Drin (Drin i zi), which rises in Lake Ohrid, and its tributary, the Radika, drain another large frontier district of Jugoslavia further to the south. It is interesting to note that these upper, Jugoslav parts of the basins of the Black and White Drins have a large Albanian population. In the far north of the country Albania contains the upper sections of several rivers draining into Jugoslavia, while further south the border with that country follows the lower course of the Buenë (Jugoslav *Bojana*), which drains Lake Shkodër. Lakes Shkodër and Ohër (Jugoslav *Ohrid*) are shared with Jugoslavia, Lake Prespa with Jugoslavia and Greece, and Little Lake Prespa with Greece only. There is easy access round the shores of the lakes into Jugoslavia.

The Albanians are generally considered to be the descendants of the Illyrians, a group of tribes that once populated the eastern coastlands of the Adriatic and their interior districts. Only in Albania did Illyrian speech survive throughout over 2,000 years of almost uninterrupted alien

71

rule of different kinds. Even so the Albanian language (*Shqip*) has been very much modified as a result of Latin, Slavonic, Greek and Turkish influences. Many place-names are Slavonic in origin and point to the intrusion of the South Slavs during the Dark Ages.

There are two distinct dialects of Albanian. The northern half of the country, down to the River Shkumbin approximately, speaks *Geg* and the southern half speaks *Tosk*. In the inter-war period the Geg speech of Elbasan, located near the dialect frontier, was officially favoured as standard Albanian, but since the Second World War the fact that the leaders of the present régime are chiefly southerners has led to the favouring of Tosk. These dialectal differences are accompanied by certain differences in temperament and outlook. The Albanian alphabet, adopted in 1908, is a Roman alphabet with several diacritical signs. Previously there had been several unofficial alphabets resulting from 19th-century literary activity in both Albania and Istanbul The name *Albania* goes back to the middle ages, *Arbanon* and *Arberia* also being used. Ptolemy had mentioned an *Albanoi* tribe as far back as the 2nd century A.D. However, it appears that some time in the 18th century the Albanian began to call his country *Shqiperia* and himself a *Shqiptar* (possibly 'one who speaks clearly', or alternatively, but more romantically, 'son of the eagle').

Until the Turkish conquest of the 14th and 15th centuries Albania, like the South Slav Adriatic lands to the north, was an area of competition, and often conflict, between the Roman and Orthodox forms of Christianity. During the Turkish period the bulk of the population was converted to Mohammedanism, but Catholicism survived in the mountains of the north and in the adjoining lowland district of Shkodër, while Orthodoxy persisted in the far south (using the Greek language for religious purposes). In the inter-war period Roman Catholics numbered about 10% of the population and Orthodox Christians about 20%. In modern times religious strife has not been as common in Albania as one might have expected and a considerable degree of mutual toleration and co-operation has tended to be the rule. Separate Christian and Mohammedan quarters have persisted in some of the towns, however. The Mohammedan population includes the formerly important *Bektashi* sect, chiefly located in the south, and noted for its liberal and even radical views by comparison with traditional (*Sunni*) Islam. The observance of all forms of religion has tended to be undermined by the impact of Marxism since 1944, but the pre-existing cultural differences of the various religious groups still survive.

In addition to the Albanians themselves the country also includes scattered communities of Vlachs and a small number of Greeks in the extreme south. The former, speaking a dialect similar to Rumanian, represent the survivors of the Romanized Balkan population. They are often pastoralists. There are also many Gypsies. Beyond the borders of the country there is a large Albanian minority of 0·92 millions (1961) in Jugoslavia, chiefly located in the Kosovo-Metohija (*Kosmet*) Autonomous Province of Serbia, but also extending into north-western Macedonia and southern Montenegro. Since the Second World War the Albanians of the *Kosmet* have enjoyed a considerable degree of administrative autonomy. Nevertheless Jugoslavia's Albanians constitute about one-third of the entire Albanian population and they are proportionately the largest national minority in Europe by comparison with the population of the homeland. There is also a now largely-submerged Albanian minority of unknown size in northern Greece.

Further afield there are tens of thousands of Albanians living in southern Italy and Sicily. They are the descendants of emigrants who left Albania centuries ago at the time of the Turkish invasion and who, rather surprisingly, have still preserved their separate identity in a number of localities. There are also many thousands of Albanians in the United States, as a result of emigration for economic reasons during the period between the end of the 19th century and 1939. Others returned home with their savings in the inter-war period. The Korçë area was a particularly important source of emigrants.

Historical Background

In the centuries before the Christian era the present territory of Albania was inhabited by Illyrian tribes, although on the coast there were also important Greek trading cities, notably *Dyrrhachion* (or *Epidamnos*) (now Durrës) and *Apollonia* (near modern Fier). The Romans conquered the coastal areas of Illyria in 167 B.C. and gradually consolidated their rule further inland. The important Roman road across the Balkan peninsula, the *Via Egnatia*, ran from Durrës up the valley of the Shkumbin, round Lake Ohrid and so on to Thessaloníki, the coastlands of Thrace, and Constantinople.

At the end of the 4th century Albania came under the rule of Constantinople (Byzantium) after the division of the Empire, but for many years afterwards it was periodically devastated by barbarian invasions. In the 7th century the Slavs made permanent settlement in the Illyrian lands, absorbing in time the greater part of both the Romanized and non-Romanized population—with the residual exceptions of the Vlachs and the Albanians respectively. In the 9th century Albania fell under the First Bulgarian Empire, which had overthrown Byzantine rule in the northern and central Balkans, but in 1018 Byzantine control was restored.

At the end of the 11th century and the beginning of the 12th the country was subjected to attacks and temporary occupation by the Normans of southern Italy. At the end of the 12th century a short-lived native principality of 'Arberia' was established, but it soon became absorbed by the Despotate of Epirus, situated to the south and ruled by a Byzantine prince. In 1272 most of the country came under the rule of Charles of Anjou, King of Sicily, who established a Kingdom of Albania. The Shkodër area in the north had already fallen under Serbian rule, however, and in the 1340s most of the rest of the country was taken. After the death of the Serbian Emperor, Stephen Dušan, in 1355, Albania broke apart into several native feudal territories.

By the end of the 14th century the Turks had taken large areas of the Balkans. Venice gained control of the coastal districts of Albania and the interior gradually fell under the sway of Turkey. There now occurred the most heroic page in Albania's chequered history–the anti-Turkish revolt of George Kastriot, son of one of the tribal chiefs. Taken as a hostage in his youth he became, as 'Skanderbeg', a brilliant military commander in the service of the Sultan. After a Turkish defeat at Niš in 1443 he returned to Albania, united the chiefs under his command and kept the Turks at bay until his death in 1468. By the beginning of the 16th century, with the cession of Durrës by Venice, Turkish control of all Albania was complete.

The Turks ruled most of Albania through a military-feudal régime, although self-governing tribal communities were tolerated in the northern mountains. The high poll tax on Christians led to conversion to Mohammedanism, especially in the 17th century. Many Albanians rose to high office in the service of Turkey. In the 18th century, as central control of the Turkish Empire weakened, Albania became split into a number of small semi-independent units. In the north territorial consolidation took place under the Bushati dynasty, who ruled an autonomous state around Shkodër after the middle of the 18th century. A similar development took place in the south. Here Ali Pasha of Tepelenë, ruler of the *pashalik* of Ioánnina, in neighbouring Epirus, gradually made himself master of large parts of northern Greece and southern Albania at the end of the 18th century and the beginning of the 19th. Turkish control was not regained until 1822 in the south and 1831 in the north. The military-feudal system of government was then abolished and a more centralized civil administration put in its place.

In 1878, after Russia's defeat of Turkey, Albanian nationalist feeling was alarmed by the terms of the Treaty of San Stefano, which would have led to encroachment by Montenegro and Bulgaria (particularly the latter) on Albanian-speaking areas. At a convention held in Prizren (in modern Jugoslavia) a 'League' was formed, with Turkish support, for the defence of the interests of the Balkan Mohammedans, especially the Albanians. In the event the Treaty of Berlin of 1878 reduced the areas to be lost by Turkey, who had meantime received some diplomatic support from the Western Powers. The League organized an army and presented demands for autonomy but the movement was suppressed by Turkey. In the late 1890s further unsuccessful petitions for autonomy were made. Armed revolts took place in 1907–8. In the latter year the 'Young Turk' revolution in Istanbul, which led to the granting of a constitution by the Sultan, raised keen hopes of Albanian autonomy. However, the nationalism of the new régime clashed with Albanian aspirations and open conflict occurred in 1910–12. In the latter year, however, the Turks agreed to make concessions.

The outbreak of the First Balkan War rapidly altered the situation. Bulgaria, Greece, Serbia and Montenegro declared war on Turkey, who, already weakened by a war with Italy in north Africa, was quickly defeated, parts of Albania being occupied as a result. An Albanian assembly, meeting at Vlorë in November 1912, made a declaration of independence, not least to try to ward off the truncation of the country that the four states intended. Representatives of the Great Powers eventually determined in London (1913) that Albania should be an independent neutral state under their control and guarantee. Austria–Hungary and Italy were keen supporters of Albanian independence, since Serbia would thereby be prevented from reaching the sea, and a small weak state would be less of a threat to these two Adriatic powers.

However, the boundaries delimited by the Powers excluded a large part of the Albanian nation, particularly the population living in the north-east (the present *Kosmet* of Jugoslavia), which was awarded to Serbia, in spite of its Albanian majority. It must be remembered, however, that this area had been part of old Serbia centuries before, and that the Albanians had settled there after a Serbian exodus in the late 17th century during the Austrian–Turkish wars of that time. From 1913 up to the time of the Second World War Jugoslavia encouraged renewed Serbian ettlement. Prince William of Wied was nominated as the new sovereign of Albania but he left in 1914 after only a few months of office. By then Albania had relapsed into anarchy and the unity of the Great Powers had been shattered by the outbreak of the First World War. During the war parts of the country were occupied for a time by Serbia and Montenegro, but after the defeat of these two countries the Austrian armies occupied the north and the centre. The Italians held most of the south, while the French, advancing from Thessaloníki, held the Korçë area. Albania was thus effectively partitioned by the opposing sides. At the conclusion of the war Italy took over the Austrian areas.

The proposals for Albania made by the victorious Western Allies included the cession of Vlorë to Italy, and of areas in the south to Greece, and the setting up of an Italian mandate for the rest of the country. A congress meeting at Lushnjë protested at this and reaffirmed Albanian territorial integrity and independence. Foreign troops then withdrew, but the Italians did not leave Vlorë until an Albanian siege had taken place. Italy received the nearby island of Sazan (Italian *Saseno*), however. This was returned to Albania after the Second World War. An International Commission made certain minor boundary adjustments in 1924. Greece has still not formally renounced an old claim to parts of southern Albania ('Northern Epirus'), however, and the border remains closed (1965).

In 1922 Ahmed Zogu, the young chief of the Mat district, became Prime Minister. Displaced in 1924 as the result of risings leading to the reformist government of the Orthodox Bishop Fan Noli, he returned to power several months later with the aid of mercenaries recruited in Jugoslavia. For the next fifteen years he exercised almost complete personal rule. A Republic was proclaimed in 1925 and a Kingdom in 1928, Zogu first becoming President and then King, as Zog I.

Modernization of the country gradually proceeded. For instance a western legal system was introduced, a National Bank was established with Italian participation, a police force was organized under British supervision, and a French *lycée* flourished in Korçë. The tribal system in the mountains began to disintegrate. Nevertheless illiteracy and disease (malaria and tuberculosis) continued to be problems and a land distribution measure of 1930 was largely ineffectual. Over 80% of the population were still engaged in agriculture. Italian influence, foreshadowed by a treaty of 1926 and facilitated by various forms of economic penetration, was allowed to become ever stronger. Finally, after making far-reaching demands, Italy invaded the country in April 1939. Zog fled abroad and a puppet assembly proclaimed the union of the Italian and Albanian crowns.

In October 1940, Italy attacked Greece through Albania, but was unexpectedly repulsed, southern Albania being taken by the Greeks. The following year, however, German forces invaded Jugoslavia and defeated Greece. Italy then extended her influence in the Balkans by annexing the adjoining Albanian-speaking districts of Jugoslavia and Greece. From 1942 onwards partisan movements were active against the Italians and the Germans, who replaced them in 1943 after Italy had made peace with the Western Allies. The two main groups were the Communist-inspired National Liberation Front, which had close connections with Tito's Jugoslav partisans, and the anti-Communist National Front. It was the former group, under Enver Hoxha, that seized power from the retreating Germans and their puppet government in late 1944 and declared a People's Republic in early 1946 after elections that were not considered to be genuine by Great Britain and the USA. Both powers eventually severed all relations. In 1946 two British warships were damaged after hitting mines in the Corfu Channel, and Albania was held responsible by the International Court of Justice. She declined to pay compensation.

Domestically there were great changes: the non-agricultural sector of the economy was nationalized, and the land of estate-owners and of the larger farmers was confiscated. Education and public health received more determined attention. Until 1948 Albania was closely influenced both economically and politically by Jugoslavia: indeed, full economic union had almost been reached and there was every likelihood of Albania eventually becoming part of the new Jugoslav federal state. This would have made possible the reunion of Albania and the Kosmet, which Jugoslavia had retrieved at the end of the war. Jugoslavia's expulsion from the Soviet bloc in 1948 gave Albania an opportunity to sever the Jugoslav connection and place herself under the protection of the Soviet Union, for whom Albania was a useful, if precarious, foothold in the Mediterranean. This relationship lasted until 1961, by which time Albania had openly aligned herself with China in defiance of the Soviet Union, in spite of the setback to the economy that this entailed.

The Land (Figs. 3 and 4)

Basically Albania may be divided into two physiographic zones–the coastal plains of the north and centre and the highlands of the interior and the south coast. In the far south, opposite Corfu, there is a much smaller area of coastal lowland, broken by hills. The country exhibits over wide areas the characteristic north-west to south-east graining of the Dinaric system (Tertiary fold-mountains). The highlands thus include a number of parallel hill and mountain ranges with broad intervening 'longitudinal' valleys and 'transverse' gorge sections, and the associated pattern of 'trellised' drainage is well demonstrated by such rivers as the Mat, Shkumbin and Vjosë. In the far north, in the so-called 'Albanian Alps', the trend-lines are almost west–east, however, and on the eastern frontier virtually north–south (e.g. Korab and Jablanica ranges).

The Alps (becoming the Prokletije Mountains beyond the Jugoslav

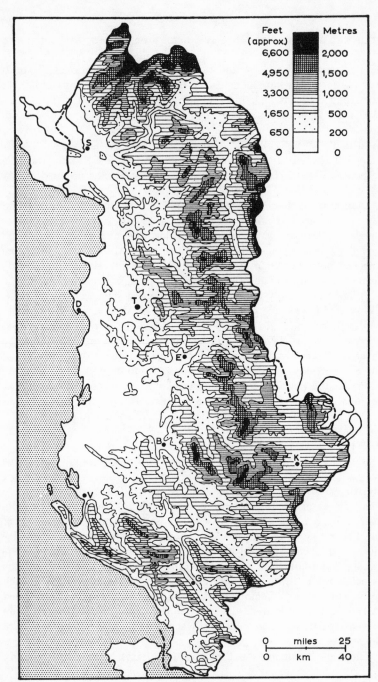

Fig. 3. Relief of Albania

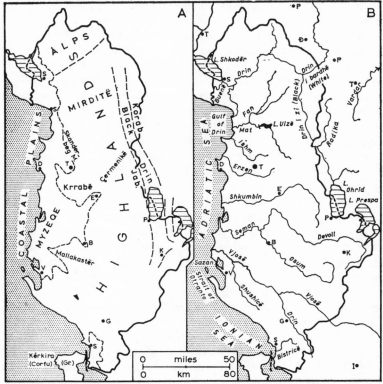

Fig. 4. Generalized physiographic regions (A) and drainage (B) of Albania

border) lie beyond the Drin and are a dissected, glaciated tableland with
cirques, over-deepened valleys and morainic deposits. They consist
predominantly of Triassic and Jurassic limestones and rise in height to
well over 2,000 m/6,550 ft (Jezercë 2,694 m/8,840 ft). To the south there
is a zone of Tertiary serpentine and other igneous rocks, especially in the
region known as *Mirditë*. These rocks, which contain a considerable
wealth of metal ores, also extend further south-eastwards, but in discontinuous fashion, outcropping, for instance, near Elbasan, Lake Ohrid
and Korçë. Apart from the igneous rocks, Tertiary limestones and softer
flysch deposits are generally dominant, especially the latter. The flysch
forms the Krrabë and Çermenikë uplands, for instance, lying to the
north of the Shkumbin, while to the south of this river limestone ranges
often alternate with broad flysch valleys. South of the Vjosë Cretaceous
and Jurassic limestones become dominant in the coastal and near-coastal
ranges. Most of the highland area lying to the south of the Alps exceeds

600 m/2,000 ft in height and a number of ranges rise to over 2,000 m/ 6,550 ft.

Along the eastern frontier there is a faulted north–south trough, overlooked by the Korab and Jablanica ranges, and followed by the Black Drin. Southwards the trough is continued by the basins of Ohrid and Korçë. Lake Prespa (height above sea-level 853 m/2,800 ft) occupies a shorter, but parallel depression further east. It drains by underground means into Lake Ohrid (695 m/2,280 ft). The north–south frontier ranges, lying on the western margins of the ancient Rodopi Block of the Balkans, consist mainly of metamorphosed Triassic rocks, although the Korab range also includes rocks of Carboniferous age. The Korab range has the highest summit in Albania (2,751 m/9,025 ft) and shows evidence of past glaciation.

The coastal plains consist of soft Tertiary deposits, largely covered by Quaternary alluvial material brought down from the mountainous interior by the rivers flowing into the Adriatic. These have steep gradients and a very large winter and spring discharge. Extensive alluvial plains and deltas have thus been built up, and also sand-barriers with lagoons or marshes lying in their rear. Low Tertiary ridges project north-westwards from the interior, so that, in detail, the coastal plains consist of several great embayments filled by the deposits of one or more rivers. Locally the descent to the coastal plains can be steep and abrupt (e.g. north of Tirana in the Skanderbeg Mountains), but in other areas (e.g. the region known as *Mallakastër*) there is a gentle transition through low hills. The largest of the coastal plains is *Myzeqe*, between the Shkumbin and the Vjosë. It is succeeded further inland by a wedge of plain and low hills that extends to Elbasan, but from here easy contact with the northern plains is obstructed by the intervening Krrabë uplands, south of Tirana. The lowlands around Lake Shkodër may also be considered as part of the coastal zone. The Shkodër basin is a depression, shared with Jugoslavia, that follows the general trend-lines, its drainage having been impeded by fluvio-glacial material from the Alps and, more recently, by fluviatile deposits. The lake's average depth varies seasonally between about 8 and 13 m/26 and 43 ft.

Climate and Soils

Over most of Albania the climate is of a 'Mediterranean' type, the mountainous areas being further characterized by a winter rainfall that locally is exceptionally heavy. Some slight 'Continental' influences become evident in the eastern frontier districts, however. The terms 'Mediterranean-Maritime' and 'Mediterranean-Continental' have been used to give emphasis to these differences.

In January almost the whole country experiences average temperatures above freezing. In lowland areas these range between 5° and 9°C/ 41° and 48°F. The sheltered coastal lowlands of the far south (the 'Riviera') have the warmest conditions, while in the high valleys of the Alps average January temperatures fall to below 2°C/28·5°F and there is snow-cover for many weeks. In July the average temperature is over 24°C/75°F over most of the country, falling to below 18°C/64·5°F in the Alpine valleys, and rising to over 25°C/77°F locally in certain enclosed lowlands, such as the Shkodër basin.

Rainfall is chiefly associated with the passage of cyclones down the Adriatic or across the Mediterranean, in the period between September and May. These impinge on the upland areas of Albania, causing heavy winter rain, November usually being the wettest month. Nearly all parts of the country have precipitation totals exceeding 900 mm/35·5 in, but along the eastern frontiers totals fall to below 800 mm/31·5 in. Most areas north of the Mat have figures of over 1,250 mm/nearly 50 in, rising to over 2,000 mm/79 in in the Alps. The upland areas in the extreme south of the country, beyond Vlorë, also receive more than 1,250 mm. By contrast the three summer months have only scanty rain, except in the northern half of the highlands, and virtually complete drought is not uncommon in some years.

The discharge of the rivers reflects these sharp seasonal differences in rainfall. In the winter the rivers are broad, deep torrents that can cause severe flooding, while in the summer braided channels trickle through vast sheets of gravel. The heavy winter rains can also cause severe erosion of over-grazed or deforested hillsides.

The accompanying climatic statistics illustrate some of the regional differences. The figures for Tirana and Vlorë may be regarded as typical of the coastal lowlands and the valleys that open out on to them. Shkodër's

TABLE 3

CLIMATIC STATISTICS · ALBANIA

Station	Average temperature January		Average temperature July		Average annual precipitation	
	°C	°F	°C	°F	mm	in
Tirana	7·0	44·6	24·2	75·6	1,094	43·1
Gjirokastër	5·9	42·6	24·3	75·7	1,865	73·4
Korçë	1·2	34·2	21·2	70·2	739	29·1
Kukës	1·4	34·5	22·6	72·7	962	37·9
Shkodër	5·4	41·7	25·1	77·2	1,860	73·2
Vlorë	9·4	48·9	24·7	76·5	955	37·6

Note: Data based on records for the 1950s only.

high rainfall is associated with its position near the western margin of the Alps, while the much smaller total for Kukës is typical of the sheltered valleys lying beyond them further to the east. Both the January and the July temperatures also show a fall compared with Shkodër. Gjirokastër and Korçë may be similarly compared in these respects.

The soils of Albania include the following chief types. Brown forest soils have developed over the greater part of the highland zone. Mountain-meadow soils occur in the Alps, however, and also in other high ranges, such as the Korab, and carbonate soils occur in the limestone districts. Alluvial soils of varying quality are found in the valleys and the coastal plains, especially the latter.

Land-Use (Fig. 5a) and Farming

Much of the original forest-cover has been either removed or modified by man, and regeneration has been hindered by soil erosion and overgrazing. Reafforestation is now being undertaken, however. In spite of widespread cultivation of the coastal lowlands and their hill margins these still retain some tracts of oak-wood and typical Mediterranean evergreen scrub (maquis). In the highlands oak-dominated deciduous forest or scrub covers large areas. In the centre and north especially the oak gives place to beech, sometimes mixed with pine, at about 1,000 m/ 3,300 ft. Stands of coniferous forest are found above about 1,500 m/ 4,900 ft, e.g. in the Alps and the Korab range. These are succeeded by Alpine meadow above the tree-line. Half of Albania, approximately, is officially reckoned to be wooded or forested, while just over a quarter is hill or lowland pasture and just under a quarter is cultivated. The regional proportions vary very greatly, however, the coastal plains having the highest proportion of arable and the northern highlands the least.

Until the late 1930s cultivation of parts of the coastal plains was hampered by the prevalence of malaria and by the need to reclaim marshes and areas liable to flooding. At the same time summer irrigation facilities were necessary. In the years before and during the Second World War anti-malaria measures were undertaken by the Rockefeller Foundation and land reclamation was carried out by the State and by Italian concerns. Since the war further areas have been reclaimed, with the result that between 1938 and 1964 the area under cultivation increased by two-thirds, chiefly at the expense of marsh, lowland pasture and hill scrub. The proportion of cultivated land under irrigation increased from 10% to 42% over the same period. Two crops a year can often be obtained with irrigation. The mechanization of arable farming has increased greatly, especially since the collectivization drive of the late 1950s. By

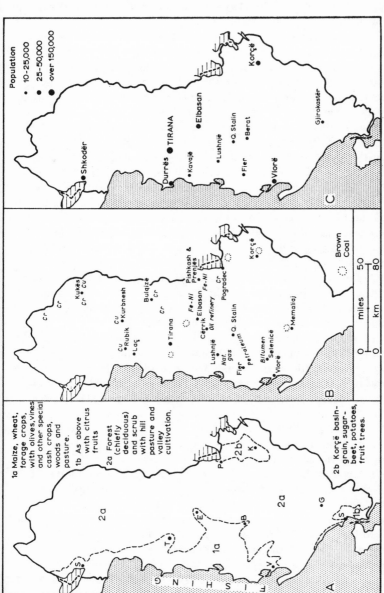

Fig. 5. Generalized land-use regions (A), mineral exploitation (B), and distribution of chief cities and towns (C) in Albania

Map A legend:

1a Maize, wheat, forage crops, with olives, vines and other special cash crops, woods and pasture.

1b As above with citrus fruits

2a Forest (chiefly deciduous) and scrub with hill pasture and valley cultivation.

2b Korçë basin-grain, sugar-beet, potatoes, fruit trees.

Map C legend:

Population

· 10–25,000

● 25–50,000

● over 150,000

1964 only 10% of the cultivated area was still privately farmed–chiefly in the highlands of the north.

These changes have also been accompanied in the plains by a much greater emphasis on special cash crops, such as cotton, tobacco, rice, vegetables, sunflowers, peaches, figs and almonds. Leguminous forage crops have become more important and the cultivation of olives and vines has also increased. Maize, for both human and animal consumption, remains the leading crop, however, with wheat second amongst the grain crops and oats a poor third. Along the sheltered Albanian 'Riviera' the cultivation of citrus fruits has been greatly expanded.

In the highland zone cultivation is generally confined to the valleys and basins, but arable fields can also be found on hillsides, especially as settlements are sometimes located high above the rivers near spring lines. Maize is again the chief crop. In the spacious, fertile basin of Korçë sugar beet is produced and also wheat, barley, oats, rye, potatoes, apples and plums. Here the agricultural area has been increased by the draining of Lake Maliq. Fruit orchards are also found locally in the valleys of the Drin basin.

Livestock are an important element of the farming economy in all parts of the country, although the quality is still often rather poor. Pastoralism, with little or no associated cultivation, remains important as a way of life in some districts. Sheep, valued for their milk and wool, are the most numerous, followed by goats. Horses, mules and donkeys are still used for rural transport, although draught oxen and buffaloes have declined. Dairy cattle, pigs and poultry have increased since 1938, but sheep and goats have shown little upward change. Some fishing takes place off the Albanian coast and also in the lakes. Vlorë has a fish cannery.

Industry and Mining

Despite much recent progress Albania may still be regarded as the least-industrialized nation of Europe. This is scarcely surprising in view of the fact that the country was liberated from Turkish rule only in 1912 and that Italian economic control from the late 1920s until 1943 was concerned with mineral extraction rather than with industrialization as such. As a result very few of Albania's present factories were built before the 1950s. During these years and up to 1961 a number of factories were built with the assistance of the Soviet Union and her partners, such as those for bricks, cement (Tirana, Vlorë), glass (Korçë, Tirana), footwear (Tirana) and textiles (including a cotton and woollen complex in Tirana and a knitwear factory in Korçë). A second textile complex is being built with Chinese aid at Berat. New food-processing and canning establishments have also been built, together with modern plants for tobacco-curing, cotton-ginning and timber-working. Engineering industries still remain very poorly represented, although spare parts for vehicles, diesel motors and simple agricultural machinery are now being produced, chiefly in Tirana. The chemical industry is at present represented mainly by oil-refining, but shortly superphosphates will be produced at Laç and nitrogenous fertilizers at Fier.

There has also been an increase in the extraction of minerals, which, as in the inter-war period, are destined for the export trade, although there is a tendency for more preliminary processing to take place in the country than previously. Assistance from the Soviet bloc has again been important. In 1964 87,000 persons were employed in industry and mining (one-quarter of these being in the city of Tirana), compared with 22,000 in 1950. There were 30 industrial organizations with more than 500 workers. Even so small-scale workshop activities still remain important, though on a co-operative basis. Mining and industry now account for about 40% of the national income. Within this whole sector, however, the food industry is by far the most important in terms of value of output.

ENERGY SUPPLIES (Fig. 5b)

In comparison with its population size Albania is relatively well endowed with petroleum and hydro-power resources and it also has some useful reserves of brown coal in a number of scattered deposits. Petroleum exploitation dates from the 1930s, when an Italian company that had also acquired British, French and American concessions, began production from wells in an area extending from south-east of Fier to Kuçovë, now Qytet (i.e. 'Town') Stalin. The crude oil was piped to the port of Vlorë for export to Italy, but eventually a very small quantity was processed at Stalin. A much larger refinery has since been built at Cërrik. Output, now almost entirely from the Fier district, has grown considerably since the war (764,000 tons in 1964, compared with 108,000 in 1938). More than half the output is now refined in Albania and the remainder is still exported through Vlorë. New resources have recently been discovered near Lushnjë, together with natural gas. Near Vlorë rock bitumen has been exploited (for asphalt) at Selenicë since the late 19th century, but little expansion has occurred in recent decades.

Brown-coal output was negligible before the Second World War but has since increased (292,000 tons in 1964), in order to serve growing industrial needs. Workings exist near Korçë (dating back to the Turkish period), Pogradec, Memaliaj, and in the Elbasan–Tirana area.

Natural conditions favour the harnessing of Albania's rivers for hydro-power generation, but before the Second World War the only hydro-plant was a small one near Korçë. The leading towns had tiny diesel stations. Since the war several medium-sized hydro-power installations have been built, notably the two neighbouring 'Marx' and 'Engels' stations on the Mat, using the impounded waters of artificial Lake Ulzë, and a station on the Bistricë. There is also a small post-war hydro-station in the hills above Tirana. The harnessing of the northern Drin is envisaged for the future. At present about two-thirds of all electricity generation is by hydro-power. On and near the oilfield gas and oil are to be increasingly used for thermal generation. Here the largest station is at Fier. A national power network is now being developed and rural electrification is proceeding.

Metallurgy (Fig. 5b)

The exploitation of metal ores is a vital element in the country's economy, in view of their important role in the export trade. Albania is by far the largest producer of chrome ore (307,000 tons in 1964) in Europe (excluding the Soviet Union) and is the sixth largest in the whole world. Exploitation began under Italian auspices in 1938 and output has expanded greatly since then. The chief areas of mining are in the north, Bulqizë and Kukës being important centres. Chrome is also exploited near Pogradec. Copper-mining began during the Second World War near Rubik, where a smelter was built for the production of blister copper. Recently mining has begun near Kurbnesh and Kukës, both of which now have concentration plants. A new smelter is to be built at Laç, where also sulphuric acid will be produced. A copper wire and cable factory has been built at Shkodër. Output of copper ore reached 145,000 tons in 1964 (blister copper, 2,200 tons).

While the chrome and copper deposits were opened up by Italian companies in the late 1930s, Albania's iron ore deposits were not exploited until the late 1950s. The ores, which occur at places between Elbasan and Pogradec, are hematite ores with 50% iron content and about 1–2 % nickel. Mining takes place near Pogradec, near the villages of Pishkash and Prenjës (near Lake Ohrid), and also further to the west in the Shkumbin valley. At present the ore is exported, but eventually part may be used in blast-furnaces to be erected with Chinese aid at Elbasan. Coking coal will have to be imported, but on the other hand Albania will be able to dispense with imports of pig-iron and steel for her small but growing engineering industry. Czechoslovakia is Albania's chief market for her iron ore (output 351,000 tons in 1964).

Distribution of Population and Chief Cities

Albania's population is the fastest-growing in Europe, and the rapid rate of growth must be considered a drawback in the country's struggle for economic development. Between 1945 and 1964 the population grew by well over 50% from 1·12 to 1·81 millions. In the latter year a birth-rate of 38 and a death-rate of 9 per 1,000 respectively gave an annual rate of natural increase of 29 per 1,000. This was achieved in spite of a rather high infant mortality rate of 82 per 1,000. Between 1945 and 1964 the percentage of the population living in towns (some, admittedly, very small indeed) grew from 21 to 33.

The coastal lowlands between Shkodër and Vlorë, the valleys leading out of them, and the hill-margins fringing them, contain about two-thirds of the population. This whole area may be roughly demarcated by a line passing through Shkodër, Tirana, Elbasan, Berat and Vlorë. It contains 14 of Albania's 20 towns with more than 5,000 inhabitants. The reasons for this predominance include such factors as the historical development of urban centres at the junction of highland and lowland, and, more recently, the growth of ports, the development of the oilfield and the expansion of agricultural villages and small towns as a result of the more intensive utilization of the coastal plains. Other areas of higher-than-average density, in addition to the main zone indicated, include the coastal district opposite Corfu and the upland basin of Korçë.

The distribution of the chief towns is shown in Figure 5c. Apart from Tirana no town has a population exceeding 50,000, although Durrës, Korçë, Shkodër, and Vlorë all have more than 40,000, with Elbasan not far behind with 35,000 (1964). Berat has 22,000. Berat, Durrës, Elbasan, Shkodër and Vlorë have all been urban settlements since Roman times, although they have undergone many fluctuations since then. While the chief towns may still be described as old-established trading and service centres, but with an increasing industrial role, it must be noted that the number and size of towns and large villages primarily devoted to mineral exploitation or processing are increasing significantly, the largest of this group being Stalin (12,000).

TIRANA (*Tiranë*) (population 157,000 in 1964) has grown rapidly since becoming the capital in 1920. After 1912 first Vlorë and then Durrës had been the capital. The population rose from 11,000 in 1923 to 25,000 in 1938 and 60,000 in 1945, since when it has risen to over two and a half times this immediate post-war figure. In 1923 Korçë and Shkodër were twice as populous as Tirana, and Elbasan was the same size. Tirana's rapid growth has been due to the increasing scope of its capital-city functions and also to its development as the leading industrial centre.

As an urban settlement it is not very old, having been established by a feudal lord in the early 17th century. It is located 127 m/417 ft above sea-level at the head of the lowland basin of the Ishm, two small tribu-taries of this river passing through the city. About 10 km/6 miles to the

east the Dajti Massif rises up steeply to 1,612 m/5,290 ft. In the 1930s and
early 1940s the centre of Tirana was replanned under Italian auspices,
with Skanderbeg Square, surrounded by public buildings, forming the
heart of the city. It is traversed by a broad north–south boulevard which
is curtailed southwards by low hills. Two thoroughfares fork westwards
in the direction of Durrës, while a third road climbs south-eastwards
over the Krrabë highlands to descend to the Shkumbin valley and Elbasan. Tirana has a number of newly-established factory industries, concerned with engineering, foodstuffs, footwear, glass and textiles. The
airport lies north-west of the city, at Rinas in the plain of Ishm.

D URRËS, with a maritime history going back several centuries before
the Christian era, is about 30 km/19 miles from the capital, to which it is
connected by road and rail. It degenerated to a mere village under the
Turks. The harbour, extended by the Italians, faces south-eastwards,
being protected on the north by a headland. Further to the south wide
beaches have favoured the development of a seaside resort. ELBASAN
lies in the heart of the country, on the old *Via Egnatia*, at a point where
the broad fertile valley of the Shkumbin narrows and quickly becomes a
gorge. K ORÇË is situated in a fertile upland basin at a height of 900 m/
2,950 ft above sea-level. With a strong Orthodox element it was formerly regarded as the most prosperous and culturally-advanced town of
Albania. The first Albanian-language school was opened here in 1887.
SHKODËR is situated at the south-eastern end of the lake of the same
name, near a point where there is a breach in the highlands surrounding
the basin. It is through this that the lake is drained to the sea by the
Buenë and an arm of the Drin. Behind it rise the foothills of the Albanian
Alps. Until the 20th century Shkodër was the leading commercial centre
not only for the highlands and plains of the north but also for adjacent
parts of Turkish-held Montenegro. Formerly, at least, it was a strong
Roman Catholic centre. VLORË lies a short distance inland from its
harbour, which is situated on the shores of a wide bay that is protected by
the promontory of Karaburun (terminating in Cape Gjuhëz) and Sazan
Island. Further to the south is the oil port.

Transport and Trade

Until the late 1940s Albania had no railways, with the exception of a
narrow-gauge line from the Selenicë bitumen mines to the port of Vlorë,
and until the First World War there had been no roads worthy of the
name. The occupying armies then did some road construction for their
own purposes. In the inter-war period and between 1939 and 1943 the
Italians did much to improve communications, so that after their withdrawal in the latter year they left a useful, if skeletal, network of asphalt

roads, together with modern bridges over the rivers. Even so, a fairly important town such as Gjirokastër still has only unsurfaced mountain roads linking it to Vlorë and Berat.

The Italians had also done much preliminary construction work on a railway system. As a result single-track standard-gauge lines have been completed since the Second World War, between Durrës and Tirana and Durrës and Elbasan, with a short branch to Cërrik. More recently a line to the north, branching off the Durrës–Tirana line, has been built as far as Laç. In 1964 the total length of the railway lines was only 151 km/ 95 miles. The road network, in spite of its shortcomings, is thus far more important than the small railway system and is responsible for about 90% of the volume of both freight and passenger movements.

Albania's links with the outside world are chiefly by sea, in view of the rather limited land communications with Jugoslavia and Greece and also the strained political relationships with both her two neighbours. Nevertheless there is some overland foreign trade through Jugoslav territory.* There is a small volume of passenger traffic by air from Tirana to Rome and Belgrade (via Titograd). Durrës is the leading port, with a turnover of 1·5 million tons in 1964, but its facilities have become inadequate for Albania's increased foreign trade. Much smaller in importance are Vlorë (petroleum and bitumen exports) and Sarandë, in the far south. Shëngjin, south of Shkodër, the only other port, deals only with a small volume of coastal traffic.

Over half of Albania's exports consist of minerals, including petroleum, bitumen, copper, and chrome and iron ores. Most of the other commodities are agricultural in character, including fruit and vegetables, wine and brandy, nuts, wool, leather and tobacco and cigarettes. Some canned fish and timber products are also exported, together with a few simple manufactures, such as cotton cloth and blankets. Imports consist mainly of industrial plant and machinery, vehicles, industrial raw materials (e.g. iron and steel, chemicals, rubber) and certain foodstuffs (e.g· wheat and sugar) and consumer goods of which Albania is short.

In spite of a useful range of primary products for export Albania has a chronically adverse balance of trade which has to be covered by foreign aid or credits, formerly from the Soviet Union and now from China. Previously Italy and Jugoslavia fulfilled a similar role. Only two-thirds of imports were covered by exports in the early 1960s and in the 1950s the proportion was sometimes as low as one-quarter. After 1961 China replaced the Soviet Union as the leading trading partner. In the former year 54% of all foreign trade was with the Soviet Union and only 7% with

---

* In 1966 Albania agreed to increased trade with Jugoslavia, and commercial contacts were restored with Greece.

China, while by 1964 China's figure had risen to 55% and the Soviet Union's trade had ceased entirely. The Socialist countries of East-Central Europe, headed by Czechoslovakia, together accounted for over a third of all foreign trade in both years. Trade with the Socialist world had thus been maintained at about 90% of the total. Post-war trade with Italy has been only a tiny fraction of its pre-war amount. In 1964 Italy accounted for less than 3% of Albania's foreign trade, compared with 50% in 1938. Even so, Italy is the largest non-Socialist trading partner. In spite of the expansion and considerable degree of modernization and diversification of the Albanian economy in recent years it can be argued that the small size of the country and its still relatively low level of development make inevitable the need for close economic association with a larger trading partner or partners. The problem is to avoid at the same time the political subordination that this has hitherto entailed.

Chapter 4

BULGARIA·BŬLGARIYA

Introduction

Bulgaria is a compact, rectangular-shaped country with an east–west span of about 450 km/275 miles and a north–south span of about 275 km/175 miles. In the south-east corner, however, part of Turkey-in-Europe forms an indentation. Bulgaria's neighbours are Rumania to the north, Turkey and Greece to the south and Jugoslavia to the west. To the north and east natural frontiers are provided by the Danube (*Dunav*) and the Black Sea respectively, except that the river frontier with Rumania (450 km/275 miles long) is succeeded in the north-east by a land frontier of about 135 km/85 miles, running across the Dobrudzha Platform from the Danube to the Black Sea. To the south and west the land frontiers with Turkey, Greece and Jugoslavia have only a partial coincidence with natural features. Certainly, for most of its length the border with Turkey runs through the Strandzha uplands, and similarly the border with Greece runs through the southern part of the Rodopi and Pirin Mountains. However, the southern boundary also cuts across the valleys of the Maritsa and its two important tributaries, the Arda and Tundzha, the Turkish city of Edirne being situated at the confluence of all three rivers near the borders of both Bulgaria and Greece. Further west the valleys of the Mesta and Struma are also crossed by the boundary. The Struma frontier does, however, broadly coincide with the Rupel gorge.

The desire for access to the maritime outlets of these valleys, on the Aegean coast of Thrace and Macedonia, affected Bulgarian foreign policy from the time of independence from Turkey (1878) until the Second World War. Indeed, for two brief periods (1912–18 and 1941–4) this goal was partly realized. (It should be noted in passing that Macedonia broadly corresponds to the Vardar basin and its fringes, and stretches from Lake Ohrid in the west to beyond the Struma valley in the east, while Thrace is the area lying between the Stara Planina range, bisecting modern Bulgaria, and the Aegean–Sea of Marmara coast, from the lower Mesta valley in the west to Istanbul in the east.) To the west the frontier with Jugoslavia follows watersheds in hilly and mountainous country to a large extent, but the valleys of the upper Strumeshnitsa and upper Dragovishtitsa (tributaries of the Struma) lie in Jugoslavia, while in the vicinity of the Dragoman Pass a considerable part of the upper Nishava basin lies in Bulgaria. These three areas were all affected by frontier changes in favour of Jugoslavia at the end of the First World War.

The Bulgarians, although possessing a distinctive linguistic and cultural identity that has existed for a thousand years, are nevertheless a people of mixed origins. They are predominantly descended from the Slavs, who entered the Balkan peninsula in the 6th and 7th centuries, and from the numerically smaller 'true' Bulgarians, later intruders of Asiatic origin, who, until their fusion with the Slavs, represented a military ruling class. The Slavs also eventually absorbed the pre-existing Romanized population of the country. Today the Bulgarians, speaking a South Slavonic language, constitute 88% of the total (1956) population of 7·6 millions (8·1 in 1964), the balance being accounted for by Turks (8%) and other very much smaller minorities. The Turks (650,000) are the descendants of settlers who entered Bulgaria during the 500 years of Turkish rule between the end of the 14th century and 1878. Many Turks left the country after 1878 and about 200,000 departed in the mid-1920s under inter-governmental arrangements. Yet another exodus occurred at the instigation of Bulgaria in the early 1950s, when about 150,000 departed. The remaining Turks, although widely scattered throughout the country, show a marked concentration in the north-east and also in the Arda basin. They tend to cling to their Mohammedan faith, as also do the 'Pomaks' (about 140,000), who are Bulgarian Mohammedans living in the Rodopi. Other Turkish influences that have survived include words in the language and dishes in the diet, while to western ears Bulgarian folk-music has a distinctly oriental flavour. Many towns still have mosques, although in many cases they are now only museums. Turkish place-names, which were formerly quite numerous, have been largely eliminated during the present century and have been replaced by Bulgarian substitutes. Other place-name changes, largely political in character, have taken place since the establishment of the present régime; some, such as the change from Varna to Stalin, Pernik to Dimitrovo and Karlovo to Levskigrad, have proved to be only temporary, however.

The other minorities include Gypsies (about 200,000), most of whom are settled, and small numbers of Rumanians, Greeks, Armenians, Jews, Russians and Tatars. The Rumanians are chiefly found in the Danube valley and the Southern Dobrudzha (although many left when this territory was retro-ceded to Bulgaria in 1940 after being in Rumanian hands since 1913). Many Greeks left the country in the mid-1920s and most of the Jewish community (fortunately little affected by Hitler's racial extermination policy) left for Israel after the Second World War. While minorities remain, therefore, notably the Turks, Bulgaria is now distinctly more homogeneous in character than when she regained her independence nearly a hundred years ago.

Finally mention must be made of the Macedonian question. In the middle ages the Bulgarian state included large areas to the west of the present country, including Macedonia, also populated by Southern Slavs. Most Bulgarians used to consider that the Macedonians, now falling chiefly within Jugoslav Macedonia, with smaller numbers living in Greek Macedonia and the extreme south-west of Bulgaria (Pirin Macedonia), were essentially Bulgarians and that their speech was a dialect of Bulgarian. It was on such historical and linguistic grounds that liberated Bulgaria sought to embrace all of Macedonia in modern times. In the event Serbia (and its successor state, Jugoslavia) became the possessor of most of Macedonia after the Turkish withdrawal. Since the Second World War Macedonian has been officially recognized as a separate language by federal Jugoslavia and a Macedonian Republic is one of its constituent states.

Historical Background

For a number of centuries before the beginning of the Christian era much of the territory of present-day Bulgaria was populated by Thracian tribes. Contacts with Greek civilization were strong and, indeed, there were Greek colonies on the Black Sea coast, e.g. *Odessos* (modern Varna). In the 1st century A.D. the Thracian lands passed under Roman rule, Sofia (*Serdica*) and Plovdiv (*Trimontium*) becoming important Romanized towns, while forts were built along the south bank of the Danube, protecting the province of Moesia from northern intruders. With the division of the Empire into eastern and western realms at the end of the 4th century the population came under the rule of Constantinople (Byzantium).

Periodic waves of invasions by barbarian tribes, both before and after this event, presumably led to some modification of the population, but the greatest change resulted from the southward influx of the Slavs in the 6th and 7th centuries. At the end of the 7th century the Slavs were in their turn overrun by the Bulgars, a Turanian people of Asiatic origin who had reached the lower Danube area after following a land route round the northern lowlands of the Black Sea. Defeating Byzantine forces they established a Bulgar-Slav state in what is now northern Bulgaria, with its capital first at Pliska and then at Preslav (north-east and south-west respectively of modern Kolarovgrad). Since the Slavs were the more numerous people it was their language that finally triumphed as fusion of the two peoples proceeded, the original Bulgarians thus leaving behind only their name.

In the early 9th century the Bulgarian state entered upon a period of territorial expansion, involving not only what is now southern Bulgaria but also other neighbouring areas, including Macedonia and Serbia, with their Slav populations. A large part of Rumania was also held. Byzantine Christianity was received in the second half of the century, the most important mission being that led by Clement of Ohrid (after whom the modern University of Sofia is named), who reached Bulgaria in 886 after being expelled from Moravia, where he had been a disciple of the Byzantine scholars Cyril and Methodius, the originators of the earliest form of the Cyrillic script and also of the Old Slavonic liturgy. As a result, the Bulgarian example influenced the early development of the Orthodox form of Christianity in the South and East Slavonic lands, including Kievan Russia.

By the early 10th century this First Bulgarian Kingdom or Empire, governed by Simeon, was at the height of its vigour, both cultural and political. Internal disintegration followed shortly afterwards, however, and the supremacy of Byzantium (or *Tsarigrad*, i.e. 'Emperor's town', as it is still known to the South Slavs) was eventually restored, first in Bulgaria proper and then in Macedonia (including Serbia), which retained its independence in the meantime. By 1018 all the old Bulgarian territories had been conquered. A successful revolt in 1185 led to the establishment in the north of a Second Bulgarian Empire, with its capital at Tŭrnovo, and to the shaping of a large powerful state under Ivan Assen II in the first half of the 13th century. Like the earlier Empire the second expanded far beyond the limits of present-day Bulgaria, but Serbia was not included. Later in the 13th century feudal struggles and Tatar invasions led to a contraction of this kingdom and to a loss of cohesion. Despite internal partition and the loss of Macedonia to Serbia, 14th-century Bulgaria nevertheless achieved a cultural level of considerable impressiveness and a legacy of church frescoes remains from this period. Medieval Bulgaria also witnessed the rise of the Bogomil movement (10th–14th centuries). This was a socio-religious movement attacking ecclesiastical abuses and favouring reversion to a simpler form of Christianity, while at the same time opposing feudalism. It spread throughout the Balkan peninsula and also found echoes in western Europe.

The mid-14th century saw the first onslaught on the Christian peoples of the Balkans by the Ottoman Turks, pressing outwards from Asia Minor. By the end of the century (1396) all Bulgaria was in their hands and the five centuries of the 'Turkish yoke' had begun. The economic and cultural position of the Bulgarians suffered a setback, since, in effect, they became second-class citizens in their own country, experiencing heavy taxation under an alien military-feudal system and discrimination against the Christian religion. Fortunately, however, the Church and the monasteries were able to preserve the cultural traditions of the nation. Over the years a considerable Turkish population settled in Bulgaria, particularly in the plains; the hills, on the other hand, remained centres of nationalist feeling. Although spasmodic revolts were ruthlessly suppressed, small-scale guerrilla activities by the 'haidut' bands were a feature of the long occupation.

From the end of the 18th century onwards a national renaissance took place in Bulgaria. By this time the Turkish Empire had already begun to shrink territorially, and the order that characterized the earlier centuries of occupation had given way to corrupt decadence and arbitrary local rule. At the same time internal and external commerce were expanding and contacts with the outside world multiplying. The Danubian and Black Sea ports increased their traffic and the first railway was built by British engineers from Ruse to Varna in 1866. The first small textile factory dates from the 1830s (at Sliven). Under these changing conditions a patriotic literary movement developed (heralded by Father Paisi's *History of the Bulgarians* in 1762), and village schools and reading rooms were opened from the 1830s onwards. In 1870 the Turks at last allowed the re-establishment of an independent Bulgarian Church, thus ending Greek ecclesiastical control, which had been an obnoxious concomitant of Turkish rule and which had been associated with attempts at Hellenization of the Bulgarians.

A liberation movement was encouraged by Russian influences and by émigré elements across the Danube in sympathetic Rumania. Several of the patriotic writers of the 19th century combined literary activities with revolutionary agitation, such as Botev, Karavelov and Rakovski. The widespread national uprising of April 1876, for which the nation had been prepared by the colourful young patriot, Levsky (executed by the Turks in 1873), resulted in cruel suppression, which in its turn led to a remarkable wave of sympathy throughout the world. The name of Gladstone, who was incensed by the atrocities, is still revered in Bulgaria. Following on Turkey's refusal to grant Bulgaria autonomy an exasperated Russia, acting in her now-traditional role as a champion of the Balkan Christians, declared war and invaded Bulgaria by way of Rumania in 1877. After epic battles associated with the siege of Pleven and the holding of the Shipka Pass, the Russian and Rumanian troops, together with Bulgarian volunteers, pressed southwards to Constantinople and as a result Turkey was forced to accept the Russian-dictated Treaty of San Stefano (1878), setting up an autonomous Greater Bulgaria, to include Macedonia and part of the Aegean coast. The fear of the other Great Powers that this large state would prove to be a pliable tool of Russia against a much-weakened Turkey led Bismarck to call the Berlin Conference of 1878. It was agreed that northern Bulgaria, together with the Sofia area to the south-west, should be an autonomous principality, while the south, to be called Eastern Rumelia, should be ruled by a Christian governor under the Sultan. Macedonia and the Aegean coast of Thrace remained under Turkish rule.

A constituent assembly meeting in the old capital, Tŭrnovo, in 1879, inaugurated an exceptionally liberal constitution (destined to be frequently violated, however) and invited Prince Alexander of Battenberg to be the first monarch. The Third Kingdom (1879–1946) thus came into existence and Sofia became the new capital. The artificial separation of north and south was ended in 1885, when, after a coup in the south, northern forces were able to annex Eastern Rumelia, despite an armed attack in protest by Serbia. In 1886 Alexander abdicated and was succeeded by another German prince, Ferdinand of Saxe-Coburg-Gotha.

Bulgaria, while still remaining an overwhelmingly agricultural country, now experienced considerable economic change, involving the extension of cash-cropping, and the growth of towns, especially Sofia, and of some small-scale factory industry. The railway net developed and foreign trade expanded, based on the export of primary produce, especially grain surpluses, in exchange for manufactures. Many Turks, especially those who had formed the ruling class, left the country, releasing considerable areas of land, especially the great semi-feudal estates ('chifliks'). In 1908 formal independence as a kingdom was declared. Apart from the development of a small business class Bulgarian society was remarkably egalitarian, being based on peasant farmers, with increasing numbers of rural immigrants forming a small nascent working class in the towns.

In 1912 Bulgaria, Serbia, Greece and Montenegro together made war on Turkey (First Balkan War) with a view to gaining the remaining areas under Turkish rule populated by South Slavs and Greeks. Bulgaria hoped to obtain territories, especially Macedonia, to which she felt historically entitled and of which she had been cheated at Berlin. Scarcely had Turkey been defeated (Treaty of London) when Bulgaria attacked Serbia over the Macedonian question and was in turn attacked by Greece, Rumania and Turkey (Second Balkan War). A defeated Bulgaria then not only had to surrender part of her gains from Turkey (Treaty of Bucharest) but also cede the southern Dobrudzha to Rumania, including the small ports of Silistra and Balchik and valuable grain lands. Nevertheless she retained territorial gains in the middle Struma and Mesta valleys, part of the Aegean coast, including the port of Dedeagach (Greek *Alexandroúpolis*), and an area on the Black Sea coast south of Burgas. This setback encouraged Bulgaria to join the Central Powers in the

First World War (1915) in the hope of gaining Macedonian territory from Serbia. Defeat put her in a worse position than before since she now lost her Aegean outlet to Greece (Treaty of Neuilly, 1919) and some western frontier districts to Serbia, now part of Jugoslavia, and also had to pay large reparations to Greece, Jugoslavia and Rumania. A further problem was the absorption of a quarter of a million embittered émigrés from Greek and Serbian Macedonia. A powerful Macedonian terrorist organization not only fomented trouble within Bulgaria but also exacerbated relations with her neighbours. The national disaster led to widespread unrest and to the election of a radical Agrarian government (1919–23), which was terminated by the assassination of its leader, Stamboliysky. Three months later nation-wide demonstrations (led by Dimitrov and Kolarov, the future Communist rulers) against the new right-wing government were severely put down. Thereafter constitutional government in Bulgaria went through a number of vicissitudes and the persecution of left-wing elements occurred from time to time. In 1935 King Boris inaugurated a period of personal rule that was to last until his death in 1943.

In the late 1930s Bulgaria gave way to increasing political and economic pressure from Nazi Germany, and in 1941 entered the Second World War as her ally, largely with a view to realizing her long-frustrated territorial ambitions. German troops were allowed to pass through the country in order to attack Greece and Jugoslavia and as a result of her co-operation Bulgaria was able to occupy Jugoslav Macedonia and part of the Aegean coast of Greece. Popular feeling against the alliance increased after the German invasion of the Soviet Union, although Bulgaria herself was careful not to declare war. Certain anti-government groups, dominated by the Communist Party and including the Agrarians, sponsored an underground Fatherland Front and partisan movement. As Soviet troops crossed the Danube in September 1944, the Front seized power from a new coalition government formed to arrange an armistice with the Allies. Bulgaria withdrew from the war relatively unscathed, but, as was to be expected, the ensuing peace treaty (1947) deprived her of her wartime gains. She was, however, allowed to retain the southern Dobrudzha, which Rumania had returned to her in 1940 (Treaty of Craiova) under German pressure. A Republic was declared in 1946 and the infant King Simeon went into exile.

Using the façade of the Fatherland Front the Communist Party, led by Dimitrov, who had spent years of exile in the Soviet Union and who had been Secretary of the Communist International, quickly obtained the reins of power. After the execution of the leader of the parliamentary opposition he proceeded to mould Bulgaria in the image of the Soviet

Union, on the basis of a new constitution of 1947 setting up a People's Republic. Nationalization of all the means of production was achieved in 1948, collectivization of the land was virtually complete ten years later, and an ambitious programme of industrialization was embarked on, with Soviet aid. Since the early 1950s, Bulgaria has experienced an impressive economic advance, especially in the industrial field, but on the other hand results in the agricultural sector have at times been disappointing. Collectivization has also caused some labour redundancy. The scope of foreign trade has widened, some manufactures now being exported, and the Black Sea tourist industry has been greatly expanded. Since the late 1950s there have been some cautious trends towards decentralization of the economy and liberalization of the régime. Although the Orthodox Church played an honourable role in preserving the national heritage throughout the Turkish occupation, and although the bulk of the population were members of it, at least nominally, until very recently, the policy of the régime is to favour atheism.

The exceptionally close nature of Bulgaria's post-war alliance with the Soviet Union was partly a natural outcome of the liberation of 1878 and the intervention of 1944, but it was also partly due to the exposed geographical position of the country, adjoining anti-Communist Greece and Turkey and heretical Jugoslavia. By the late 1950s tension with these neighbours had been greatly reduced, although it is scarcely to be expected that relationships with Greece and Turkey will become positively friendly in view of long-established antipathies. Nor is the recent rapprochement with Jugoslavia likely to lead to the federation that was seriously discussed between Dimitrov and Tito after the Second World War until the idea was quashed by Stalin and in any case rendered impracticable by Jugoslavia's exclusion from the Soviet bloc in 1948. Only in 1964, after the stumbling-block of the payment of Bulgaria's post-war reparations had been overcome, were normal relations established with Greece, after nearly a quarter of a century of enmity. Bulgaria will gain traffic links to the Aegean coast and Greece will benefit by joint schemes for the regulation of rivers.

The Land (Figs. 6, 7, 8)

The physiography of Bulgaria, while complicated in detail, nevertheless presents a fairly simple general picture. Briefly, a central mountain belt with interior basins runs across the country from west to east, separating two great plains, while in the south-west of the country a fourth major zone is the Macedonian–Thracian Massif (or Rodopi Block), broken by the important north–south Struma and Mesta valleys. The chief range of the central mountain belt is the Stara Planina ('Old

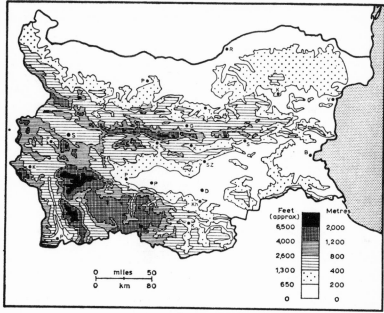

Fig. 6. Relief of Bulgaria

Mountain-range'), alternatively known as the Balkan Range. The Stara Planina, an extension of the Carpathians and thus a member of the Tertiary fold-mountain system of Europe, enters the north-western part of the country from Serbia and after swinging south-eastwards towards Sofia runs due east across the country. The range exhibits plateau surfaces and rounded summits, and escaped glaciation owing to its relatively low elevation. Triassic and Jurassic rocks, especially limestones, predominate, but ancient crystalline rocks are exposed in the western and central portions, while Tertiary rocks are dominant in the east. With the exception of this eastern portion most of the range rises to over 750 m/2,500 ft above sea-level, with Botev and Vezhen, near Karlovo, reaching 2,376 m/7,800 ft and 2,198 m/7,400 ft respectively, while Midzhur, on the Jugoslav border, rises to 2,168 m/7,100 ft. To the east of Sliven there is a marked loss of height and here, moreover, the Stara Planina branches out into a number of minor ranges, one of which runs out to sea as Cape Emine. While the Stara Planina has a number of passes, including those of Shipka and of the Iskŭr gorge, it nevertheless acts as a barrier to easy north–south movement, particularly since its southern side is marked by steep fault-scarps.

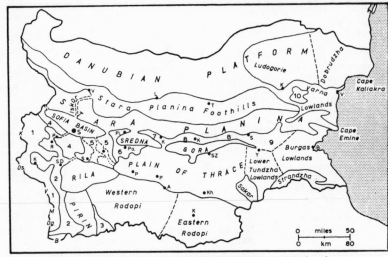

Fig. 7. Generalized physiographic regions of Bulgaria

Key: 1. Struma frontier ranges: **B**–Belasitsa, **K**–Kraishte, **M**–Maleshevo, **Og.**–Ograzhden, **Os.**–Osogovo, **V**–Vlakhina. **2.** Struma valley and basins. **3.** Mesta valley. **4.** Vitosha-Lyulin-Viskyar. **5.** Ikhtiman Sredna Gora. **6.** Pirdop basin and Panagyurishte foothills. **7.** Upper Stryama (Karlovo) basin. **8.** Upper Tundzha (Kazanlŭk) basin. **9.** Sliven basin. **10.** Provadiya plateau.

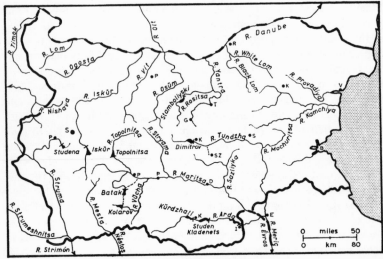

Fig. 8. Drainage of Bulgaria

By contrast the land slopes much more gently towards the north, where there is a broad foothill zone with a number of sizeable depressions, e.g. those of Botevgrad, Sevlievo and Elena. North of a line running very approximately through Vratsa, Tŭrnovo and Kolarovgrad is the Danubian or northern plain of Bulgaria. This is more accurately described as a northward-sloping platform, however, since much of it is over 125 m/400 ft above sea-level and there are often cliffs overlooking the Danube. Towards the Stara Planina foothills the land rises to 300 m/1,000 ft. The platform consists of horizontally-bedded rocks of Cretaceous and Tertiary age, chiefly limestones and clays, and is covered with loess over wide areas. Crossing it from south to north are a number of rivers which, with their tributaries, have cut broad, deep valleys into the surface, the dissection of which has led locally to the development of low tabular hills. It should be noted that all these rivers rise in the Stara Planina, with the exception of the Iskŭr, which, rising far to the south in the Pirin Mountains, crosses the Sofia basin and then cuts through the Stara Planina by means of a gorge. Eastwards the Danubian Platform increases in elevation to become the Ludogorie and Dobrudzha plateaux, locally rising to over 450 m/1,500 ft. To the south are the Varna lowlands, largely corresponding to the valleys of the two Kamchiya rivers and the Provadiya. Between the latter and the Golyama Kamchiya is the low Provadiya plateau.

South of the Stara Planina and running parallel to it, from south-east of Sofia to Yambol, is a second, but discontinuous and lower range with rounded forms, consisting of igneous and metamorphic rocks, and known as the Sredna Gora ('Central' or 'Middle Forest'). It may be regarded as an outlying component of the Rodopi Massif, from the main part of which it is now separated by the great Tertiary subsidence depression of the Plain of Thrace. Alternatively the Sredna Gora is sometimes known as the Anti-Balkan range. It consists of three elements–the Ikhtiman Sredna Gora, south-east of Sofia (and within which lies the Ikhtiman Basin), the 'True' (*Sŭshtinska*) Sredna Gora, between the R. Topolnitsa and R. Stryama, and the 'Deer' (*Sŭrnena*) Sredna Gora, to the east of the latter river. The True Sredna Gora reaches a maximum height of 1,604 m/5,260 ft (Bogdan). The Sredna Gora is succeeded westwards, towards the Jugoslav border, by Vitosha (Cherni Vrŭkh 2,290 m/7,510 ft), lying immediately to the south of Sofia, and the Lyulin and Viskyar ranges to the west of the capital. The two latter, like the Ikhtiman Sredna Gora, reach a maximum height of about 1,200 m/nearly 4,000 ft. Between the Stara Planina and the Sredna Gora ranges are elongated Tertiary fault-depressions, these being, from west to east, the basins of Sofia, Pirdop, Karlovo, Kazanlŭk (upper Tundzha valley) and Sliven

(Tundzha and Mochuritsa confluence). The Pirdop and Karlovo basins merge southwards into the Plain of Thrace and are drained by the Topolnitsa and Stryama respectively.

South of the Sredna Gora is the southern plain of Bulgaria, drained by the Maritsa and known as the Plain of Thrace (*Trakiyska Nizina*). This Tertiary depression, partly covered with more recent deposits, extends eastwards from the neighbourhood of Pazardzhik to the low watershed between the Sazliyka and the Tundzha. Further to the east the plain of the Tundzha and the Burgas Lowlands, based largely on weathered volcanic rocks, are also separated from each other by only a low watershed, so that they give, in effect, a seaward extension to the Plain of Thrace. To the south these lowlands are delimited, near the Turkish border, by the Strandzha and Sakar uplands, largely consisting of crystalline rocks. Like the Sredna Gora these uplands are also outlying members of the Rodopi Massif.

The south-west of the country consists of part of the ancient block of metamorphic and igneous rocks often known as the Rodopi Massif, but perhaps more appropriately called the Macedonian–Thracian Massif, since the Rodopi Mountains proper form only a part of the whole. It was around this ancient block that the Tertiary fold-mountain system of the southern part of the Balkan peninsula was raised up. The block itself was also affected by these earth movements, leading to uplift, faulting and igneous activity. The Eastern, Low Rodopi, consisting of hilly country, with a partial Tertiary cover, frequently volcanic in character, and drained by the Arda and its tributaries, contrasts with the much loftier and less dissected Western or High Rodopi, drained by right-bank tributaries of the Maritsa. Here there are wide areas of ancient plateau surfaces, and fault-scarps overlook the upper part of the Plain of Thrace. Golyam Perelik and Syutkyar rise to 2,191 m/7,200 ft and 2,186 m/7,170 ft respectively. The highest summits in Bulgaria are, however, found in the neighbouring Pirin Mountains (Vikhren 2,915 m/9,550 ft) and Rila Mountains (Musala 2,925 m/9,660 ft), where above about 2,500 m/7,750 ft certain features of mountain glaciation, including cirques, are found. Between the Rila Mountains and the Vitosha and Ikhtiman Sredna Gora ranges is the Samokov basin (over 800 m/2,625 ft). West of the Pirin and Rila ranges is the important Struma valley, with several constituent Tertiary basins, including those of Pernik, Radomir, Kyustendil, and Stanke Dimitrov, while between the Western Rodopi and the Pirin Mountains is the smaller Mesta valley. Between the Struma and the Jugoslav frontier are hill and mountain ranges (including Osogovo, Maleshevo, Kraishte, Ograzhden and Vlakhina) of varied composition, including schists and Jurassic limestones. Ruen, in the Osogovo range, reaches 2,252 m/7,400 ft. Several passes give access to the valleys of left-bank tributaries of the Vardar. Between the Strumeshnitsa valley and the Greek frontier is the Belasitsa range, rising to over 2,000 m/ 6,550 ft.

The coastal districts of Bulgaria have an interesting variety of features, the cliffs of the Dobrudzha (Cape Kaliakra) and of Cape Emine contrasting with shallow embayments and lagoons, as at Varna and Burgas. North of Burgas the ancient little port of Nesebŭr (Greek *Mesembria*) is located on an island linked to the mainland by a *tombolo*. Locally fine beaches provide a basis for the growing tourist industry, especially near Varna and Burgas.

Climate and Soils

From the climatic point of view Bulgaria shows some interesting transitional features, situated as it is on the borders of the Mediterranean lands and the continental interior of eastern Europe. North of the Stara Planina the Danubian Platform, open to atmospheric influences from central and eastern Europe, experiences a Continental climate. Cold winter winds sweep across the countryside from the north-east, while in the summer hot, dusty conditions prevail, broken periodically by thunderstorms. Annual rainfall varies between 500 and 650 mm/20 and 25 in, most of the total falling in the summer months. Average July temperatures are 22 to 24°C/71·5 to 75·0°F and average January temperatures −2 to −3°C/26·5 to 28·5°F. In parts of the Dobrudzha winter temperatures are slightly lower and annual precipitation falls to below 450 mm/17·5 in in its coastal districts.

South of the Stara Planina, which exerts a considerable influence on air movements, a somewhat modified Continental climate prevails, slight Mediterranean influences being felt. Compared with the climate of the Northern Platform the summers are longer and winters rather less cold, with a shorter period of snow-cover. Annual precipitation tends to be a little smaller, however, particularly in the upper Thracian Plain, sheltered on three sides by mountainous areas. In the far south Mediterranean influences become clearly recognizable, especially in the lower Struma, Mesta and Maritsa valleys and the Arda basin. These rather limited areas experience considerably warmer winters and summers than the rest of Bulgaria and also have a winter rainfall maximum. Even so winter conditions are not sufficiently mild for the successful growing of Mediterranean crops such as the olive and citrus fruits.

Lastly there are those areas greatly influenced by altitude or by proximity to the sea. Temperatures are lower and precipitation higher in the mountainous districts than in the adjoining lowlands; January

TABLE 4

CLIMATIC STATISTICS · BULGARIA

Station	Average temperature January		Average temperature July		Average annual precipitation	
	°C	°F	°C	°F	mm	in
Sofia	−1·6	29·1	21·5	70·7	644	25·4
Kŭrdzhali	+1·6	34·9	23·4	74·1	625	24·6
Pleven	−1·7	28·9	23·6	74·5	585	23·0
Plovdiv	0·0	32·0	24·0	75·2	539	21·2
Varna	+1·4	34·5	22·6	72·7	474	18·7

temperatures fall to below −4°C/25°F and precipitation rises to over 1,000 mm/nearly 40 in. Along the Black Sea coast maritime influences result in a smaller temperature range than occurs further inland, but rainfall is slightly lower. The accompanying climatic data for Sofia (height 550 m/1,800 ft), Kŭrdzhali (in the hills of the Arda basin), Pleven, Plovdiv and Varna, illustrate some of these regional differences.

As regards soils the Danubian Platform has various categories of 'black-earths' of excellent fertility, based on loess to a large extent. These give way to grey forest soils as the Stara Planina foothills are reached. In the southern lowlands the soils are also of good quality, consisting of (a) the black 'smolnitsa' or 'pitch' soils (developed on lacustrine clays), situated in the Plain of Thrace, Tundzha lowlands and Burgas lowlands (also the Sofia basin), and (b) flanking zones of 'cinnamon-coloured' soils at higher levels. These cinnamon soils also extend into the Strandzha and eastern Rodopi hills, where they become slightly podzolized, however, and they are also found in the Struma and Mesta valleys. Brown forest soils and mountain-meadow soils occur in the Stara Planina and in the Rila, Pirin and Western Rodopi mountains. Alluvial soils, often of good quality, are found along the rivers, especially the Danube and the Maritsa, and also in the Tertiary basins.

Land-Use (Fig. 9) and Farming

Despite felling by man for timber and for charcoal-burning considerable areas of Bulgaria are still forested, or at least well wooded. Extensive stands of coniferous trees occur in the Pirin, Rila and Western Rodopi mountains, while deciduous forests, of beech and oak predominantly, are found on their lower slopes and also in the Stara Planina, Sredna Gora, Strandzha and the Struma frontier ranges. Such areas support local

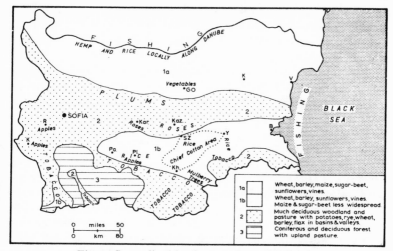

Fig. 9. Generalized land-use regions of Bulgaria

timber industries. Scattered areas of deciduous trees are also to be found in the intermediate areas between mountain and plain, but here scrub is often the appropriate description. Over-grazing has often led to soil-erosion on steep hillslopes and as a result the goat has been virtually banned in recent years and reafforestation and terracing encouraged. In the northern and southern plains the natural wooded-steppe grasslands have been completely transformed over the centuries by arable cultivation. Planted shelter-belts of trees can be advantageous in the semi-arid Dobrudzha, where considerable progress has been made in this respect. In the Ludogorie patches of oak scrub remain from a formerly more extensive cover. In the Struma and Mesta valleys and the Strandzha uplands Mediterranean evergreen shrubs locally appear, although oak and beech are more typical of the latter area.

Climate and soils offer Bulgaria considerable advantages for arable farming, but periodic summer drought can, unfortunately, lead to wide fluctuations in crop yields. The leading areas of arable cultivation are the northern and southern plains, but there are important differences between the two areas as well as local variations within each. Generally speaking the Danubian Platform has a much greater emphasis on grain crops, including wheat, barley and maize, while the south, although an important grain producer, has a higher ratio of other crops and owing to its rather drier summers engages in maize-growing only to a slight extent. Within the north there is a distinction between the east and the west, the former being less suited to maize-growing because of its drier summers, and as a result the importance of maize decreases eastwards while that of barley increases. In addition to the grain crops of the northern and southern plains sunflowers are widely grown as a source of vegetable oil, and sugar beet is cultivated where moisture conditions allow and where there is accessibility to refineries, the north being far more important than the south. Vines are also widely grown on suitable sites in both plains, both for the table and for wine-making, and commercial vegetable growing, some of it for the export trade, is also important, in value, if not always in area. In the southern plains special cash crops achieve great importance, especially in the Plain of Thrace. Cotton is grown in an area lying between Stara Zagora, Yambol and Khaskovo, while rice is grown under irrigated conditions near Stara Zagora, along the Tundzha, and in the Plovdiv–Pazardzhik area along the Maritsa. In the latter area there is also much fruit and vegetable growing, especially for the export market. Specialities include strawberries, melons, quality grapes (for wine-making and dessert), tomatoes and red peppers. Apricots, peaches and apples are also important. In the north there is an important vegetable-growing district around Gorna Oryakhovitsa. There are also specialized areas of fruit and vegetable production in the Black Sea coastlands.

The hilly areas and upland basins, while not self-supporting in food-stuffs, nevertheless contribute some valuable crops to the national economy. In the central part of the Stara Planina foothills plum trees, for the making of plum brandy, are an important feature of the rural landscape. The hill country of the Arda basin has a particular specialization in tobacco production, chiefly for the export trade, which began at the end of the 19th century. There are outlying areas of cultivation in the Sakar and on the northern slopes of the Western Rodopi. In all these areas eroded soils, poor in organic matter, are ideal. Tobacco-growing also occurs in the lower Struma and Mesta valleys. In the Kyustendil and Radomir basins there are important apple orchards. The 'Rose Valley' (Karlovo and Kazanlŭk basins) is noted, as the name implies, for its cultivation of rose-bushes, the blooms being used for the production of attar of roses (rose-oil). This valuable product is destined for export chiefly, as a raw material in the perfume industry. The commercial cultivation of roses dates back some two hundred years and is related to the specific advantages of the local soil and microclimate.

Despite the emphasis on arable crops (covering over 80% of the farmed area) there is at the same time a considerable attention to live-stock, although until recently its quality left much to be desired. A large part of the maize produced is destined for pigs and poultry, while the pedigree dairy herds now being gradually built up on the collective farms depend on leguminous forage crops, barley and silage to a large extent. Sheep, which are rather more numerous than people in Bulgaria, are widely distributed and are a familiar sight not only on upland pastures but also on lowland stubble after the July grain harvest.

During the 20th century Bulgarian agriculture has undergone considerable changes in response to the possibilities afforded by foreign markets. While the grain surpluses accruing in good years continue to be a useful element in the export trade other products have tended to increase in importance. Tobacco and rose-oil were already important before the First World War, while between the wars fruit and vegetables, both fresh and preserved, became significant, and also eggs and poultry. The output of rose-oil fell very greatly, however, in the 1930s and 1940s, chiefly owing to competition from chemical substitutes, but the industry has subsequently shown some revival. Since the Second World War these various high-value products have been further stimulated by the government, with the aid of new irrigation schemes, technical advice and large-scale organization both of cultivation and marketing. One-sixth of the arable area is now irrigated. Much of Bulgaria's fruit and vegetable produce finds guaranteed markets in the Soviet Union, Czechoslovakia and Eastern Germany. Organizationally the country's small farms, once totalling over a million, have been consolidated into less than a thousand large collective farms, although small private plots for household use are still permitted. Finally mention should be made of the fishing industry. While small by world standards, the total catch landed at Danube and Black Sea ports is increasing as a result of reorganization and re-equipment.

Industry and Mining

Industry and mining have increased greatly since the Second World War, although output in many sectors is still small by West European standards. Nevertheless the value of output from industry and mining now exceeds that from agriculture, and in view of the fact that before the war Bulgaria was one of the least industrialized countries of Europe her progress in recent decades must be treated as a remarkable achievement. Engineering industries have made particularly rapid progress.

Craft industries were, in fact, fairly important in Bulgaria during the Turkish period, and textiles especially found a ready market in the Empire. The entry into Bulgaria of foreign manufactures from the latter part of the 19th century onwards tended to undermine many of these small-scale industries. However, food-handling establishments, such as flour-mills, vegetable-oil mills, sugar beet refineries and fruit- and

vegetable-processing factories, showed considerable development, especially in the inter-war period. Since the last war engineering industries,
hitherto very poorly represented, or not at all, have been developed, such
as shipbuilding (Varna), motor-cycles (Lovech), mining machinery
(Pernik), electric motors (Troyan), electric hoists (Gabrovo), electric
pumps (Vidin), telephonic equipment (Belogradchik), tractors (Karlovo)
and agricultural machinery (Ruse). A motor-vehicle industry is planned.
The chemical industry has also expanded and includes fertilizers
(Dimitrovgrad and Stara Zagora), soda (Reka Devnya, near Varna),
penicillin (Razgrad) and sulphuric acid (non-ferrous metal refineries). A
petrochemical industry is being developed in association with the new
Burgas oil refinery. Large cement works have been built at Dimitrovgrad, Reka Devnya and near Pernik and Vratsa. The textile industry,
formerly rather small-scale in character, showed until recent times a
marked localization in towns on the margin of the central mountain belt,
especially Gabrovo and Sliven. Here supplies of wool and water were
important factors historically. The building of modern textile mills in
other places (e.g. Sofia and Plovdiv) has reduced this emphasis, however.
Despite the considerable output of factory textiles the peasant-woman
with her distaff can still be seen in the countryside. Bulgaria also has a
small natural silk industry, which, although scattered, is particularly well
represented in the Eastern Rodopi and Plain of Thrace. Here the mulberry is cultivated. A synthetic fibre industry is being established at
Yambol.

A certain amount of industrial development is quite obviously
advantageous, both to reduce the need to import items that could
reasonably be made within the country and to provide employment for
the 'surplus' rural population (a chronic problem further exacerbated by
continued population growth and the larger-scale methods associated
with collectivization), but the relatively small size of the domestic market
may place a limit on the widespread development of large-scale industry.
On the other hand, it is true that Bulgaria now has an increasing volume
of industrial exports; these are taken by the Soviet Union to a large
extent, however, and are a means of repaying credits for the supply of
factory equipment. Further intensification and specialization of agriculture for the export trade, together with the further development of tourist
facilities, are scheduled to accompany the process of industrialization.
In 1964 the numbers working in industry (888,000) were more than three
times the total in 1948, and industrial production was more than nine
times that of 1948. Rather less than half the labour force is now employed
in agriculture, compared with about 80% in the 1930s.

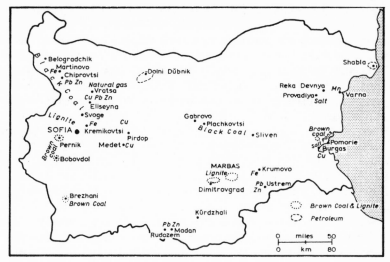

Fig. 10. Mineral exploitation in Bulgaria

ENERGY SUPPLIES (Fig. 10)

Bulgaria's chief sources of energy are brown coal, lignite and hydro-power. Reserves of the two former are substantial and there is still some unharnessed hydro-power potential. On the other hand petroleum and black coal resources are insufficient even for Bulgaria's rather modest present needs. The chief source of brown coal is the Pernik basin in the upper Struma valley, located about 30 km/19 miles south-west of Sofia. State-owned mines were developed in the 1890s and the straggling workers' settlement of Pernik grew up. Other significant brown-coal mining areas, also in the Struma valley, are at Bobovdol and Brezhani. Apart from the Struma fields there is also a small field north of Burgas. Lignite working is of more recent development and output is dominated by fields in the Maritsa basin ('Marbas'), where there has been a great expansion since the 1940s. The deposits now being worked extend from near Dimitrovgrad in an easterly direction to beyond the Sazliyka. Here there is the newer 'Marbas Iztok' (i.e. 'East') field. Dimitrovgrad, where the lignite is used for chemical industries and thermal electric power generation, is a new town built near the pre-existing railway junction of Rakovski. Thermal power generation is now growing impressively in Marbas Iztok. Other lignite workings are found in the Sofia basin, both to the east and the west of the capital. The national output of brown coal and lignite amounted to 9·8 and 14·0 million tons respectively in 1964.

Black coal is obtained in the Stara Planina range from a number of small mines with rather difficult geological conditions. One area of mining extends from Belogradchik to the Iskŭr gorge area (where some anthracite is mined at Svoge) and another from Gabrovo to Sliven (the 'Balkanbas'). Total output is very small, however, amounting to only 0·6 million tons (1964). Coal of coking quality is processed at the small coke works at Plachkovtsi. Thus a large part of Bulgaria's needs of black coal and coke has to be met by imports, chiefly from the Soviet Union. Similarly there is a reliance on foreign supplies of petroleum, the output (0·2 m tons in 1964) from the Shabla field, north-east of Varna, being inadequate. A new field is now being developed at Dolni Dŭbnik, near Pleven. A refinery for imported Soviet petroleum has been built at Burgas (initial annual capacity 2 m tons). An older and smaller refinery exists at Ruse. Natural gas is now being exploited near Vratsa.

Several small hydro-stations were in operation before the Second World War, but since then much new capacity has come into use, often associated with river-control and irrigation schemes. The largest schemes by far are in the Rodopi and involve (a) dams on the Arda river above and below Kŭrdzhali (including Ivaylovgrad near the Greek frontier) and (b) the associated Kolarov and Batak schemes on tributaries of the Maritsa. On the upper Iskŭr, south-east of Sofia, there is a chain of small stations associated with the Iskŭr reservoir, occupying the northern end of the Samokov basin, which lies above the gorge by which the river descends to the Sofia basin. In the Rila Mountains there are small stations on the 'White' Iskŭr and the Rilska (tributary of the Struma), while on the upper Tundzha, in the Rose Valley near Kazanlŭk, there is a scheme associated with the Dimitrov dam, which also supplies a station at Stara Zagora, before the water is used for irrigation. The Stamboliyski and Topolnitsa irrigation reservoirs and the Studena reservoir, which supplies water to Pernik, are also used for hydro-power generation. There are other small and scattered hydro-plants in the Stara Planina foothills. Large new hydro-power schemes are under construction on the Vŭcha and at Sestrimo, on a tributary of the upper Maritsa in the Rila Mountains. Thermal power-stations are chiefly concentrated in the Sofia–Pernik and Dimitrovgrad–Marbas East districts, using brown coal and lignite respectively, but new stations using Soviet coal are now coming into operation at Ruse and Varna, and a cable connection over the Danube with the Rumanian power network is being established. The power-deficient areas of the north and east obtain electricity from the main thermal and hydro areas by means of a national network and they also rely partly on local diesel plant. Three-quarters of the output of electric power was by thermal means in 1964.

METALLURGY (Fig. 10)

Bulgaria produces substantial amounts of lead, zinc, copper and manganese and is able to export surpluses of these metals. Lead-zinc ores are mined in the western part of the Stara Planina (Chiprovtsi and Eliseyna) and also in the Eastern Rodopi, the latter being the leading area of production. Here Rudozem and Madan are new mining towns with flotation plants and there are refineries at Kŭrdzhali and Plovdiv. Another mining centre is Ustrem. Total output of lead and zinc was 179,000 tons by metal content in 1964. Copper (20,000 tons by metal content in 1964) is chiefly obtained in the Burgas area (Rosen) and in the western part of the Stara Planina, south of Vratsa and near Pirdop (where there is a smelter and refinery). The ores to the south of Pirdop, at Medet in the Sredna Gora, are the largest deposits now being exploited, however, and a smelter and refinery have been built here. Manganese (52,000 tons of crude ore in 1964) is obtained near Varna.

The Bulgarian iron and steel industry, although still one of the smallest in Europe, has grown considerably since the 1940s. East of Pernik a medium-sized integrated works has been built up, initially using scrap for steel-making and subsequently pig-iron produced from iron ore brought from Krumovo (south of Yambol) and Martinovo (in the north-west of the country). In the mid-1960s a much larger integrated plant began to come into operation at Kremikovtsi (about 25 km/15 miles north-east of Sofia), based on newly-exploited local ores. Total output of iron ore (by metal content) was 257,000 tons in 1964, while pig-iron output reached nearly 0·5 million tons and steel about the same.

Distribution of Population and Chief Cities

The distribution of population in Bulgaria, as might be expected in a country where agriculture is still the most important form of livelihood, shows a broad correlation with land-productivity. As a result, therefore, the higher parts of the Stara Planina, Sredna Gora, Western Rodopi and Pirin and Rila Mountains have only a sparse population, while both the Danubian Platform and the southern plains have moderately high rural densities. Frequently, however, densities become greater in areas that are transitional between the plains and the mountains. This is due not only to the more varied range of economic possibilities presented by contrasting environments, but also to the fact that during the Turkish period there was some withdrawal of the Bulgarians from the plains, where Turkish feudal estates were often the rule, and an accompanying tendency to the clustering of population in foothill areas outside direct Turkish control. In such areas craft industries often developed as an alternative means of livelihood. There is, however, a difference in settlement type between the plains and the hills. In the former, rural settlements are larger, further apart, and are distinctly nuclear in character, whereas in the hills settlements tend to be smaller and somewhat scattered. Apart from the capital and the ports, the towns of Bulgaria are still chiefly service centres for their rural hinterlands and places for food-processing, but the growth of manufacturing industries is gradually leading to greater economic diversification as well as to a rapid growth of the urban proportion of the population (40% in 1963 compared with 26% in 1946). Only a few urban centres can be described as predominantly industrial

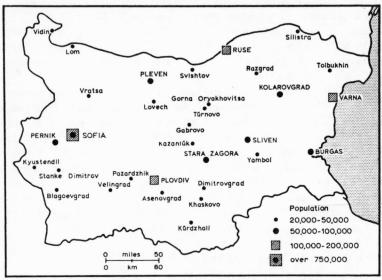

Fig. 11. Distribution of chief cities and towns in Bulgaria

or mining towns, the leading examples being Dimitrovgrad and Pernik. The distribution of the leading towns is shown in Fig. 11.

SOFIA (*Sofiya*) (812,000 in 1964, including suburban areas) has a long history as an important urban settlement. Under the Romans the city was known as *Serdica*, after the Serdi, a local Thracian tribe, while the early Slavs called it *Sredets*, meaning 'centre', an indication of its geographical nodality within the Balkan peninsula. Eventually the city took the name of one of its early churches, St Sophia, which still survives, although much restored, in the heart of the city.

One of the leading towns of medieval Bulgaria, Sofia was captured by the Turks in 1386 and it became the chief seat of administration for a large part of the Turkish-held Balkans ('Rumelia'), as well as a centre of handicrafts and trade. At the time of the liberation of Bulgaria it had only 20,000 inhabitants, however, and presented a typically Turkish appearance. Since then the city (Fig. 12) has grown rapidly in area and population and its centre has been remodelled (although several old churches and mosques remain), the most recent stages of redevelopment being necessitated by damage caused in Allied air raids in 1944. The central area of the city has a rather mixed and incoherent aspect, and

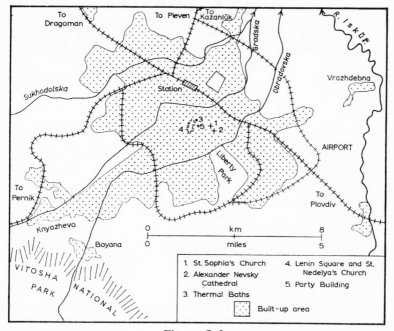

Fig. 12. Sofia

Lenin Square is little more than a major street intersection, with the church of St Nedelya occupying a constricted site in the middle. While boulevards and squares on the grand scale are lacking, the city can boast of numerous public gardens.

Although the general setting of Sofia is impressive, with wooded mountains rising as a backcloth, the actual site of the city is almost flat. The central area is situated between two small streams, now regulated as ditches, flowing north-eastwards to join the Iskŭr. On a very slight rise between these two streams stands the old church of St Sophia and its more grandiose neighbour, the early 20th-century Alexander Nevsky cathedral. The Sofia basin is an elongated depression some 80 km/50 miles long and up to 25 km/15 miles wide, stretching south-eastwards from the hills on the Jugoslav border. Here the Dragoman Pass gives access to the valley of the Nishava, a tributary of the Morava, which it joins at Niš in Jugoslavia. Sofia lies approximately midway along this depression at a height of about 550 m/1,800 ft. Immediately to the south it is overlooked by the Vitosha Massif (Cherni Vrŭkh 2,290 m/7,500 ft), to the foot of which the city's suburbs now extend.

Routeways radiate outwards in a number of directions, following passes of varying difficulty, so that, despite its location, little more than 50 km/30 miles from the Jugoslav border, Sofia nevertheless enjoys satisfactory communications by road and rail with the rest of the country. It must be admitted, however, that the west–east division of the country by the Stara Planina would have rendered difficult the selection of a suitable capital nearer to the heart of the country. Nor must it be forgotten that during the early years of independence it was assumed that sooner or later Macedonia would be united with Bulgaria, thus extending the frontier much further westwards.

Sofia is not only a major administrative, cultural and commercial centre, but it is also the chief industrial city of Bulgaria, accounting for about one-quarter of total industrial output. Substantial industrial growth has occurred during the 20th century. In addition to a varied range of food-processing and consumer-goods industries, new engineering, electrical, radio and cotton-textile factories have recently been developed.

PLOVDIV (198,000), situated on the road and rail route from Sofia to Istanbul, has always been the leading urban settlement of southern Bulgaria and especially of the fertile upper Thracian Plain. As *Eumolpias*, a Thracian tribal centre, it grew up on and around a group of syenite eminences located on the right bank of the Maritsa only a short distance north of the High Rodopi. It was captured by Philip of Macedonia in the 4th century and renamed *Philippopolis*, by which Greek name the city was generally known to the outside world until the twentieth century, when its Slavonic name gradually gained acceptance. Under the Romans it was known as *Trimontium* (after the three hills on which the ancient city developed) and under the Turks as *Filibe*. After capture by the Turks in 1364 it continued to be an important commercial centre, attracting Greeks, Armenians and Sephardic (Spanish) Jews, as well as a considerable Turkish population.

Today Plovdiv is the second city of Bulgaria and has a number of industries, many of which are concerned with the processing of produce from the rich hinterland, such as tobacco, fruit, grain and vegetables. Cotton textiles, footwear, non-ferrous metals and engineering are also represented. Across the river are new suburbs and the permanent buildings of the biennial international trade fair, initiated in the 1930s. The Plovdiv Fair may be said to be the modern successor of the great fair held for several centuries at Uzundzhovo, north-east of Khaskovo.

VARNA (162,000), one of the two leading seaports of Bulgaria, dates back to the ancient Greek trading colony of *Odessos*. In 1444 it was the scene of the defeat and death in battle of the Polish king, Władysław III, who led the last Christian campaign against the Turkish invasion of the Balkans. The trade of Varna began to increase in the 18th century and grew rapidly in the second half of the 19th century, particularly after the building of the Ruse–Varna railway (1866). It was chiefly concerned with the export of grain from the north-east of Bulgaria, and the loss of the southern Dobrudzha led to a decline of this trade in the inter-war period. In recent decades trade has expanded considerably and has become more diverse, while at the same time industrial activity has increased, involving shipbuilding and the manufacture of domestic electrical appliances and diesel engines. Textile and food-processing industries are also represented.

The city lies on the north side of the small Bay of Varna, overlooking the harbour, which is located seawards of the filled-in mouth of a large lagoon (Varna Lake). Stretching for 20 km/12 miles northwards along the coast there is a chain of rest-homes and hotels, including the resorts of Druzhba ('Friendship') and Zlatni Pyasŭtsi ('Golden Sands'), developed since the 1950s for the international tourist trade.

RUSE (118,000), once a fortified Roman harbour, is the leading river-port of the country and also the chief focus of rail and road traffic with Rumania, as a result of the location a short distance downstream of the 'Friendship' Bridge over the Danube. Built in 1954 this double-decker bridge carries both road and railway and replaces the pre-existing ferry service to Giurgiu on the Rumanian side of the river. The harbour lies below the town at the foot of a steep bank descending to the Danube, near the mouth of the Ruse Lom river. Industries include the manufacture of agricultural machinery, river-craft, textiles and food-products. There is also an oil-refinery.

Transport and Trade

The railway network of Bulgaria is somewhat skeletal by West European standards and has a high proportion of single-track mileage. Sofia, although located in the west of the country, is a focus of lines radiating in a number of directions. The international route from Belgrade to Istanbul reaches Sofia from Jugoslavia by way of the Nishava valley and the Dragoman Pass, and after leaving the Sofia basin proceeds through the Ikhtiman Sredna Gora, the Ikhtiman basin and the Momin

('Maiden') Pass and Gorge, cut by the upper Maritsa and a tributary, to the Plain of Thrace. Passing through Plovdiv and Dimitrovgrad it follows the Maritsa to the Turkish border at Svilengrad. This line is also an important domestic route and has several junctions along it, notably at Plovdiv and Dimitrovgrad. From Plovdiv there is also a line to Burgas, via Stara Zagora and Yambol, with a connection at Karnobat for Varna (via the Luda Kamchiya valley through the eastern ranges of the Stara Planina). Northwards from Sofia another international line proceeds through the Iskŭr gorge and on to Pleven and the junction-town of Gorna Oryakhovitsa, whence a route continues to Ruse and so, by means of the Friendship Bridge, to Bucharest in Rumania. The other Danube ports are connected to the northern main line by spurs, e.g. Vidin and Lom having a connection at Mezdra, and Svishtov at Levski. From Gorna Oryakhovitsa a line continues to Varna via Kolarovgrad. Varna is also linked across the Dobrudzha to the Rumanian port of Constanţa, and Vidin has a ferry to Calafat across the Danube. Southwards from this northern main line there are spurs to Tŭrnovo, Gabrovo, Lovech, Troyan and other towns, the Tŭrnovo line continuing by tunnels through the Stara Planina and Sredna Gora to Stara Zagora. In the future it is possible that a tunnel may be driven between Troyan and Karlovo to provide a direct link between Pleven and Plovdiv. Running through the Rose Valley and the other depressions south of the Stara Planina is a line from Sofia to Sliven and Karnobat, only fully completed since the Second World War. Finally south-westwards of Sofia there is a line to Pernik and Kyustendil and also a line down the Struma valley to the Greek frontier. The whole network thus resembles an oval, with Sofia at the western end and Varna and Burgas at the eastern end, and with the Rose Valley line bisecting it, while extensions from the northern and southern trunk lines give connections with the Danube ports and the Rodopi towns. Electrification is proceeding on some of the most heavily-used sections of the network.

Road traffic was formerly hampered by the poor state of many roads, but this deficiency is gradually being remedied and freight traffic is increasing as regards both domestic and foreign trade. In particular there has been a development of lorry traffic carrying fruit and vegetables to other European countries. Internal and external air traffic is also increasing, with the international airport at Sofia being the most important. Airports at Burgas and Varna cater for the Black Sea tourist traffic to a large extent. Water transport is limited to the Danube and Black Sea, none of the internal rivers being navigable. Varna and Burgas handle virtually all of Bulgaria's sea trade, the other coastal ports being chiefly concerned with fishing, and they also handle some transit trade for other

Socialist countries. Ruse is the leading Danube port for both internal and external traffic, but other ports also have a considerable traffic, such as Lom, Vidin, Svishtov and Silistra. Tonnages (millions) handled in 1964 were: Burgas 3·8, Varna 3·6, Ruse 1·5 and Lom 0·8.

The foreign trade of Bulgaria tends to increase both in volume and scope as the economy expands. While agricultural products still hold first place in the export trade there has been a general trend towards increased emphasis on the higher-value items, such as fruit, vegetables, wine and livestock products, rather than on grain. This process was already well under way before the Second World War. Tobacco remains the most important single commodity of this group. Tomatoes are also a leading item. A similar trend is seen in the field of minerals, where refined non-ferrous metals (lead, zinc and copper) are now exported. The development of Bulgarian industry leads both to an increased import of machinery and certain essential raw materials (e.g. coal, petroleum) and also to the export of an increasing range of manufactured goods (e.g. textiles, cement, chemicals and engineering products). About 80% of Bulgaria's foreign trade is with the Soviet Union and with the other Socialist countries, especially Czechoslovakia and Eastern Germany, but at the same time transactions with West European countries, such as West Germany and Italy, and underdeveloped countries are tending to increase. A relatively new element in the Bulgarian economy is the tourist industry. With its advantageous climate, increasing reliance on irrigation and its traditional horticultural skills Bulgaria is not only an important area of market-gardens and orchards for Socialist Europe, but its 'Black Sea Riviera', centred on Varna and Burgas, is also becoming a major playground. There are also mountain resorts in the south-west and various spa-centres. Western tourists are now keenly encouraged as they provide Bulgaria with useful hard currency.

Chapter 5

CZECHOSLOVAKIA · ČESKOSLOVENSKO

Introduction

Czechoslovakia has an elongated shape and stretches for about 750 km/over 450 miles from west-north-west to east-south-east, while its width varies from 275 km/175 miles to less than 100 km/60 miles. It is bordered by Poland to the north, the Soviet Union to the east, Hungary and Austria to the south, and West and East Germany to the west. The modern republic of Czechoslovakia came into being in 1918 after the collapse of the Austro–Hungarian Empire at the end of the First World War, but it must not be forgotten that the important Kingdom of Bohemia (including Moravia) had existed up to 1620. The population is 14·1 millions (1965).

As its name implies, the country is populated by the Czechs and the Slovaks, closely-related peoples speaking almost identical languages that fall within the West Slavonic group. The area populated by the Czechs forms the western half of the country approximately, and corresponds to Bohemia (*Čechy*) and Moravia (*Morava*), together with very small parts of ancient Silesia (*Slezsko*) (the remainder of which constitutes south-western Poland), adjoining northern Moravia. These areas are often known collectively as the Czech Lands (*České Kraje*). Their population is 9·75 millions (1965), while that of Slovakia is 4·35. The number of Czechs is about 9·2 millions, and Slovaks 3·9, some of the latter being resident in the Czech Lands.

Within the Czech Lands there also exist German and Polish minorities. The German minority of 140,000 (1961) forms only the vestige of a formerly very much larger group, numbering about 3·3 millions on the eve of the Second World War. This minority, descended from settlers who had entered the country at various times, was concentrated in the northern, western and southern borderlands of Bohemia and Moravia–Silesia, where German speakers frequently formed over three-quarters of the local population and in some places as much as 90%. They played a major role in the industrial development of the country, both in medieval and modern times. These German-speaking fringe areas were formerly known, in German, as the 'Sudetenland', after the Sudet Mountains (*Sudety*) of north-eastern Bohemia. This name was geographically rather misleading, since numerically the Germans were at least as important in the north-west, in the vicinity of the Ore Mountains. The Sudeten German Party, supported by most of the German-speaking minority, played a leading part in precipitating the international crisis of 1938. This was followed by the Great Power settlement, known as the Munich Agreement, authorizing the ceding of the borderlands to Germany. In 1939 Germany occupied the remainder of the Czech Lands. Apart from those in the 'Sudetenland', sizeable German minorities also existed in certain cities and towns in the heart of the Czech Lands, notably Prague, Brno and Jihlava.

The liberation of Czechoslovakia from German control in 1945 was followed by the transfer to Germany of the greater part of the German-speaking minority, despite the dislocation that this involved, at least temporarily, in the industrial life of the country. The removal was authorized by the Potsdam Agreement of the victorious Allies. Some key workers and their families were retained, however, and some persons who had been antagonistic to the German occupation were also allowed to remain. Czechs and Slovaks gradually moved into the largely depopulated towns and villages, and the more superficial signs of former German occupance were all removed. Urban populations have now reached, or even exceeded, the pre-war level, although the rural population is smaller and some difficulties have been experienced in ensuring the full utilization of agricultural land. As a result of these evictions and the cession (1945) of the easternmost province of the country to the Soviet Union (see below), the population of Czechoslovakia is still (1965) half a million fewer than it was a year before the Second World War, despite subsequent natural growth.

The Polish minority (68,000 in 1961) is found in the Karviná–Těšín district, lying near the Polish border, to the east of the industrial city of Ostrava. Těšín is separated from its parent settlement of Cieszyn (in Poland) by the little River Olše (Polish *Olza*). Much of the Polish minority is associated with coal-mining and the iron and steel industry. The area historically formed part of Silesia and was awarded to Czechoslovakia after the First World War (1920). Poland was never reconciled to this, however, and occupied the area in 1938 after Czechoslovakia had been weakened by the Munich Agreement. The area reverted to Czechoslovakia at the end of the Second World War, and the subsequent immigration of Slovaks to offset the labour shortage in the heavy industries has led to a reduction of the Polish proportion of the population.

Slovakia (*Slovensko*), forming the eastern half of the country, also contains important minorities. The fertile foothills and lowland margins of the Carpathians have a strong Hungarian minority, chiefly rural in character, numbering 534,000 (1961). These areas were taken from

Czechoslovakia by Hungary after the Munich Agreement, but, like the Karviná–Těšín area, they were returned to her in 1945. After the war, part of the Hungarian minority was exchanged for Slovaks living in Hungary. Small German minorities also existed in Slovakia before the Second World War, especially in the towns and mining centres. As in the Czech Lands they were expelled after 1945.

In north-east Slovakia, especially in the Prešov area, there is a Ukrainian (Ruthenian) minority (55,000, including some Russians). Before the Second World War the Ukrainian minority of Czechoslovakia was much larger, owing to the fact that the country then extended further east and embraced 'Carpathian Ukraine' ('Ruthenia'), a rather backward territory with a mixed Ukrainian and Hungarian population. In 1945 Czechoslovakia ceded this area to the Soviet Union and it was united with the Ukrainian Soviet Socialist Republic. The transfer of this territory was not without strategic significance, since it conveniently gave the Soviet Union a common frontier with Hungary.

Pre-war Czechoslovakia also contained many Jews, both Czech- and German-speaking. Prague had been for centuries one of the most important centres of Jewish culture in Europe. Most of those who had not succeeded in leaving the country before 1939 were exterminated by the Germans. Many gypsies were also victims of the German racial policy, but considerable numbers survive, especially in Slovakia.

Historical Background

At the dawn of the Christian era Celtic communities, including the *Boii* (hence the origin of the name 'Bohemia'), were being overrun by Germanic tribes, including the *Marcomanni*, who in the 2nd century A.D. attacked the frontier of the Roman Empire, the *limes Romanus*, lying more or less along the Danube, immediately to the south of modern Czechoslovakia. There was later penetration by the Slavs, coming from their presumed homeland between the Vistula and the Dnepr, and in course of time they became the dominant people, despite incursions of the Huns and the Avars.

By the 9th century a 'Great Moravian Empire' had come into existence, which, at its greatest extent, under its ruler Svatopluk, also embraced Slovakia, Bohemia and Lusatia (a territory lying to the north of Bohemia and populated by a Slav people, the Sorbs or Wends, of whom a small number survive to this day in Eastern Germany). Two hundred years previously there is mention by the chroniclers of an earlier Empire, ruled by Samo. The Moravian Empire (where one of the important centres was Nitra, in modern Slovakia) received Christianity from both western and eastern sources; Germanic missionaries came from

the East Frankish kingdom and Greek missionaries from Byzantium.
The latter were led by the two famous brothers, Constantine (usually
called Cyril) and Methodius, who were familiar with the Slavonic
tongues. They had compiled a special Slavonic alphabet, based on Greek
characters (the Glagolitic, a forerunner of the Cyrillic alphabet proper),
and they provided an easily-understood liturgy. In the event, however,
the Roman rite triumphed and the Byzantine missionaries withdrew
before the end of the 9th century.

By the beginning of the 10th century the Empire broke apart, as a
result of both internal and external factors. The Bohemian tribes had
split away and come under the influence of the East Frankish kingdom,
and the penetration of the Magyars into the Pannonian Basin not only
severed the hitherto continuous link between the Western Slavs and the
Southern Slavs, but also threatened the Danubian lowlands of Moravia
and Slovakia. Slovakia became part of the new Magyar Kingdom of
Hungary at the beginning of the 11th century, and the Slovaks thereafter
remained for nine hundred years a downtrodden minority living in the
Carpathian valleys. Meanwhile the fortified settlement of Prague had
become the capital of a Kingdom of Bohemia which expanded to embrace
Moravia and many of the other territories of the old Moravian Empire,
except Slovakia. One of the earliest rulers of Bohemia was Vaclav, the
'Good King Wenceslas' of the English Christmas carol.

Although part of the Holy Roman Empire the medieval Bohemian
Kingdom was able to maintain a vigorous internal independence under
dynasties elected by the Czech nobility, who, together with the Church,
including the monasteries, owned the land on a feudal basis. Economic
and cultural progress, particularly marked from the 13th century onwards, involved the expansion of trade, the growth of handicrafts and
the mining of metal ores, the building of churches and the development
of towns. The latter often tended to be largely German in character,
however, as a result of the immigration of craftsmen, miners and merchants from the German-speaking lands of the Empire.

In the second half of the 13th century Přemysl Otakar II annexed a
large part of modern Austria and Slovenia, thus extending his sway to
the Adriatic. He also helped the Teutonic Knights in their campaigns
against the heathen Lithuanians and so temporarily established himself
on the Baltic coast. Přemysl lost his southern territories to Rudolf of
Habsburg, the Holy Roman Emperor: they eventually became the heart-
land of this dynasty's growing territorial possessions. A later king, John
of Luxembourg, annexed large parts of Silesia and Lusatia. Charles I,
his son (1346–78), not only extended these gains but succeeded in becoming Emperor (as Charles IV), and his reign was one of the most brilliant

in Bohemia's history. As seat of the Imperial Court Prague became one of the leading cities of Europe, growing in size and economic and cultural importance. Charles founded the earliest university in this part of Europe in 1348, and he rebuilt the stone bridge over the Vltava; both still bear his name. He also began the rebuilding of the cathedral of St Vitus. Cultural relations were established with France and Italy and also with England, through the marriage of Charles's daughter, Anne, to Richard II.

Contacts with England, where the activities of John Wycliffe and the Lollards attracted interest, helped to stimulate the Hussite movement at the beginning of the 15th century. Jan Hus (John Huss), Rector of Prague University and an eminent scholar associated with the translation of the bible into Czech, preached against the sale of indulgences and other practices of the Church. Summoned to a Council at Constance he refused to recant and was burnt there at the stake in 1415. This act provoked a powerful reformist movement both religious and social in character, which also had nationalist overtones. Hussite forces gained control of the leading towns of Bohemia and the economic power of the Church was destroyed. The anti-Hussite crusades of King Sigismund, supported by the Pope, failed to suppress the armies of the movement, led until his death by the warrior Jan Žižka, noted for his famous victory at Vítkov Hill overlooking Prague (1420). A Council, meeting at Basel in 1431, offered a truce and eventually agreed to recognize a reformed Church–the Calixtine ('Chalice') Church, so-called because the Hussites had fought for the right of all communicants, not only priests, to receive wine.

During the reign of Jiří (George) of Poděbrady (1458–71) opposition by the Pope was renewed, but his champion, the Hungarian King Matthias, was repulsed. After Jiří's death there was a contest between Matthias and the Polish Prince Władysław for the Bohemian crown, to which the latter had been elected. This was settled by the former's death in 1490, when Władysław also became King of Hungary. The Czech and Hungarian Kingdoms were henceforward to be associated in various ways until 1918.

In 1526 King Ludvík, ruler of both countries, met his death against the Turks at the disastrous Battle of Mohács in southern Hungary, and a large part of Hungary subsequently passed under Turkish rule. The election of Ferdinand of Habsburg, ruler of Austria, to the two vacant thrones, intended as a protective measure against the Turkish threat, proved to be unwise since reconversion to Catholicism was now encouraged and the privileges of the towns were reduced. Western and northern Hungary, with Slovakia, also came under Habsburg rule and Bratislava now became the Hungarian capital. Feeling against the Habsburgs reached a crisis in 1618, when representatives of the Czech Estates 'defenestrated' the two Royal Governors at Prague castle. Frederick of the Palatinate, a Protestant and son-in-law of James I of England, was elected king, but despite some assistance from Protestant lands, the nationalist armies were defeated a little to the west of Prague at the Battle of the White Mountain in 1620. This defeat signalled the complete destruction of national independence, which was not to be regained for three hundred years. The Czech Lands became mere provinces of the Habsburgs, Catholicism was forcibly reimposed, and the land and property of the rebels were given to Austrians and foreigners who had assisted the Habsburg forces. Many Protestants fled the country, among these being the eminent philosopher and educationalist, Bishop Jan Komenský (Comenius). The introduction of foreign Catholic elements into the nobility and urban classes was a severe blow to the leadership of the Czech nation, whose condition was further worsened by the effects of the Thirty Years' War (which the 'defenestration of Prague' had initiated).

In the 18th century, however, material improvement was considerable, especially in the second half of the century during the reigns of Maria Theresa and Joseph II, whose administrative and economic reforms encouraged the development of trade and industry. The loss of Silesia, with its textile industries, to Prussia in 1742, had the effect of stimulating the textile industries of Bohemia. Serfdom was abolished and religious toleration permitted, but on the other hand the influence of the German language became stronger. Many churches were rebuilt in the Baroque style in the 18th century, and a number of impressive palaces of the nobility, especially in Prague, are also a heritage of this period.

During the 19th century the Czech Lands became the 'workshop' of the Habsburg Empire. Modern textile and engineering factories developed, coal-mining and metallurgical activities expanded and railways were built, the line of 1832 from Linz to České Budějovice (using horses) being the first on the Continent. Towns grew as a result of immigration from the countryside and the Czech element in them was thereby considerably strengthened.

In the year 1848, when the Empire was shaken by revolutions and all but disintegrated, the Czechs played a prominent role in the struggle for national rights. Despite the suppression of the revolutionary movements and the period of absolutist rule that followed, certain cautious concessions to national feeling were eventually granted, particularly after the introduction (for the Empire) of the 'February' constitution of 1861. Such concessions, combined with growing prosperity (despite emigration to the USA), led to considerable quiescence in the period before the First

World War, although the working-class movement grew in size and vigour. Federalism, rather than complete independence, was looked upon as the ultimate goal. Nationalist feeling was to a certain degree canalized into the cultural field, as exemplified by the essentially patriotic music of the composers Dvořák and Smetana and the building by public sub-scription of a National Theatre. Other instances of this 'cultural nationalism', which was already evident before the 1848 Revolution, included the study of Czech history (with which is particularly associated the name of Palacký) and the foundation of the nation-wide gymnastic association, *Sokol* (Falcon). A Czech university in Prague was established in 1882.

The effect of the First World War was to stimulate Czech and Slovak nationalism and Czechs and Slovaks fought on the Allied side both in Russia and in Western Europe. The collapse of Austria–Hungary in October 1918 was followed by the declaration of an independent Czecho-slovak state. The Allies had been prepared for such an eventuality by the advocacy of Masaryk and Beneš. Czechoslovakia was the most politically stable of all the countries of East-Central Europe during the inter-war period. Parliamentary democracy was successfully maintained and the substantial Communist Party was never outlawed as it was in many other countries. The influence of the Catholic Church, regarded by many as having been too closely linked with the Habsburgs, was reduced, par-ticularly in the Czech Lands, and a new national Church received con-siderable support. The large estates were greatly reduced and their land redistributed. The boundaries of the new state largely corresponded to the traditional limits of Bohemia, Moravia and Slovakia, to which were added small parts of Silesia and the Carpathian Ukraine. Owing to the inclusion of peripheral minorities of Germans, Hungarians, Ukrainians and Poles, only two-thirds of the population of the new state were 'Czechoslovaks' in the strict sense, however.

The union of Slovakia with the Czech Lands created certain problems. It must be remembered that although Czechs and Slovaks had been nominally united under the Habsburgs for several hundred years the Czech Lands had been administered as part of Austria, and Slovakia as part of Hungary. From 1412 to 1772 certain small towns in the Hornád and Poprad valleys (*Spiš* district) were under Polish rule. After the *Ausgleich* of 1867, whereby the Habsburg Empire became the 'Dual Empire', consisting of the Austrian territories and the Hungarian terri-tories, each internally autonomous and administered from Vienna and Budapest respectively, the position of the Slovaks tended to worsen. For centuries they had been largely a nation of peasants scattered throughout the valleys and basins of the Carpathians and economically dominated by the more influential Hungarian and German minorities, who tended to be concentrated in the market-towns and small metal-mining centres. Under such conditions Slovak cultural, economic and political development was retarded. Even so there had been nationalist opposition to the revolutionary Hungarian government of 1848–9 and in 1862 a cultural organization, *Matica*, was founded. The writer Štúr popularized the use of the Central Slovak dialect as a national language.

Emigration became widespread in the 19th century, and as a result Budapest, rather than Bratislava, contained the largest number of urban Slovaks. In the years following the *Ausgleich* unrestrained Hungarian nationalism led to a policy of 'Magyarization' in Slovakia. Secondary education was provided only in Hungarian, for instance, and *Matica* was suppressed. Apart from its mines and associated metallurgical activities (precious and non-ferrous metals and iron), which played quite an important role in the Hungarian economy, it was essentially a backward area. This condition was partly due to rather unfavourable environmental conditions for agriculture in the Carpathians and partly due to the lower economic level of the Hungarian territories as a whole compared with the Austrian.

Union with the Czech Lands led to free cultural expression in Slovakia and a great educational expansion, including the opening of a Slovak university at Bratislava, but the lack of a sufficient number of highly-educated persons meant inevitably that the country tended to be governed to a large extent by Czech officials. At the same time Slovakia's small metallurgical industries, separated from their Hungarian markets and suffering competition from the Czech Lands, tended to languish. There developed a strongly nationalist anti-Czech movement, with which certain elements in the Catholic Church were identified, and eventually, when the time was ripe, in 1939, the authority of Prague was challenged.

The Czech Lands, with their important manufacturing and mining activities, accounting for about three-quarters of the industrial output of the old Empire, were, at least on the surface, in a strong economic position. After the immediate post-war upheavals had been overcome economic activity and foreign trade expanded considerably in the 1920s, aided in certain instances by Western capital. Large-scale production on American lines was introduced by the Bat'a family at their large new footwear-manufacturing complex at Zlín (now Gottwaldov) in Moravia. Political security for the new state was sought by means of an alliance with France and also by the 'Little Entente', aimed at preventing Hungarian irredentism, the other partners being Rumania and Jugoslavia.

The Great Depression of the early 1930s hit the Czech Lands sharply.

Trade declined, partly owing to economic nationalism in traditional export markets, including the other 'succession states' of the old Empire, and unemployment increased. Recovery was slow, especially in the industrialized German-speaking borderlands, but by the late 1930s production had regained the pre-Depression level.

By the mid-1930s the Sudeten German Party had developed, which, while ostensibly merely championing the rights of a minority, became ever more insistent in its demands, particularly after Germany's annexation of Austria in March 1938. The Czech Lands were now surrounded by German territory on three sides. Hitler then used the Sudeten German movement for the fomentation of a crisis having as its ultimate object the destruction of Czechoslovakia, a bastion standing in the way of German expansionism.

Fig. 13. Dissolution of Czechoslovakia, 1938–9

After Mr Neville Chamberlain's two dramatic flights to discuss the problem with Hitler the Munich Agreement of September 1938, signed by Germany, Italy, Great Britain and France, authorized the transfer to Germany of those areas that were more than 50% German-speaking (Fig. 13). The Czech government was prevailed upon to accept the Agreement by the two Western powers.* Poland and Hungary quickly claimed the areas containing their minorities (Fig. 13). Linguistic nationalism, fanned by external influences, thus triumphed, leaving Czechoslovakia as a truncated country, inhabited almost entirely by Czechs and Slovaks, together with the Ukrainians in the east. One-third of the population had been lost, including many Czechs and Slovaks in

* In his broadcast to the nation, at the height of the crisis, on September 27th, 1938, Mr Chamberlain said: 'However much we may sympathize with a small nation confronted by a big powerful neighbour, we cannot in all circumstances undertake to involve the whole British Empire in a war simply on her account. If we have to fight it must be on larger issues than that' (*The Times*, 28.9.1938).

the transferred areas. The viability of the country was seriously impaired by the loss of its frontier defences, the severance of important railway routes and the loss of much industrial potential. Separatist agitation in Slovakia gave Hitler a pretext for helping the break-away of a pro-German independent Slovak state the following March, and simultaneously the new Czech President, Hácha, under strong German pressure, agreed to the setting-up of a German 'Protectorate' of Bohemia and Moravia (Fig. 13). This proved to be nothing short of an outright German occupation that lasted until the defeat of Germany in May 1945. The dismemberment of Czechoslovakia was completed by the Hungarian annexation of what remained of Carpathian Ukraine.

After the outbreak of the Second World War, many Czechs and Slovaks outside the country joined the Allied armies, and eventually a government-in-exile was formed, headed by Beneš, who had resigned as President after Munich, and Masaryk, son of the first President. As Soviet troops approached the Carpathians an armed revolt broke out in Slovakia in the summer of 1944 but it was suppressed, although partisan activity continued. Soviet troops did not break through the Dukla Pass from southern Poland until the autumn. A coalition formed of the government-in-exile and leading Communist émigrés in Moscow took over the administration of the country as it was liberated. The Czech Lands were not freed by Soviet troops until the spring of 1945. American forces freed the Plzeň area. Prague, capital of the country whose dissolution by Germany in March 1939 had finally disenchanted the Western Powers of Hitler's good faith, was, ironically, the scene of the last stand of the German forces during the Second World War. A popular rising at the time of the German surrender in May 1945 was sharply counter-attacked by the local German forces, leading to the destruction of the Old Town Hall. Physical damage due to the war was, however, remarkably light compared with that in many countries and, indeed, some useful wartime industrial plants were inherited. However, six years of forced labour for the German war machine accompanied by ruthless persecution of all opposition had caused death and suffering.

Between 1945 and 1948 the country was ruled by an uneasy coalition of non-Communists and Communists, the latter admittedly having obtained nearly 40% of all votes cast in the elections of 1946. An essentially Socialist programme, as promulgated by the coalition at Košice in 1945, was put into effect. Large businesses, banks and mines were nationalized; most of these had in any case been taken over some years before by German interests. The 1938 boundaries were reinstated, except that Carpathian Ukraine was ceded to the Soviet Union. The bridgehead across the Danube from Bratislava was enlarged at Hungary's expense.

The Sudeten Germans, the willing tools of Hitler's expansionism, were expelled.

The extent of Moscow's influence over liberated Czechoslovakia was revealed when the government was persuaded to refuse the offer of American aid to Europe ('Marshall Aid') in the summer of 1947. The following February a Cabinet crisis was caused by the resignation of most of the non-Communist ministers as a protest against Communist infiltration of the police. The outcome was a new government of Communists and left-wing Social Democrats which then proceeded to consolidate its power, aided by the introduction of a new constitution. The general elections already scheduled for the summer merely took the form of a vote for or against the new régime and in the circumstances the outcome was a foregone conclusion.

In the years following 1948 Communist rule of a stern character was firmly established. The earlier political and social upheavals were thus followed by further radical changes. Nationalization of the non-agricultural sectors of the economy was quickly completed. All anti-Communist influences were suppressed and the Catholic Church was circumscribed. By various stages the peasantry was brought into a completely collectivist system by the early 1960s. Industrial output was greatly expanded, despite shortages of labour and the need for importing many raw materials, as well as food supplies. A policy of industrialization was embarked on in Slovakia in order to increase employment and iron out the considerable differences in level of economic development between Slovakia and the Czech Lands. Such a policy was under way before the establishment of the Communist régime and had involved some removal to Slovakia of textile machinery from the Sudetenland. Even so Slovakia continued to be an important source of labour in the 1950s for the factories and mines of the Czech Lands. In 1961 over 300,000 Slovaks were living there.

The death of Stalin in 1953, his posthumous exposure by Khrushchev in 1956, and the events in Poland and Hungary in the same year were not accompanied by any striking changes in Czechoslovakia. There were, however, cautious trends towards some liberalization of the régime. In 1960 a new constitution changed the name of the country to the Czecho-slovak Socialist Republic. Economically the early 1960s were charac-terized by stagnation in a number of industrial sectors and attempts have been made (1965) to remedy this by less rigid planning methods and more incentives and autonomy for individual enterprises.

Relations between the Czechs and the Slovaks are now more amicable, at least officially. Within the framework of the present régime Slovakia enjoys a considerable degree of home-rule, under a 'National Council', and it has claimed lavish capital investment from the Czech Lands. This great development of the economy has, however, tended to reinforce rather than diminish the nationalism of the Slovaks, while the persistence of a high birth-rate amongst this traditionally fervent Catholic people constantly tends to reduce their numerical inferiority by comparison with the Czechs.

The Land (Figs. 14, 15, 16)

Czechoslovakia embraces both Hercynian and Alpine elements. Bohemia is essentially an ancient Hercynian massif, while a large part of Slovakia coincides with the western ranges of the Carpathians, forming part of the Tertiary fold-mountain system of Europe. Moravia, situated between the two and important for its north–south corridor, is a transitional zone including both Hercynian and Alpine elements. Such a threefold division, useful though it may be as an introductory statement, conveys an inadequate impression of the rich variety of land-forms to be found in each; Czechoslovakia is, indeed, a veritable mosaic of physiographic units.

Bohemia is sometimes quoted as an excellent example of geographical correlation–here the well-defined Bohemian 'diamond' or 'quadrilateral', delimited by mountains or uplands on all sides, broadly corresponds to the drainage basin of the upper Labe (German *Elbe*) and its tributaries. Prague, the capital, lies in the north-central part of Bohemia not far from important confluences. It would be unwise, however, to press too closely this coincidence of an old-established political unit with a major physiographic and hydrological entity. Again, although the elevated margins of the Bohemian Massif would seem to pose a physical barrier, it is none the less true that they were crossed by German settlers many centuries ago. On the other hand, we cannot overlook the contrast between Bohemia and Slovakia as regards the development of independent nationhood and the accompanying contrast in their physiography. How far is the long submergence of the Slovaks to be explained in terms of the limitations imposed on cultural and political assertiveness as a result of the physiographic compartmentation of their country? There was a lack of any natural focus for the valleys and basins that constituted the homeland of the Slovaks after their retreat into the Carpathians under Magyar pressure from the south. Moravia, somewhat curiously, never developed the same degree of distinctive individuality as Bohemia. While a 'Great Moravian Empire' certainly existed in early times, Moravia had become essentially an appendage of Bohemia by the middle ages and its role as a corridor of north–south movement thus seems to have been irrelevant– or perhaps even detrimental–to the emergence of a separate nationhood.

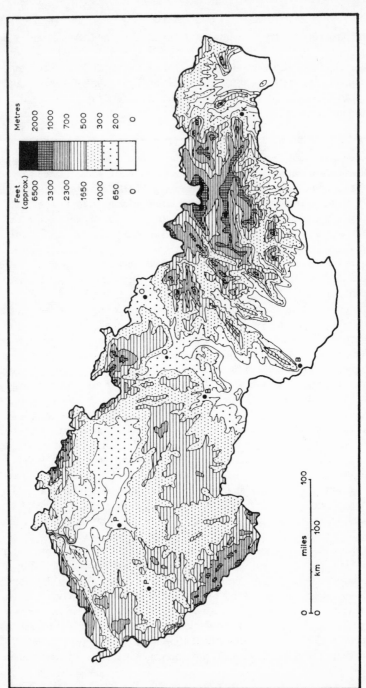

Fig. 14. Relief of Czechoslovakia

BOHEMIA is an ancient 'horst' that once formed part of the Hercynian mountain system. Extensive peneplanation of the Hercynian ranges was followed by their submergence and by the deposition of newer sedimentary rocks. These were later greatly eroded after an uplift taking place as a result of the Alpine earth movements of Tertiary times, and only the wide cover of Cretaceous rocks in northern Bohemia has survived. Other effects were faulting and tilting, especially on the margins, and volcanic activity. Lakes filled a number of faulted depressions, leaving a legacy of Tertiary deposits, and the river system was rejuvenated, leading to the incised valleys and deep gorges that are typical of the upland areas of Bohemia. Loess deposits later masked the surface in certain lowland areas, notably the Labe plain north of Prague. This long sequence of events finds its expression in the varied landscapes of Bohemia, such as the steep inward-facing fault-scarp of the Ore Mountains (*Krušné hory*) overlooking the Tertiary depression of the Ohře valley, the incised meanders of the Vltava, the rolling horizons of the peneplaned uplands of southern and eastern Bohemia, and the conical hills of volcanic origin in the north.

The highland margins that delimit the 'Bohemian Diamond' present certain contrasts. Firstly, let it be said that only on three sides is there any serious barrier to movement. On the east the Bohemian–Moravian Uplands (*Českomoravská vrchovina*), rising to more than 750 m/2,500 ft in the Jihlava and Žd'ár Heights, form a lofty part of the elevated peneplaned surfaces of the southern half of Bohemia rather than a range of mountains, and passage-ways are not difficult between the Labe and Morava basins, whether through the Třebová Hills or by way of the Sázava valley further south. The Ore Mountains (Klínovec 1,244 m/ 4,080 ft) in the north-west and the Bohemian Forest (*Český Les*) and *Šumava* ranges (Plechý 1,378 m/4,520 ft) in the south-west act as much more important barriers to movement, however, although the latter certainly have important passes linking Plzeň and České Budějovice with Bavaria and Austria respectively. In the north-west the most important routeways are located at either end of the Ore Mountains, utilizing, respectively, the Cheb basin and the Labe gorge. Despite the considerable barrier presented by the Ore Mountains thick clusters of German-speaking population developed on both sides of the Bohemia–Saxony frontier. By contrast the borderlands between Bohemia and Bavaria and Austria, formed by the Bohemian Forest–Šumava, are much less well populated, possibly owing to the sheer width of this highland zone and also to the paucity of natural resources.

The ranges of the north-east, sometimes collectively known as the

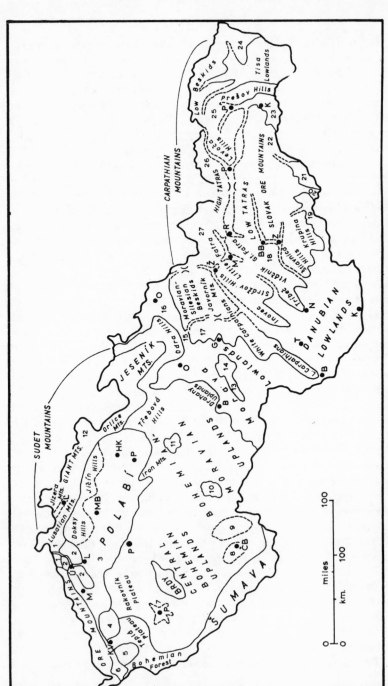

Fig. 15. Generalized physiographic regions of Czechoslovakia

Sudet Mountains* (Sněžka 1,602 m/5,255 ft), include the Jizera, Lusatian (*Lužické*), Giant (*Krkonoše*), Broumov, Orlice and Jeseník Mountains. They are of a much more broken character and there are a number of routeways into Lower Silesia (Poland). The international boundary shows several important anomalies in that it deviates frequently from the main watersheds. Geologically the Sudet Mountains, like the Ore Mountains, the Bohemian Forest–Šumava ranges and the Bohemian–Moravian uplands, are predominantly of crystalline rocks, but the Lusatian Mountains (see below) are of Cretaceous sandstone, while Carboniferous rocks occur in the small Trutnov coalfield and also in Moravia in the lower part of the Jeseník Mountains (Culm Measures). The higher parts of the Jeseník Mountains also contain Devonian rocks.

The territory lying within this outer framework may conveniently be split into a northern and a southern portion, the north consisting largely of plain and the south largely of plateau. The contrast in relief is matched by a contrast in population density and intensity of economic activity. This broad division must be modified for the north-west of Bohemia, however. Here the steep inward-facing scarp-slope of the Ore Mountains overlooks an elongated but discontinuous depression filled with Tertiary deposits and drained by the upper Ohře and the Bílina.

The upper Ohře valley, following the Cheb and Sokolov depressions, is delimited on its inner side by the Slavkov Forest (granite) and the Doupov Mountains (volcanic), the latter also effectively separating the Cheb and Sokolov depressions from the much larger Most depression, drained by the Bílina, which extends as far as the river-port of Ústí-on-Labe, at the confluence of the Bílina with the Labe. While the soils of the Tertiary depressions are of only moderate quality, the presence of great deposits of brown coal has led to the proliferation of mining towns and associated industries. The western part of the Most depression almost merges southwards with the lower Ohře valley, but the two are separated further east by the intervention of the Bohemian Mid-Mountains (*České Středohoří*) of Tertiary volcanic origin, through which the Labe has cut a steep-sided valley between Litoměřice and Ústí. The valley of the

---

* In fact Czechoslovakia rarely uses the term (*Sudety*), but Poland, sharing the ranges, generally does use it.

Key: **1.** Děčín Walls. **2.** Bohemian Mid-Mts. **3.** North Bohemian Lowlands. **4.** Doupov Mts. **5.** Slavkov Forest. **6.** Cheb-Sokolov Basins. **7.** Plzeň Basin. **8.** Č. Budějovice Basin. **9.** Třeboň Basin. **10.** Jihlava Hts. **11.** Žďár Hts. **12.** Broumov Mts. **13.** Ždánice Forest. **14.** Chřiby. **15.** Moravian Gate. **16.** Ostrava Lowlands. **17.** Hostýn Hts. **18.** Kremnica Hills. **19.** Ipel' Basin. **20.** Fil'akovo Hills. **21.** Rimava Basin. **22.** Slovak Karst. **23.** Košice Basin. **24.** Vihorlat. **25.** Čerchov Hills. **26.** Spiš Magura. **27.** Orava Magura.

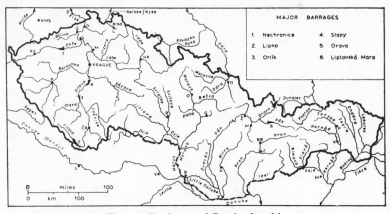

Fig. 16. Drainage of Czechoslovakia
Key to major reservoirs: 1. Nechranice. **2.** Lipno. **3.** Orlík. **4.** Slapy. **5.** Orava. **6.** Liptovská Mara.

lower Ohře is a fertile agricultural district with loess soils and it stretches eastwards to the Plain of the Labe.

Extending for nearly 150 km/90 miles from Litoměřice south-eastwards to beyond Pardubice, is the Plain of the Labe, developed on Cretaceous marls, partly covered by loess, with alluvial deposits near the rivers. The lower part of the Plain, with its very fertile soils, is known as the *Polabí* ('along-Labe'). Some distance south of the Labe there is a fairly well-marked rise to the Central Bohemian Uplands, but northwards there are low hills of Cretaceous sandstone (Doksy and Jičín Hills), culminating in the Lusatian Mountains. The latter may, indeed, be considered as part of the highland margins of Bohemia. West of the Lusatian Mountains the sandstone is cut into by the Labe to give the 'Děčín Walls' (Děčínské stěny). Between Mělník and the Lusatian Mountains the sandstone country is further diversified by the occurrence of striking conical hills of phonolite. The erosion and dissection of the Cretaceous sandstone areas of northern Bohemia have led to the formation of picturesque gorges and curious erosional rock formations, and a small tourist industry has therefore resulted. The sandstone also occurs in the Třebová Hills south-east of the Polabí.

Central and southern Bohemia contrast in elevation and land-forms with the Tertiary and Cretaceous lowlands of the north, and have the character of a lofty, rolling plateau (about 300–450 m/1,000–1,500 ft) diversified by (*a*) areas of higher but subdued relief, such as the *Brdy* (rising to over 850 m/2,800 ft), (*b*) deeply incised river valleys, especially that of the Vltava, (*c*) major depressions, notably the Carboniferous basin of Plzeň and the Tertiary depressions of České Budějovice and Třeboň. Geologically there is a contrast between the predominantly crystalline rocks south-east of the Brdy and the Pre-Cambrian and Palaeozoic rocks (Cambrian to Carboniferous) found in the Brdy and in the area stretching north-westwards (including the Rakovník and Teplá plateaux) to the Slavkov Forest and the Doupov Mountains.

MORAVIA, as its name implies, corresponds largely to the drainage basin of the Morava, although it is true that the lower part of the basin lies in Slovakia and Austria. The river (German *March*) forms the boundary between the two for over 50 km/30 miles, until its confluence with the Danube is reached a short distance upstream from Bratislava. A detached upland of flysch, formed by the Chřiby and Ždánice Forest, separates the main valley of the Morava from the lowlands drained by a major tributary, the Dyje. The western tributaries of the upper Morava and the Dyje drain the Bohemian–Moravian Uplands, including the out-lying hills known as the Drahany Uplands. These consist of Carboniferous Culm Measures and Devonian limestone, the latter being associated with the 'Moravian Karst', north-east of Brno. The upper Morava and its tributaries also drain the Třebová Hills and the Jeseník Mountains. The eastern tributaries of the Morava drain the outer flysch ranges of the Carpathians, including the Hostýn Heights and the White (*Biele*) Carpathians. The Morava lowlands, including those of the Dyje and its tributaries, were once occupied by arms of the Miocene Sea, which covered the Pannonian Basin to the south-east. The Miocene rocks are, however, widely covered by loess and other superficial deposits, the lower part of the Morava valley near the Austrian frontier also being locally characterized by marshy and sandy conditions. The Morava corridor, one of the natural routeways of Central Europe, gives an easy connection between the Vienna basin, to the south, and the Moravian Gate, to the north. The latter is an easy passage-way between the Odra Hills (Carboniferous Culm) to the west and the Beskids (*Beskydy*) to the east, and it corresponds to a low watershed between the Bečva, a tributary of the Morava, and the upper Odra. North of the Moravian Gate, and lying partly in Silesia, is the Ostrava coal-basin, drained by the upper Odra. This important black-coal mining area forms the southern part of the great Upper Silesian coal-basin, most of which lies across the frontier in Poland. Surface deposits include glacial sands in the coal-basin and loess further west near Opava.

SLOVAKIA consists of two contrasting parts–the mountains and valleys of the Carpathian system and the fringing plains and foothills to the south and east, which continue over the border into north Hungary. Accompanying contrasts in relief, soils and climate are reinforced by ethnic differences, since large areas of the lowlands of southern and eastern Slovakia have a mixed Hungarian and Slovak population.

The Carpathian ranges, although brought into being by the Tertiary earth movements and thus forming part of the 'Alpine' system, have only a limited resemblance to the Alps proper. Only the impressive range of the High Tatras, situated on the Slovak–Polish border, with some of their jagged, fretted peaks rising high above the tree-line to over 2,500 m/ 8,200 ft (Gerlach 2,655 m/8,700 ft) recalls the majesty of the Alps themselves. The other ranges, while often major obstacles to movement, are much lower in elevation (although Ďumbier in the Low Tatras reaches 2,043 m/6,700 ft), and a more subdued appearance is presented by their rounded forms.

Geologically there is considerable variety in the Slovakian Carpathians. The broad three-fold character of the Alpine system is present, i.e. old crystalline rocks, limestones of Triassic, Jurassic and Cretaceous age, and softer, flysch material of Cretaceous and Tertiary age. The crystalline rocks and the limestones occur in varying proportions in the Little (*Malé*) Carpathians, Inovec, Tríbeč, Tatras and Fatras and in the Slovak Ore Mountains (*Slovenské Rudohorie*). The flysch extends as an outer, northern arc running from south-west to south-east, and including the White Carpathians, the Jarvorník Mountains, the Moravian–Silesian Beskids, the Levoča Hills and the Low (*Nízke*) Beskids. Karstic conditions occur locally in the Low Tatras and the Ore Mountains, and one area near the Hungarian border is, in fact, known as the 'Slovak Karst' (*Slovenský kras*). Further complicating the geological map of the Slovakian Carpathians are wide areas of Tertiary volcanic rocks, as for instance, the Štiavnica and Krupina Hills in central Slovakia and the Prešov and Vihorlat Hills in the east. Quaternary deposits include morainic accumulations at the foot of the High Tatras and wide loess tracts in the southern lowlands. Lying between the main channel of the Danube and its lesser, northern arm, the Little Danube, is a great spread of both coarse and fine alluvium sometimes known as 'Rye Island' (*Žitný ostrov*), which, although much drained and reclaimed in modern times, still offers a contrast with the more fertile, loess-covered plains and low, gently-rolling hills to the north, which are more densely settled. In the Tisa (Hungarian *Tisza*) lowlands of eastern Slovakia there are similar contrasts as regards drainage conditions and the character of superficial deposits. Marshy conditions occur locally and there is considerable scope for reclamation.

The Carpathians ranges are separated from each other by a network of cultivable valleys and basins, sometimes tectonic in origin, that are often linked to one another by passes of varying difficulty. Settlement, especially urban settlement, is largely restricted to these areas. While the drainage pattern, with its longitudinal and transverse elements, lends a certain coherence to Slovakia, there is at the same time the lack of any clearly-defined major focus, since the rivers radiate outwards in a number of directions: the Váh, Nitra, Hron and Ipel' (Hungarian *Ipoly*) to the Danube; the Hornád, Slaná and tributaries of the Bodrog to the Tisa, and the Poprad to the Vistula. It is not surprising, therefore, that the largest towns of Slovakia–Bratislava and Košice–should lie on the margins of the Carpathians, at either end of the country, where they command the fringing lowlands. In central Slovakia no one town enjoys a clear dominance over the others. Banská Bystrica is, however, the administrative capital of the 'Central Slovakian' Region and there is a civil airport at Sliač, to the south, near Zvolen. Martin was the scene of Slovakia's declaration of secession from Hungary in 1918 and it contains the Slovak National Museum. Žilina is at the junction of the two most important railway routes of Slovakia, where the line from Bratislava, coming up the Váh valley, meets the line from Ostrava to Košice. This latter line makes use of the Jablunkov Pass, and then, proceeding eastwards, follows the upper Váh and Hornád valleys, using the low watershed between the Liptov (upper Váh) and Poprad basins. These together form a long, broad, faulted depression situated between the High and Low Tatras.

Climate and Soils

Climatic conditions reveal both Oceanic and Continental characteristics, in consequence of the country's general geographical position. Compared with the Atlantic lands of north-west Europe Czechoslovakia has a smaller average rainfall, combined with a summer maximum, and a wider range between January and July temperatures, but compared with the Continental climate of Russia the country has a greater frequency of westerly winds, a more evenly-distributed rainfall and a smaller temperature range. Oceanic influences are most evident in Bohemia with northern Moravia–Silesia, but within this area differences in altitude and exposure lead to important variations. Thus the higher parts of the frontier mountains have a much greater annual precipitation (over 1,000 mm/40 in) than the sheltered Labe–lower Ohře plains (in places under 475 mm/19 in), and there is also an accompanying contrast as regards temperature conditions. The climatic statistics (Table 5) for Liberec, in the Sudets, Prague, in the sheltered Vltava valley, and Žatec, in the lower Ohře plain, reveal these differences. The lowlands of southern Moravia and southern and eastern Slovakia show a slightly greater range of temperature than the Bohemian plains, but total rainfall tends to be higher owing to the sheltered location of the latter, and to the fact that some autumn rain from the Adriatic reaches the former areas (see figures for Brno and Bratislava). The Carpathian ranges, owing to their altitude and exposure, show much cooler and moister conditions than the plains of Slovakia, the higher areas experiencing more than 1,000 mm/40 in of precipitation, while in the High Tatras the total rises to over 1,500 mm/60 in. The valleys and basins of the Carpathians

TABLE 5

CLIMATIC STATISTICS · CZECHOSLOVAKIA

Station	Average temperature January °C	°F	Average temperature July °C	°F	Average annual precipitation mm	in
Prague	−0·5	31·1	19·5	67·1	487	19·2
Bratislava	−1·6	29·1	20·2	68·4	670	26·4
Brno	−2·0	28·4	18·8	65·8	563	22·2
Košice	−3·4	25·9	19·1	66·4	663	26·1
Liberec	−2·6	27·3	16·7	62·1	918	36·1
Poprad	−5·7	21·7	16·3	61·3	620	24·4
Žatec	−1·5	29·3	18·9	66·0	441	17·4

experience climates that are greatly modified by local conditions of relief and aspect; temperatures are lower than in the plains, but precipitation is not necessarily higher. The figures for Poprad should be compared with those for Bratislava and Košice.

The best soils of Czechoslovakia are, as might be expected, associated with the lowland areas. Here good conditions for arable farming are offered by black-earths, brown forest soils and alluvial soils, although the latter vary in their quality. In Bohemia there is a zone of black-earths, based on loess, stretching from north-west to south-east along the lower Ohře and the Labe, from Žatec to Pardubice and reaching as far south as Prague. Brown forest soils, together with alluvial soils near the rivers, cover the remainder of the Labe–lower Ohře plains, except that between the Jizera and Pardubice there is a wide area of calcareous soils developed on the Cretaceous marls. Brown forest soils also extend up the Berounka and Vltava valleys.

A rather similar range of soils occurs in the Morava lowlands. Brown forest soils predominate, but locally the soils are alluvial or calcareous in character and an important zone stretching in a broad curve from Brno to Olomouc, and including the Haná valley, is noted for its black-earths.

In the Danubian lowlands of south-west Slovakia there is a fairly simple three-fold pattern. Firstly there are the alluvial soils, of varying texture, found in the Rye Island and along the north bank of the Danube. Such soils extend northwards into the valleys of the Danube's tributaries, especially the Váh. Next there are the black-earths, forming a discontinuous arc broken by the Váh valley, with a western tract situated on the eastern side of the Little Carpathians and a more extensive eastern tract located between the Váh and the Hron. North of the black-earths there is a zone of brown forest soils stretching northwards into the Carpathian valleys and eastwards into the Ipel' basin. In eastern Slovakia alluvial soils are found in the Tisa lowlands, with fringing areas of brown forest soils at the higher levels, and the Košice and Slaná basins have similar conditions.

Contrasting with the generally fertile soils of the lowlands of Czechoslovakia are the poorer soils of the uplands and mountain districts. Podzols of moderate fertility cover the plateaux of southern Bohemia and the lower slopes of the Czech frontier ranges and the Carpathians. Skeletal mountain soils are found at higher altitudes, and there are also some areas of peat-bog in the Ore Mountains, the Bohemian Forest and the Šumava. There are also areas of peat in the Tertiary basins of southern Bohemia. In the Carpathian valleys and basins restricted tracts of relatively fertile alluvial soils contrast with the poorer soils of the mountains.

Land Use (Fig. 17) and Farming

The natural vegetation has been either removed or modified by man over large areas of the country, especially in the Czech Lands. The natural grasslands and open deciduous woodland of the Labe plain, the Morava lowlands, the Slovakian lowlands, and their margins, were removed in past centuries as the area of cultivation was extended. Similarly much of the original forest-cover has been removed from the plateaux of southern Bohemia. Nevertheless nearly one-third of the surface of the Czech Lands is covered by forest, very considerable areas occurring in the frontier ranges, where coniferous trees, especially spruce, predominate. Large tracts of forest also occur in southern Bohemia, again with spruce predominating, although the Scots pine is also very important. There are also large stands of Scots pine in the sandy districts of the lower Morava basin, especially on the Slovak side. Oak-woods occur in the Labe and Morava lowlands and on the eastern slopes of the Bohemian–Moravian uplands. Most of the Czech forests have been subjected to management and replanting for a considerable time. Until the First World War large private estates were the rule, but in the inter-war

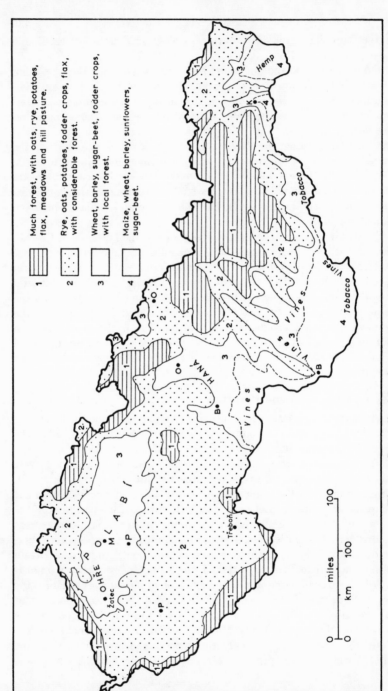

1. Much forest, with oats, rye, potatoes, flax, meadows and hill pasture.

2. Rye, oats, potatoes, fodder crops, flax, with considerable forest.

3. Wheat, barley, sugar-beet, fodder crops, with local forest.

4. Maize, wheat, barley, sunflowers, sugar-beet.

Fig. 17. Generalized land-use regions of Czechoslovakia

period many areas passed into state hands and today all forests are publicly owned.

In the Carpathians, where, generally speaking, the forests have been less exploited and also less well managed, except in Moravia, three zones can be distinguished. The northern zone, including the Tatra, Fatra and Javorník ranges, have extensive coniferous forests, dominated by spruce, while the Chřiby, the White Carpathians, Little Carpathians, the southern ranges and the hills of eastern Slovakia have beech-woods at the higher levels, but as the plains are approached oak-woods become more typical. Rather more than one-third of Slovakia is forested.

Forest industries have long been important in Czechoslovakia, although they have tended to be better developed in the Czech Lands than in Slovakia. The coniferous forests form the basis of lumbering and paper and furniture industries, while the beech-forests also find a market in the furniture industry. Timber-using industries are concentrated in the vicinity of the Sudet Mountains, the Šumava, the Bohemian–Moravian Uplands and at a number of centres, both Moravian and Slovakian, in, or on the margins of, the Carpathians ranges. Formerly there was considerable timber-rafting on some of the rivers, especially the Vltava and the Váh, but improvements in communications in the present century and the recent building of barrages on these two rivers have virtually eliminated this method of transport. Despite the large home demand Czechoslovakia has an export trade in timber and wood-products, especially to neighbouring countries with inadequate forest resources.

Distinctive combinations of climate, soil and terrain have led to the emergence of several very broad types of land-use (see Fig. 17). Firstly there are the mountainous areas, with their poor soils and rather cool, damp conditions. A large part of the surface is forested. Cultivation is much restricted by physical conditions and is chiefly concerned with oats, rye and potatoes. There is also some livestock rearing, especially sheep. In the Carpathians particularly there are abrupt contrasts in land-use between the often very spacious valleys and basins and the pastures and forests overlooking them. Secondly there is the farming typical of the plateaux of southern Bohemia, with their broad sweeping horizons of field and forest. In view of the podzol soils and the climatic effect of elevation there is an emphasis on the rye–potato combination, together with oats, fodder crops and some flax, but there is a smaller proportion of forest than in the mountainous areas. A similar type of land-use prevails in northern Moravia and in the outer, lower ranges of the Carpathians. In the large Tertiary basin of Třeboň fresh-water fishing is important, utilizing an artificial system of lakes developed for this purpose by feudal landowners centuries ago.

Finally there are the fertile lowland regions, enjoying warmer summers, better soils and an annual rainfall ranging between 450 mm/18 in and 625 mm/25 in. Except in the more southerly lowlands of Moravia and Slovakia production is dominated by wheat, barley, sugar beet and fodder crops, and there is a higher ratio of dairy cattle to cultivated area than in the rye–potato areas. Some localities are noted for special cash crops, such as hops, tobacco or market-garden produce. The Polabí–lower Ohře plains and the Haná district of central Moravia are the premier arable areas of the whole country; here the exceptionally fertile character of the soils leads to excellent grain and sugar beet crops, although it is true that summer drought can occasionally be a hazard. The barley of the Haná is especially important and also the hops of the lower Ohře valley, including the district near Žatec. These are the ingredients for the famous breweries of Prague, Plzeň and České Budějovice. In the Polabí vine cultivation has a small outpost at Mělník, overlooking the confluence of the Vltava with the Labe. Vines are also grown in south-west Slovakia. The extreme south of Moravia and the southerly parts of the Danubian lowlands and of the lowlands of eastern Slovakia have rather warmer summer conditions and here maize and sunflowers become important crops, while wheat, barley and sugar beet are less prominent. Tobacco and hemp are grown locally and also vines. As regards livestock pigs become more numerous relative to cattle.

Despite a fairly high level of agricultural efficiency Czechoslovakia is not self-supporting in food and has to import substantial quantities of grain and meat. Collectivization, which proceeded by stages throughout the 1950s, was virtually completed by the early 1960s. The consolidation of the fields and farms of the peasantry and the accompanying growth of mechanization have so far had rather disappointing results, as far as production is concerned. In contrast to the other East-Central European countries, there are also shortages of young agricultural workers, especially in the Czech Lands, owing to the superior attractions of industrial employment. This transfer of manpower from the land is hastened not only by the loss of a personal stake in agriculture but also by the very dispersed character of industry and the well-developed passenger-transport network, which enables widespread easy access to factory employment.

Food-processing tends to be concentrated either in the larger towns or in the main food-producing areas, such as the Polabí, the Morava lowlands and the Danubian lowlands of Slovakia, where many of the towns have grain-mills, sugar beet factories, milk-processing depots and fruit- and vegetable-preserving factories. The important brewing industry has already been mentioned. Czechoslovakia is the sixth largest producer of beer in the world.

Industry and Mining

After Eastern Germany Czechoslovakia is the most industrialized Socialist country in the world and also enjoys a relatively high standard of living. In *per capita* production of solid fuels, electric power and steel she matches the great industrial powers of Western Europe. Under 25% of the employed population is engaged in agriculture and forestry–a proportion similar to that of France. Although there has been a great increase in industrial investment since the Second World War, within the framework of a series of five-year plans, it must be remembered that many of the country's industries have a long history, the Czech Lands having been the most industrialized part of the Habsburg Empire. They accounted for the greater part of the Empire's output of coal, iron and steel, engineering products, sugar, textiles, pottery, glass and chemicals. This high level of industrial development was the result of several factors–the important geographical position of the Czech Lands in relation to the trade routes of central Europe, the occurrence of useful deposits of solid fuels and metal ores of various kinds, the existence of old-established craft industries (especially in the border areas, where, in any case, agricultural possibilities were limited), and the traditional 'industriousness' of both Czechs and Germans. Moreover, before the First World War German industrial capital found the Czech Lands a convenient foothold within the Habsburg Empire.

ENERGY SUPPLIES (Fig. 18) (see also Fig. 44)

Although Czechoslovakia has a good endowment of solid fuels the deposits are not ideally located. Thus the chief reserves of brown coal

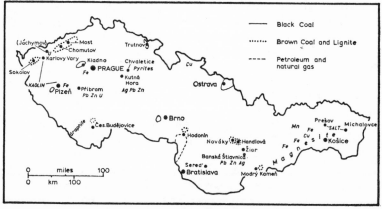

Fig. 18. Mineral exploitation in Czechoslovakia

are found in the extreme west of the country. This drawback has been demonstrated by the transport difficulties incurred in satisfying Slovakia's increasing requirements of solid fuel for her industrial expansion. The recent electrification of trunk railway lines is partly aimed at increasing their carrying capacity. The development of a national electric-power network and of gas pipe-lines also bears witness to the growing demand for energy supplies and the need to bring about a wider and more efficient diffusion of them. The West Bohemian brown-coal field plays a key role in this context. The newly-constructed Soviet oil pipe-line, initially terminating at Bratislava (where a large refinery and petro-chemical complex have been built), is also of great importance. An extension has now been built to Most in the West Bohemian brown-coal field.

The chief source of black coal in the country is the Ostrava–Karviná coal-basin (Fig. 44), which accounts for much the greater part of the total national output of 28·2 million tons (1964). About 40% of the coal raised is of coking quality and as such is not only of importance to Czechoslovakia, but also to neighbouring Socialist countries where coking coal is either absent or deficient. There are also very much smaller black-coal basins, the largest being in the Kladno–Rakovník district (about 3 million tons per annum), west of Prague. Other fields are at Žacléř, near Trutnov (in the Giant Mountains), the Plzeň basin and a field to the west of Brno.

In western Bohemia there is a large output of brown coal, obtained chiefly by open-pit methods from the Tertiary deposits at the foot of the Ore Mountains. Over two-thirds of the national output of brown coal, reaching 71·5 million tons (1964), is obtained from the main field around Chomutov and Most. The smaller Sokolov field to the west is second in importance in the country, producing nearly one-third of the national total. The brown coal is used as (a) a domestic or industrial fuel, (b) a fuel for local power-stations and (c) a raw material for the heavy chemical industry, especially the synthetic petrol plant built near Most during the Second World War by the Germans. This complex of activities is not without its attendant problems, however. Some of the smaller settlements have had to be demolished in order to allow mining to proceed, or else they remain as 'peninsulas' within the mining areas. There is considerable air and water pollution from the chemical industry, and also a shortage of water for the needs of the power-stations. The new reservoir at Nechranice on the Ohře should remedy this, however. Apart from the large brown-coal fields of western Bohemia there are much smaller areas of exploitation near Modrý Kameň and Handlová, both in Slovakia. Close to Handlová lignite is exploited at Nováky, near which is the town of Prievidza, housing the miners. There are also small lignite fields near České Budějovice and near Hodonín in southern Moravia. Thermal power-stations are located close to all the various coalfields and also in the large cities. Soviet coal imports are used for a large thermal station in eastern Slovakia.

Hydro-electric power installations have increased considerably since the Second World War and are chiefly located on the Vltava and the Váh. Even so, hydro-electric power accounts for only about 10% of total output. Small pre-war barrages above Prague are now overshadowed in importance by the three new ones at Lipno, Orlík and Slapy. On the Váh a series of medium and small barrages with lateral canals (known collectively as the *Váhostroj*) has been partly completed on the section below Žilina. Above Žilina a major scheme is in progress at Liptovska Mará, and on the Orava, a tributary of the Váh, a large power-station and barrage were completed in the 1950s. In the far east of Slovakia, in the Laborec basin, several barrages for hydro-electric generation and river control are either under construction, or projected, in order to aid industrialization in this part of the country and to prevent spring flooding and provide summer irrigation water. A new barrage is also being constructed, in collaboration with Hungary, at Gabčíkovo, on the Danube.

Other energy sources include the petroleum and natural gas obtained from a field extending southwards from Hodonín across the Morava in the direction of Bratislava. The field also extends into Austria. The gas is more important than the petroleum, but the combined output is of only slight importance to the national economy. A further supply of natural gas will be provided by a new pipe-line from the Dashava field in the Soviet Ukraine. This will terminate at Šal'a (on the Váh, south-west of Nitra), which is already connected to the Slovakian gas-field. A chemical complex will be developed here. Uranium should also be mentioned in the context of energy resources. Jáchymov, in the Ore Mountains, has long been known for its radio-active metals, and the area was an important source of uranium ore in the late 1940s and 1950s, when the Soviet Union was the recipient, but output is now negligible and other employment has had to be found for the inhabitants of Ostrov, a nearby town specially enlarged for the miners and their families. Uranium is still obtained from some localities in the plateaux of central Bohemia, however. An atomic power-station has been built near Piešt'any in western Slovakia.

METALLURGY (Fig. 18)

Czechoslovakia has a long history of precious and non-ferrous metal-ore mining. The Ore Mountains of Bohemia attracted German settlers in the middle ages, although today mining is negligible, being chiefly con-cerned with small quantities of tin and uranium. In central Bohemia two famous old silver-mining towns are Příbram and Kutná Horá, in the vicinity of which metal ores are still mined, chiefly lead and zinc, although some silver and antimony are also obtained. Copper-mining occurs in the Jeseník Mountains. The Slovak Ore Mountains, unlike those of Bohemia, still justify their name and a number of ores are obtained in useful quantities, including copper (Krompachy) and iron ore and manganese west of Košice. Banská Štiavnica retains some importance as a precious-metal mining centre, although copper, lead and zinc are the leading metals today. A short distance to the north is Kremnica, a famous old gold-mining centre, where a mint is still main-tained. The country is far from self-sufficient in non-ferrous metals and, moreover, costs tend to be high. Imports are thus increasing and un-economic mines closing down. Bauxite imports from Hungary are the basis of the aluminium works at Žiar-on-Hron, and Albanian and Cuban nickel is refined at Sered' (on the lower Váh).

The iron ores of Czechoslavakia have been exploited for many centuries, but large-scale extraction did not begin until the mid-19th century. The Brdy uplands of Bohemia once had an important charcoal iron industry, but this gradually declined as coke-using blast-furnaces developed, especially those of nearby Kladno. Iron ore is still mined at various places between Prague and Plzeň and is used in the blast-furnaces of Kladno and those of the much smaller centre of Králův Dvůr, south-west of Prague. These furnaces, the only surviving ones in Bohemia, also use some imported ores, and coke is made from both local and Ostrava coal. Gas from Kladno's coke-ovens is piped to Prague. Electric steels are a speciality of Kladno. There are also steel furnaces at Plzeň and steel-tube mills at Chomutov.

The leading producer of iron and steel in Czechoslovakia is, however, the Ostrava area, situated in northern Moravia and Czech Silesia. Some iron ore is derived from Bohemia and eastern Slovakia but the greater part is imported from abroad. Coking coal is mined locally. Ostrava itself has two large integrated plants, at Vítkovice and Kunčice (1954), and a third is located to the south-east at Třinec. There are also several associated steel-mills and other finishing works in the Ostrava area, at Bohumín, Karviná and Lískovec (Frýdek-Místek).

Slovakia's small-scale iron and steel industry suffered an eclipse during the inter-war period. Some works were closed down and others stagnated, owing to competition from the Czech Lands. The present centres are Istebné-on-Orava (near Dolný Kubín) and Podbrezová. Both are chiefly concerned with electric steel production. In 1964 Slovakia produced only

56,000 tons of pig-iron, but 0·3 m tons of steel. The Czech Lands, by contrast, produced 5·7 m tons of pig and 8·0 m tons of steel. This great disparity will be changed as a result of the gradual coming into operation, from 1965 onwards, of the large new 'East Slovakian' integrated plant, located a short distance south-west of Košice. Destined to play a key role in the further industrialization of Slovakia the new plant will draw chiefly on Ukrainian ore and Ostrava coking coal. A 90-km/55-mile extension of the Soviet Union's broad-gauge rail system takes ore direct to the plant. Other quantities of ore continue the journey to Ostrava after trans-shipment and the wagons so used bring back coking coal.

Although Czechoslovakia produced 2·8 m tons of iron ore in 1964 a further 9·3 m tons had to be imported. The chief supplier was the Soviet Union (7·7). Other leading suppliers were India, Brazil, Sweden and Morocco. Manganese ore is imported from the Soviet Union and India, although some is produced in Slovakia (84,000 tons in 1964).

OTHER MINERALS

Other notable mineral deposits include salt (for domestic and chemical uses) and magnesite (for refractory bricks) in Slovakia, graphite (for pencil-making) near České Budějovice, and kaolin (for ceramics) near Plzeň and Karlovy Vary. Fireclay is important in the Plzeň–Rakovník area, and pyrites (for sulphur) are exploited at Chvaletice, north-east of Kutná Hora in the Polabí. Limestone is quarried for cement-making at a number of places, production being particularly important at or near Králův Dvůr and Radotín (south of Prague), Brno, Hranice (in the Bečva valley), Žilina, Banská Bystrica, Bratislava and Turna-on-Bodva (south-west of Košice). There is thus a high degree of regional self-sufficiency.

ENGINEERING

Czechoslovakia, more particularly the Czech Lands, has a wide range of engineering industries, some individual enterprises having been in existence for more than a hundred years. Metal-working by craftsmen had a long tradition in a number of districts with good access to supplies of iron, including Prague, Brno and Plzeň. In these larger centres engineering factories were developing before the middle of the 19th century. Heavy products, including armaments, became typical of Brno and Plzeň, while Prague was more concerned with medium and light engineering, including transport engineering. These differences are less marked today, however.

In the 20th century, and especially since the Second World War, there has been both an enlargement and a further diversification of the engineering industries, accompanied by a wider geographical distribution. Engineering as a whole now accounts for a much larger proportion of total industrial output than before the war. The recent spread of the industry reflects both the need to find available labour supplies and the government policy of bringing new employment to the smaller towns and less-industrialized districts.

Perhaps the name best known abroad is that of the 'Škoda' works of Plzeň, with their traditional specialization in heavy engineering products, including armaments. Today the 'Skoda' trade-mark also covers the motor-car industry of Mladá Boleslav, north-east of Prague. Mladá Boleslav and its smaller neighbour, Mnichovo Hradiště (where lorries are made), are supported by a number of component factories in northern Bohemia, both in the Polabí and the Sudets. Prague manufactures a wide range of products, including motor-cycles, buses, lorries, aircraft, locomotives, railway wagons and electrical and precision instruments. Brno is noted for boilers and other heavy engineering products, as well as tractors, typewriters and ball-bearings. Bratislava has developed as an electrical engineering centre much more recently. Komárno builds river vessels.

The Ostrava district is not, as might be expected, a major centre of engineering; indeed government policy aims at avoiding the introduction of new industries that might affect the labour supply of the coal-mining and metallurgical industries. However, industries relying on Ostrava steel have been developed or expanded not far away, in a number of new and pre-existing engineering centres in Moravia and the Váh valley of Slovakia. The building of the Košice steelworks is intended to give an impetus to engineering activities in eastern Slovakia. In some small towns of Czechoslovakia the degree of commitment of the labour force to engineering is exceptionally high, as, for instance, at Strakonice and Týnec on Sázava (motor-cycles), Kopřivnice ('Tatra' cars) or Považska Bystrica (motor-scooters).

CHEMICALS

The chemical industry shows considerable development at places along the Labe, reflecting proximity to the West Bohemian brown-coal supplies and the role of the river as a source of water and a transport medium for the procurement of external raw materials, including salt from Germany and oil-seeds from overseas. Once the area was also a convenient 'bridge-head' for the penetration of German capital. Industries include vegetable-oil processing (Ústí and Děčín), fertilizers (Ústí), rayon (Neratovice, north of Prague), dyestuffs (Pardubice), petroleum refining (Kolín) and synthetic rubber (Kralupy, on the lower Vltava). There is a coal-chemical

industry (synthetic petrol) near Most in the brown-coal field. Both Most
and the Labe chemical centres will benefit by the extension of the Soviet
oil pipe-line. There is also a coal-based chemical industry in the Ostrava
district. Bratislava, which already processes rubber and manufactures
rayon, is becoming a major petro-chemicals centre, as is Šal'a to the east,
on the Váh. Rayon is also made at Svit (Poprad basin) and synthetic
fibres at Planá (south of Tábor on the Lužnice) and Humenné (north-east
of Košice on the Laborec). Humenné may be regarded as a forerunner of
other chemical plants in eastern Slovakia, to be based on Soviet natural
gas, local salt, and coke-oven by-products from the new Košice steelworks. Prague has a pharmaceutical industry.

TEXTILES, CLOTHING AND FOOTWEAR

Traditionally the greatest concentration of textiles was in the area of
the Sudet Mountains in northern Bohemia, where restricted agricultural
possibilities and the combination of water for power and processing and
wool from hill sheep, encouraged the development of small-scale,
domestic textile industries several centuries ago. These became converted
to a steam-power factory basis in the 19th century, when also cotton was
introduced. It should be noted that a broadly similar sequence of
development occurred on the other side of the Sudet Mountains in
Lower Silesia and even more so beyond the Ore Mountains in Saxony.
With the transfer of the German-speaking population after the Second
World War the textile industries underwent a contraction. Much equipment was declared redundant, some being transferred to Slovakia, however, and empty factories were often converted to other uses, particularly
engineering. The new settlers from the rest of the country thus have a
rather better-balanced employment structure than their predecessors.
Nevertheless, the Sudet textile industry, extending approximately from
Varnsdorf in the west to Náchod in the east, still remains very important.
Liberec, in the Nisa valley, lying between the Lusatian Mountains and
the Giant Mountains, is the largest town of the group. The Sudet textile
zone is succeeded south-eastwards by another group of textile towns in
north-west Moravia and Silesia, including Svitavy, Šumperk and Krnov,
and to the south of them are Brno, the chief centre for woollens, and
Prostějov, the largest centre for ready-made clothing. Some textile
industries also exist in the upper Ohře valley, and since the war new
factories have been built in Slovakia.

Footwear manufacture is especially associated with the former Bat'a
factory complex at Zlín (now Gottwaldov), located a few miles east of
the River Morava, up the valley of the Dřevnice. Between the two World
Wars Zlín developed from a village into a specialized company town

recruiting its labour from the Morava valley and the hills and valleys of the Moravian–Slovakian borderlands. The factories of Gottwaldov and those at nearby Otrokovice are also engaged in leather- and rubber-processing. There is also a large footwear factory at Partizánske in the Nitra valley.

Other notable industries include the glass industry of northern Bohemia, initially related to supplies of suitable sand and charcoal. The industry embraces ornamental glassware, including glass buttons, glass 'jewellery', chandeliers, tableware and Christmas-tree decorations. This group of products is particularly concentrated at Jablonec, south-east of Liberec, and neighbouring villages. At Nový Bor, between Liberec and Děčín, a new glass-making complex is being built. A second area of glass-making occurs in the West Bohemian brown-coal basins in and near Teplice and Sokolov, but here the industry is chiefly concerned with sheet-glass and plate-glass.

Distribution of Population and Chief Cities

The distribution of population in Czechoslovakia is extremely uneven, largely owing to wide differences in natural conditions for agriculture and in resources for industry. In the Czech Lands there are two broad zones that show a higher rural density and a greater frequency of urban settlements than the remaining areas. The first corresponds to northern and central Bohemia as far as a line from Chomutov to Pardubice that curves southwards to include Prague. This zone admittedly includes a number of thinly-populated areas, including the frontier ranges, the Doksy Hills and the Mid-Mountains, but it also includes the Chomutov–Most brown-coal basin, the river-ports of Ústí and Děčín, the Sudet textile and glass-manufacturing zone, the fertile Labe–lower Ohře plain, with its fairly high rural density, and numerous small and medium-size towns and the capital city. In the west and south of Bohemia are three isolated population concentrations–the Cheb–Sokolov depression, including the spa-town of Karlovy Vary, and the Plzeň and České Budějovice basins. In Moravia–Silesia there is a second major populous zone, but less compact in character, corresponding to the fertile Morava lowlands and the Ostrava district, linked together through the Moravian Gate. The area includes the large towns of Brno, Ostrava, Olomouc and Gottwaldov, as well as a rather dense network of market-towns and agricultural villages.

In Slovakia, separated from Moravia by the thinly-populated ranges of the Little Carpathians, White Carpathians and Javorníks, physiographic conditions and population density are closely related. North of the Rye Island there is a zone of high rural density enclosed by a line joining Bratislava to the towns of Nové Zámky, Nitra and Trnava and corresponding to the fertile loess plains. This populous area has long branches extending northwards up the Váh valley to Žilina and up the Nitra valley to the Handlová coalfield. In central and eastern Slovakia there is a complicated patchwork of densities, since widely scattered rural and urban settlements in valleys and basins contrast with the lacunae presented by the intervening mountain ranges. The distribution of the chief cities and towns is shown in Fig. 19.

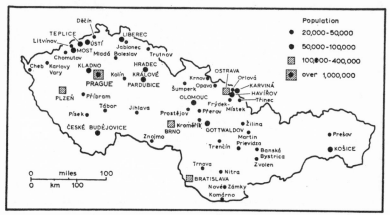

Fig. 19. Distribution of chief cities and towns in Czechoslovakia

PRAGUE (Czech *Praha*, population 1·02 million in 1964) has a dramatic setting along the incised meanders of the Vltava (Fig. 20). The early importance of Prague related to its function as a stronghold and as a great cross-roads centre located where the river could be reached for fording within a gorge section of the valley. The earliest stronghold was the *Vyšehrad*, but this was superseded by the *Hradčany* (Prague Castle) in early medieval times. The chief civil settlement, the Old Town or *Staré Město*, grew up on the right (east) bank on a narrow stretch of flood-plain situated within a bend of the river and overlooked by the steep, undercut slopes of Letná Hill and the loftier Hradčany Hill on the opposite side of the river. At the time of Charles IV (14th century) Prague consisted of the *Hradčany* (castle and cathedral of St Vitus), the Little Quarter (*Malá Strana*) lying at its foot, and the larger *Staré Město* across a stone bridge over the river. Charles extended the city very considerably by bringing into being the New Town or *Nové Město*, lying east and south of the Old Town, the city walls then stretching as far south as the *Vyšehrad*.

Apart from sporadic development in Smíchov, opposite the New

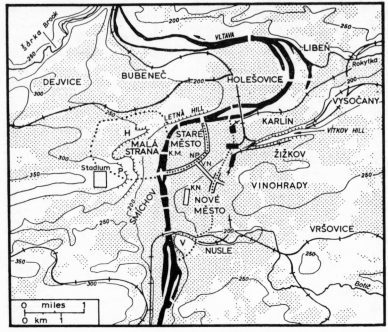

Fig. 20. Prague

Key: H–Hradčany. **KM**–Karlův most (Charles Bridge). **KN**–Karlovo náměstí (Charles Sq.). **NP**–Na příkopě. **P**–Petřín Hill and Park. **V**–Vyšehrad. **VN**–Václavské náměstí (Wenceslas Sq.).

Former defensive walls shown by dotted lines. Contours in metres.

Town, the city did not change in area until the 19th century, when a great expansion occurred, especially after the arrival of railways beginning in the 1840s and the removal of the defensive walls of the New Town. The old Horse Market, occupying rising ground just outside the Old Town, became Wenceslas Square, the heart of the modern city, and the street at right angles to its lower end, aligned along the former ditch of the Old Town (hence its name *Na Příkopě*), became the chief shopping thoroughfare. On the slopes east of the New Town the residential area of Vinohrady ('Vineyards') developed. Further north industrial quarters grew up in Karlín, Vysočany, Libeň and Holešovice and also to the south in the Botič valley. Across the river, Smíchov also developed as an important industrial quarter, overlooked by steeply-rising Petřín Hill, with its wooded park. In the first half of the 20th century residential development took place beyond the Hradčany and Letná Hill in Dejvice and Bubeneč and east and south of the 19th-century accretions on the right bank. Prague, a rich treasure-house of Gothic and Baroque architecture and remarkable for its sweeping urban panoramas, fortunately suffered relatively little war damage, the chief casualty being, however, the Town Hall in the Old Town Square.

BRATISLAVA (266,000) is located on the north bank of the Danube at the southern extremity of the Little Carpathians, the last eminence of which is crowned by the castle. It was the Hungarian capital (*Poszony*) for a long time both during and after the Turkish occupation of lowland Hungary (until the 19th century). The modern city stretches eastwards down the river, where the harbour and industrial quarters are located, and also northwards along the eastern slopes of the Little Carpathians. The old city lies back a little from the river, and the intervening low-lying ground was not fully built over until the 19th century, when public buildings and an embankment were constructed. Situated at a point where the German, Hungarian and Slovak languages converge, Bratislava was essentially a city of mixed populations until the inter-war period, when the Slovak element gradually assumed dominance. As the administrative, cultural and economic nerve-centre of a resurgent Slovakia, Bratislava has grown rapidly in recent decades. There is an important road and railway bridge across the river.

BRNO (327,000), dominated by the twin spires of its cathedral, developed on Petrov Hill, rising above low ground within the angle of confluence of the Rivers Svitava and Svratka. On a neighbouring hill is the fortress of *Hrad* (or *Špilberk*), once a notorious Habsburg prison. In the 19th century industrial districts with textile and engineering factories grew up beyond the old fortifications on the surrounding lowlands. Local supplies of coal and of charcoal-iron were early locational factors. Before the First World War the old city was largely German in character, while the industrial quarters were largely Czech. The city is noted not only for its textile and engineering products, but also for its annual International Trade Fair, the most important in Czechoslovakia, which is held on an extensive permanent site.

KOŠICE (100,000), the second city of Slovakia, is situated on the Hornád in a fertile basin on the eastern margins of the Slovak Ore Mountains. With a strong German element it developed as a prominent town of medieval Hungary, commanding a trade route to Poland. Slovaks have become dominant only in modern times and a Hungarian minority still persists. Košice was reincorporated in Hungary from 1938 to 1945. There are food-processing, engineering and textile industries and the city controls the important railway route to the Soviet Union. Magnesite is mined and processed in the vicinity and the new 'East Slovakian' iron and steel plant has been built to the south-west.

OSTRAVA (259,000) is a relatively modern municipality of an amorphous kind, embracing not only Moravská (Moravian) Ostrava and its smaller neighbour Slezská (Silesian) Ostrava, across the little River Ostravice, but also adjoining places, including Vítkovice, with its old-established iron and steel works, Kunčice, with its large new plant, and Poruba, a new satellite town beyond the Odra to the west. Pit-heaps and metallurgical establishments are embedded in the older built-up areas. To the north and east are other smaller towns economically connected with the coalfield and the iron and steel industry, such as the mining town of Karviná, the railway junction of Bohumín and the new residential town of Havířov. Further to the south are the metallurgical centres of Frýdek-Místek and Třinec. Ostrava and the surrounding industrial and mining region have a total population of well over 600,000.

PLZEŇ (139,000), situated in a relatively fertile Carboniferous basin where five small rivers join to form the Berounka, has a long history as a trading centre, to which a great square with a massive church bears witness. Its economic life has been dominated for a hundred years by the Škoda heavy engineering complex and the famous breweries. Iron ore and fireclay are obtained in the vicinity, but today the output of coal is very small.

Transport and Trade

The road and rail transport networks vary considerably in density. The Czech Lands are better served than Slovakia, while within the Czech Lands the northern half of Bohemia and the Morava lowlands have the densest networks. A further difference between the Czech Lands and Slovakia lies in the fact that many of the railway lines in Slovakia were built as part of a system radiating from Budapest, with some consequent neglect of west–east routes, although the northern trunk route from Žilina to Košice is an exception. In Bohemia, on the other hand, the overwhelming importance and existing nodality of Prague were strong enough to ensure its rise as a major focus of railways, despite the need for tunnelling to reach the centre of the city. In Moravia the railway pattern reflects the function of the Morava lowlands as north–south corridors, but at the same time there are important links with Bohemia to the west and Slovakia to the east, although those with the latter proved inadequate after 1918 and further connecting links thus had to be provided between the Morava and Váh valleys.

From Prague lines radiate in numerous directions–for instance, northwards down the Labe valley to Ústí and Děčín, north-eastwards to Liberec and other places in the Sudets, eastwards to Pardubice and thence, by way of the junction of Česká Třebová, to Olomouc and Brno.

Brno can also be reached by two lines from Havlíčkův Brod in the Sázava valley, south-east of Prague. Prague also has connections to České Budějovice, to the Cheb basin (by way of either Karlovy Vary or Plzeň), and also to the Most coal-basin. Some of these routes extend over the frontiers to give international connections with Dresden, Wrocław, Vienna and Nuremberg.

The Moravian Corridor is followed by the main south–north line from Vienna to Upper Silesia and Warsaw, via Ostrava and Bohumín, with connecting lines to Brno and Bratislava from Břeclav and to Olomouc from Přerov. Today the Corridor route is much less important as regards internal and international freight than the west–east routes that cross it. These link the Czech Lands and East Germany with Slovakia, the Soviet Union and south-east Europe and carry large quantities of industrial raw materials, coal, foodstuffs and machinery. From Bratislava there are lines north-eastwards up the Váh, Nitra and Hron valleys, and also south-eastwards to Komárno and to Budapest. There is also a line westwards to Vienna, only about 60 km/40 miles away. In central and eastern Slovakia a rather skeletal network links the main valleys and basins together and there are some connections northwards to Poland and southwards to Hungary. An important line links the Ostrava coal-basin to the Žilina–Košice route already referred to. Beyond Košice the line continues eastwards into the Soviet Union (former Czechoslovak Carpathian Ukraine). Electrification of main lines is now proceeding. Conversion of the west–east axial line from Most to Čierna, on the Soviet border, has been completed.

Although obviously much denser in character, the road network shows a general pattern reminiscent of that of the railways, with Slovakia showing a lower density than the Czech Lands and also somewhat inferior surface conditions. The disparity has narrowed considerably, however, in the last few decades. There is a very well-developed bus network throughout the country that enables the rural population to take up industrial employment. Private-car ownership, although increasing and also proportionately high amongst the Socialist countries, nevertheless lags behind the levels reached in neighbouring Austria and Bavaria. As yet there are no modern motor-ways in the country. Passenger traffic on the railways now shows little growth. Internal air-links connect Prague with the four largest towns of Moravia and also with Bratislava and Košice. Some of the spa-towns and mountain resorts are served by special flights. Prague airport, at Ruzyně, west of the city, has important international connections.

Inland waterways chiefly relate to the lower Vltava and the Labe, giving connections with Germany and the North Sea, and to the Danube, giving connections with the Black Sea. Prague is accessible to small craft, but traffic is limited by the low summer water-level and by winter freezing. Further downstream Ústí and Děčín are very much more important. Bratislava and Komárno are ports on the Danube, the latter having shipyards. Although the volume of waterway traffic now exceeds pre-war totals it is still very small compared with the volume of freight carried by rail. The construction of a canal link between the Odra and the Danube, via the Morava, has been projected for some time but has been repeatedly postponed. Apart from the Vltava–Labe and Danube waterways, Czechoslovakia is also able to use the Polish river-port of K źle on the Odra, particularly for Swedish iron-ore imports. Foreign trade is chiefly conducted through the Polish ports of Szczecin, Gdańsk and Gdynia and the West German port of Hamburg. Rijeka and the Black Sea ports are also used. Most of the traffic travels by rail rather than waterway, however.

The foreign trade of Czechoslovakia shows a high degree of dependence on the import of raw materials, fuels and foodstuffs (totally nearly three-quarters of the import bill) and the export of manufactures, especially engineering products. There are also some specialized food exports, such as beer. Over two-thirds of all foreign trade is with the other Socialist countries, the chief trading partner by far being the Soviet Union, followed by East Germany, Poland and Hungary. Amongst other countries a leading place is held by West Germany. Despite a very considerable home production there is some importing of coal, but on the other hand there are also exports of coal, especially coking coal, to neighbouring countries. Iron ore and non-ferrous metals are imported in large quantities. In recent years trade with underdeveloped countries has increased, and factories are often built in exchange for various foodstuffs and raw materials. Tourists are now encouraged as a source of foreign exchange. The lack of a sea-coast is a drawback, however, and stress is therefore laid on the spa-towns (such as Karlovy Vary, Františkovy Lázně and Mariánské Lázně in north-west Bohemia, and Piešt'any and Sliač in Slovakia), the mountain resorts (Tatras and Giant Mountains), and the architectural attractions of Prague and other towns.

Chapter 6

HUNGARY · MAGYARORSZÁG

Introduction

Modern Hungary is bordered on the north by Czechoslovakia, on the north-east by the Soviet Union (Ukraine), on the east by Rumania, on the south by Jugoslavia, and on the west by Austria. It is a small country, extending for about 400 km/250 miles from east to west and for about 250 km/150 miles from north to south. It occupies the greater part of the lowlands of the Hungarian or Pannonian Basin, a vast Tertiary depression situated in the heart of Europe and drained by the Danube (*Duna*) and its tributaries.

The outer margins of the Pannonian lowlands today lie beyond Hungary's frontiers. Before the First World War, however, the limits of the Hungarian Kingdom, an equal partner with Austria and her territories in the Habsburg Empire, extended over a much wider area, reaching the Carpathians in the north and east and the Sava in the south, with a salient extending south-westwards to the Adriatic coast, while to the west the border ran through the foothills of the eastern ranges of the Alps. To a large extent 1914 Hungary (Fig. 21) was, in fact, a fairly well-defined physiographic and hydrographic unit.

On three sides it was embraced by the Austrian territories: Slovenia, Austria proper and Moravia to the west, and Galicia and the Bukovina to the north and north-east. Moreover, to the south, beyond the Sava, lay Bosnia-Hercegovina, taken by the Empire from Turkey in 1878 and officially annexed in 1908. The only 'foreign' frontiers of Hungary were those with Serbia and Rumania, to the south and east.

The defeat of the Austro-Hungarian Empire at the end of the First World War led to the loss of Hungary's peripheral territories. Slovakia and adjoining Carpathian Ukraine (or Ruthenia) became part of the new state of Czechoslovakia; Transylvania, Crişana, Maramureş and part of the Bánát (of Temesvár) were united with Rumania; the remainder of the Bánát, most of Bácska, and Croatia-Slavonia joined Serbia, Bosnia-Hercegovina and Slovenia to form the new Kingdom of the Serbs, Croats and Slovenes (Jugoslavia); and a largely German-speaking area in the west (Burgenland) was joined to neighbouring Austria. In all Hungary lost over 70% of her territory and over 60% of her population, which was reduced from 22 millions to 8. Only in the Burgenland were these

Fig. 21. Hungary before and after the First World War

changes (Treaty of Trianon, 1920) confirmed by plebiscites, and, while the transferred territories certainly had overall non-Hungarian majorities, substantial Hungarian populations (totalling about 3 millions) were left, against their will, outside the boundaries of the shrunken Hungarian state. Most of these Hungarians lived just beyond the new frontiers, but some of them (known as the Széklers) formed a large detached 'island' in Transylvania. As a result of the boundary changes many Hungarians left the ceded territories. particularly landowners and government officials.

It was the desire to reincorporate at least some of these areas that eventually led Hungary to co-operate with Hitler's Germany and thereby regain territory from Czechoslovakia, Rumania and Jugoslavia in the years 1938–41. Such gains (including southern Slovakia, Carpathian Ukraine, northern and eastern Transylvania, rest of Bácska) were nullified by the defeat of Germany and her allies, and the 1938 frontiers were duly restored; moreover, Czechoslovakia was allowed to enlarge her Bratislava bridgehead. The Hungarian minority in Slovakia was substantially reduced by a post-war agreement between Czechoslovakia and Hungary whereby many Hungarians were transferred from Slovakia in exchange for Slovaks from Hungary. Some Hungarians also left Jugoslavia and Rumania. Despite these changes about 2·75 million Hungarians still live in Czechoslovakia, Jugoslavia, Rumania and the Ukraine, where their effective rights of self-expression tend to vary considerably. Relative to the population of the homeland this is the most important minority of its kind in Europe, with the exception of the Albanian minority in Jugoslavia.

The frontiers of modern Hungary have only a limited relationship to natural features. In the north-west, however, the boundary follows the Danube as far as Esztergom, and then the Ipoly for most of its course. In the north-east, east and south-east the boundary rarely shows coincidence with rivers–indeed it crosses them–and follows a somewhat erratic course. In the south-west the Dráva is followed for a considerable distance, while in the west the border, while still set mainly in the Alpine foothills, lies further to the east than in 1914, with the result that Austria now contains part of the 'Little Plain' (*Kisalföld*) and also the greater part of Lake Fertő (German *Neusiedlersee*).

Hungary is populated by 10·1 million persons (1964), of whom nearly all are Magyars. The largest minority consists of some 50,000 Germans, chiefly located in Budapest and in certain districts of western Hungary, e.g. in and around Pécs, Sopron, and the Transdanubian range. Before the Second World War the German minority was much larger, however (over 500,000). Many Germans either left Hungary with the German armies in 1944–5 or were subsequently expelled. The Jewish population was also much larger, but was greatly reduced by wartime extermination in German death-camps. There are also small minorities of Croats, Rumanians and Slovaks, as well as Gypsies.

Historical Background

The territory of present-day Hungary was inhabited by a succession of different peoples before being occupied by the Magyars (Hungarians) in the 9th century. In the 1st century A.D. the frontier of the Roman Empire ran along the Danube, and western Hungary, then with a Celtic population, largely corresponded to the province of *Pannonia*. Fortified posts were located along the river, *Aquincum*, just north of modern Buda, being the most important of these. With the waning of Roman power the country was penetrated by several waves of barbarian invaders, including the Huns and the Slavs, the latter being temporarily subjugated by the Avars. The fact that the country was a stronghold of the Huns led to the name Hungary, and variants, being used by the peoples of western Europe. When, at the end of the 9th century, the Hungarians entered the Basin that was later to bear their name, they probably found a somewhat sparse population, largely Slav in character, that formed a bridge between the western and southern Slavs. The Hungarian invasion severed this connection and was itself a factor leading to the disintegration of the 'Great Moravian Empire', which at that time extended southwards into the basin.

The invaders reached the Hungarian Basin after a series of westward migrations, possibly from somewhere in the region of the Middle Volga. Their language was of the Finno–Ugrian group, showing distant connections with Finnish, Estonian and Lapp. Western Hungary, lying beyond the Danube, received the name of *Dunántúl* ('Transdanubia'), while the area east of the Tisza was called *Tiszántúl* ('Trans-Tisza'). Further east, between the Bihor Massif and the Carpathians proper, was *Erdély* ('forested'), otherwise known in Latin as 'Transylvania'. After a period of far-ranging marauding expeditions, stemmed in the west by the Emperor's victory at Lechfeld, near Augsburg, in 955, the Hungarians adopted a more sedentary way of life and received the Western form of Christianity. The Pope granted a special crown to István (Stephen) I (c. 1000–1038), who is regarded as the effective founder of Hungary, and the 'Holy Crown of St Stephen' was revered as the symbol of the nation until after the Second World War. Under Stephen's rule the foundations were laid for the development of a feudal society and of the system of counties, ruled through the nobility, that was to become such an important feature of internal administration. The conquest of adjoining territories rapidly proceeded northwards and eastwards, as far as the Carpathians; Slovakia and Transylvania thus fell under Magyar rule, while to the south-west Croatia–Slavonia was attached to the Hungarian crown by the end of the 11th century. In the far east of Transylvania control over the Carpathian borderland was consolidated by early colonists closely related to the Magyars (the 'Széklers').

In the medieval period there was frequently a need to preserve the independence and territorial integrity of the Kingdom against external pressures. These came chiefly from the Holy Roman Empire, to the west, and, to a lesser extent, the Byzantine Empire, to the south-east, the threat from the latter quarter being eventually replaced by that of the Turks. The Tatars invaded the country in 1241, causing widespread devastation before being repelled. The Cumans, who fled into Hungary before the Tatar advance, were absorbed, however, and left a legacy in the two regional names of Little Cumania (*Kiskunság*), lying in the Danube–Tisza Interfluve, and Great Cumania (*Nagykunság*), lying between the Lower Körös and the Tisza. Other arrivals were Germans (12th–13th centuries), who were invited chiefly to work the metal ores of Slovakia and Transylvania and also, like the Széklers, to consolidate Hungarian control in the Carpathian districts. In Transylvania they became known, erroneously, as the 'Saxons' and they tended to concentrate in and around seven municipalities that enjoyed a number of rights; hence the German name of *Siebenbürgen* for Transylvania.

After the ancient Árpád dynasty died out at the beginning of the 14th century, Hungary was vigorously ruled for some seventy-five years by Robert Charles of Anjou (1308–42) and his son, Lajos (Louis) I, 'the Great' (1342–82). Lajos also became King of Poland and his territories extended from the Baltic to the Adriatic and the River Dnepr. By the end of the 14th century the Turks, having conquered most of the Balkans, were becoming a threat. Władysław, King of Poland and Hungary, fell in battle against the Turks at Varna (Bulgaria) in 1444, but in 1456 János Hunyadi forced them to retire from Belgrade, on the southern borders of Hungary, and thereby temporarily preserved the country from further attacks. His son, Matthias Corvinus (1458–90), a patron of the Renaissance, increased Hungarian power by gaining control of Austria and Bohemia.

In the early 16th century Hungary was greatly weakened by ineffectual rule, dissension amongst the powerful nobles, peasant disaffection, and renewed Turkish encroachments. At Mohács, in 1526, Hungary was defeated by the Turks and King Lajos II was killed. After a temporary Turkish withdrawal and a period of dispute for the crown, a three-fold partition took place in 1541 under Turkish auspices after a second invasion. Western and northern Hungary, including Slovakia, became a rump kingdom under Ferdinand I of Habsburg (subsequently Holy Roman Emperor), central and southern Hungary were occupied by the Turks, while Transylvania and its north-western fringes (including Debrecen) became a Turkish vassal state under its own princes. As such it was able to keep alive the spirit of Hungarian independence, and Protestantism was also able to flourish to a degree that was not possible in the Habsburg-held areas. This three-fold partition lasted for nearly a hundred and fifty years.

The last great thrust of the Turks into Central Europe was terminated by their defeat near Vienna in 1683. This was followed by their gradual withdrawal, under Austrian pressure, from all of Hungary except the Bánát of Temesvár (Peace of Karlovci/Karlowitz, 1699). The Bánát was freed in 1718 (Peace of Požarevac/Passarowitz). The vacuum left by the Turkish withdrawal was filled by Austria, but not without strong Hungarian nationalist opposition. During Austria's involvement in the War of the Spanish Succession a revolt (1703) led by Ferenc Rákóczi resulted in a brief period of independence, extinguished in 1711 by a reimposition of Habsburg rule, with some guarantees, however. The Pragmatic Sanction of 1723, on the other hand, confirmed that the Hungarian crown was no longer elective but linked automatically to that of Austria.

During the second half of the 18th century great economic and cultural progress was made during the period of 'enlightened absolution' under

Maria Theresa and Joseph II, although at the same time there were strong Germanizing influences. In the Bánát and Bácska the depopulated areas lying to the north of the new Turkish frontier, following the lower Sava–Danube line, were systematically recolonized by agricultural settlers drawn from many parts of the Habsburg territories, and a mosaic of villages speaking different languages came into being. In the Bánát German 'Swabians' were especially prominent.

The first half of the 19th century, often known as the 'Reform Period', was noted for a remarkable development of national consciousness (Magyar becoming the official language in place of Latin) and a yearning for economic and political changes, which were fostered by the liberal aristocrat Count István Széchenyi (founder of the Academy of Sciences) and the radical political writer, Lajos (Louis) Kossuth. Revolution in Vienna and Budapest in 1848 led to the Emperor's acceptance of the 'March reforms' granting a type of Home Rule to Hungary. Unfortunately, however, the minorities were soon antagonized by Magyar nationalism. In Vienna Imperial authority was restored.

The volunteer *Honvéd* army had to fight against both Austrian and Croat forces, but the reimposition of Habsburg control was not easy. In April 1849 complete independence was declared in Debrecen. In August, however, the Hungarian forces were defeated at Világos by interventionist Russian forces. Defeat was followed by the execution of many of those prominent in the revolution and by the imposition of the repressive 'Bach system', whereby Austrian officials gained close control of the nation's life. Austria's humiliating defeat by Prussia in 1866 at last made her ready to acknowledge the claims of Hungary in an attempt to strengthen internal cohesion. The *Ausgleich* ('Compromise') of 1867 gave Hungary (including Transylvania and Croatia-Slavonia) its own government, except that joint ministries controlled foreign affairs, defence and finance.

Between 1867 and the First World War there was much economic progress. Budapest grew rapidly as one of Europe's most gracious capital cities, with a radiating network of railway lines extending to the Carpathians and the Adriatic. Agricultural output expanded, partly as a result of land-reclamation and flood-control schemes, and there was a growth of processing industries. Mineral extraction increased, especially in the Central Range, the Bánát and Slovakia, and manufacturing industries developed in Budapest. The growth of the rural population began to lead in time, however, to rural unemployment and land-hunger, especially as large areas of the country formed part of the vast estates of the magnates and the Church. Emigration to America was thus becoming important by the end of the 19th century. Politically there was tension with the minorities as a result of the policy of 'Magyarization'. Only the Croats enjoyed a measure of autonomy.

With the defeat and collapse of the Habsburg Empire at the end of the First World War the way was open for the minorities to assert their independence, especially as the Western Powers regarded Hungary as a defeated enemy. Economic difficulties and the exasperation resulting from the loss of the peripheral territories led to the downfall of a radical government under Count Károlyi and to the establishment for a few months in 1919 of a Socialist Republic under Béla Kun. Hungarian forces clashed with Czech, Rumanian and Serbian troops and the régime collapsed as the Rumanians advanced on Budapest. Admiral Horthy became Regent and continued as head of a monarchical form of government until 1944.

Inter-war Hungary was ruled by a succession of largely authoritarian conservative governments, closely associated with the still-powerful aristocracy. The loss of territories that had formed part of Hungary for centuries was keenly felt, not only emotionally but also economically, and relationships with Czechoslovakia, Jugoslavia and Rumania were understandably strained, the more so since these countries formed what was effectively an anti-Hungarian alliance, the 'Little Entente'. Much less was done as regards land redistribution than in other countries of East-Central Europe and thus rural unemployment and land-hunger continued to be severe problems, while externally there were periodic difficulties in marketing agricultural produce. In the middle and late 1930s Hungary was drawn closer to Germany and Italy, politically and economically, and for a number of years derived certain benefits from this association, including territorial gains at the expense of her neighbours (1938–41). Her participation in the Second World War as an ally of Germany was rather lukewarm and she was able to avoid direct German control until 1944, when, after Hungarian feelers for an armistice had been put out, the country was taken over by Germany and the Hungarian Fascist party installed in power.

Soviet troops entered eastern Hungary shortly afterwards and a provisional government at Debrecen obtained an armistice. Budapest was heavily defended by the retreating Germans during the winter of 1944–5. Parliamentary government was uneasily reinstated under the shadow of the Soviet occupation forces. Large estates were confiscated and redistributed to landless peasants and various nationalization measures were put into effect. Little by little all political forces antagonistic to further socialization and to Soviet influence were undermined, and in 1949 a 'People's Republic' was inaugurated. The powerful Catholic Church, the last stronghold of opposition, was shorn of its influence and its leader imprisoned after a trial. In the economic field nationalization was completed in the non-agricultural sectors, collectivization of the land embarked on, and an industrialization programme put into effect within the framework of five-year plans.

After a wave of demonstrations in Budapest in October 1956, 'liberal' Communist elements, led by Imre Nagy (who had headed the government in 1953–5), organized a new government with non-Communist participation, which made far-reaching concessions to the people. International neutrality was declared and a return to a conventional parliamentary system envisaged. Soviet armed forces, after an initial withdrawal, attacked and captured Budapest and helped into power a new Communist government. Members of the deposed government were subsequently executed. The frontiers were quickly sealed again, some 200,000 Hungarians having fled the country in a matter of days. The damage due to the fighting, together with the disorganization of life during and after the rising, led to a great setback to the economy. By the early 1960s there had been a marked improvement in living standards, however, and the régime, although insisting on the completion of the collectivization programme, had become more flexible in an attempt to win the confidence of the nation. The 1956 rising had not been entirely in vain.

The Land (Figs. 22, 23, 24)

Hungary corresponds to the inner part of the Pannonian or Middle Danube Basin. In Tertiary times it was an area of subsidence, around the margins of which encircling young fold-mountains had been raised up (Alps, Carpathians, Dinaric ranges). Previously there had existed an eroded, fragmented Hercynian massif upon which Mesozoic sediments, chiefly limestones, had been deposited during periods of submergence. The Tertiary earth movements led not only to subsidence and to submergence by the Miocene Sea, but also to much volcanic activity. There followed a period of emergence, during which the volcanic areas were peneplaned, succeeded by renewed submergence (the Pannonian Sea of Pliocene times) and further uplift. Thereafter differential rising and sinking of the various parts of the Basin, extending into the Quaternary period, led to the present pattern of relief, and in particular to the contrast between the Great and Little Plains and the intervening 'Central Range' or 'Middle Mountains' (*Középhegység*). The uplift of the latter was accompanied by the eastward shift of the Danube from a north–south course between the present Rába and Dráva to the present route, which utilizes a line of weakness through the mountains further to the east (Visegrád gorge). Much superficial matter, both aeolian and fluviatile, was deposited in the Quaternary period.

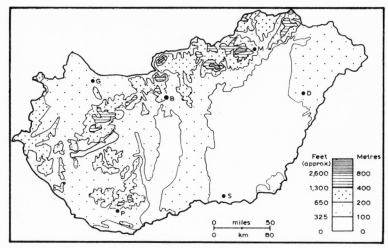

Fig. 22. Relief of Hungary

Stretching from south-west to north-east across the northern half of Hungary is the so-called Central Range, a name more appropriate when the territory of Hungary was much larger. Conventionally the mountains are divided into the 'Transdanubian' and 'Northern' ranges, separated by the Visegrád gorge of the Danube. In the former Pilis reaches 757 m/

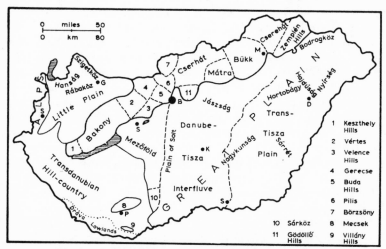

Fig. 23. Generalized physiographic regions of Hungary

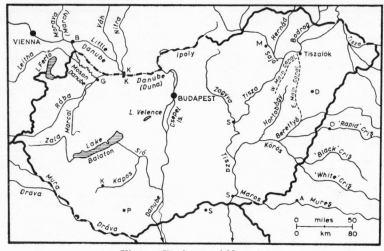

Fig. 24. Drainage of Hungary

2,485 ft, and in the latter Kékes reaches 1,015 m/3,330 ft. The ranges, which are block-faulted and peneplaned, consist chiefly of Mesozoic and Tertiary limestones (with karstic features) and Tertiary volcanic rocks (chiefly andesitic lava and tuffs). Their flanks are often covered with loess. Triassic and Tertiary limestones predominate in the Transdanubian range, although the Velence Mountains are of granite (a surviving fragment of the Hercynian massif) and part of the Pilis range consists of volcanic rocks. At the southern foot of the Keszthely Hills and the Bakony stretches Lake Balaton, occupying a tectonic depression. Only 72 km/ about 45 miles long, the lake is rarely more than about 4 m/about 13 ft deep, and the south shore has wide, shallow beaches used as a summer resort by both Hungarian and foreign holiday-makers. Further east is the smaller and shallower Lake Velence, partly covered by reeds.

In the Northern range volcanic rocks increase in importance, especially in the Börzsöny, Mátra and Zemplén ranges and the southern part of the Bükk (the rest of which consists of a high limestone plateau). The Cserehát and Gödöllő hills, by contrast, consist of Tertiary material with a loess cover. Broad valleys with alluvial fans forming a foothill zone open out from the Northern range on to the Great Plain.

Other upland areas occur in the west and south-west of the country. Along the western borders the easternmost spurs of the Alps penetrate into Hungary, notably the Sopron Mountains and Kőszeg Mountains (near Szombathely). Much of the south-western quadrant of Hungary is known as the Transdanubian Hill Country. This chiefly consists of dissected Tertiary rocks covered with loess and sands. A large area south and south-west of Lake Balaton is characterized by straight, north–south parallel valleys with intervening flat-topped ridges, the origin of which is not yet fully understood by Hungarian geographers. In the south the raised block of the Mecsek Mountains, a smaller replica of the Transdanubian range, consisting of Permian and Mesozoic limestones, overlooks the city of Pécs. Further south are the Villány Hills, which are lower and less extensive but geologically similar.

The lowland areas of Hungary consist chiefly of two plains–the 'Little Plain' (*Kisalföld*) in the north-west and the 'Great Plain' or 'Plain' (*Nagyalföld* or merely *Alföld*) forming the eastern half of the country south of the Northern range. Both are still subsiding very slightly. The Little Plain, which extends into Austria and Slovakia, lies between the Alpine foothills and the Transdanubian range and is covered with thick deposits of superficial material. The low-lying north-central part consists of recent fine alluvial material, while the marginal areas variously consist of coarse alluvial fans or Tertiary hills of soft material. The damp, north-central area itself consists of several distinctive units, including the *Szigetköz*, between the Moson Danube and the main channel of the river; the *Hanság*, a largely reclaimed marsh adjoining the shallow, reed-covered Lake Fertő (only about 1 m deep); and the *Rábaköz*, lying between the Rába and the Hanság.

The Great Plain also exhibits considerable variety. The northern part of the Trans-Tisza Plain (*Tiszántúl*) includes the *Nyírség*, a low sandy plateau, originating in an old alluvial fan deposited by the Tisza and its Rumanian tributaries; the *Bodrogköz*, a damp flood-plain area between the Tisza and the Bodrog, and the rather similar *Rétköz* between the Bodrog and Nyírség; the *Hajdúság*, an area of loess near Debrecen; and the adjoining, but lower, *Hortobágy*, an area of alluvium that became an arid steppe with poor alkaline soils in the last century as a result of flood control of the Tisza. The Hortobágy still retains a few picturesque *gulyás* or 'cowboys', but recent irrigation schemes with the aid of the new Eastern Main Canal have transformed large areas of it. The southern half of the Trans-Tisza Plain has wide areas of loess, as in Great Cumania (*Nagykunság*), but there are also sandy patches as well as areas of swamp reclamation, especially near the confluence of the Berettyó with the Körös (*Sárrét*).

That part of the Great Plain lying between the Danube and the Tisza, known as the 'Danube–Tisza Interfluve' (*Duna–Tisza–Köze*), is broadly similar to the Nyírség, being a low sandy plateau, with loess tracts becoming more important in the south. The sands are the remains of the great alluvial fans that were deposited by the Danube when its former course ran diagonally across the area, from Budapest to Szeged. Lower-lying flood-plain tracts near the Danube and the Tisza border the Interfluve to east and west (including the Plain of Solt). To the north-east is the *Jászság*, the flood-plain of the Zagyva.

West of the Danube the *Mezőföld* is broadly similar to the Great Plain (although higher) and consists of Tertiary rocks covered by loess, with some sandy areas. It descends by loess cliffs to the Danube. To the south of the *Mezőföld* is the damp *Sárköz*, while to the south of the Trans-danubian Hill Country are the Dráva lowlands, bordering Jugoslavia.

Climate and Soils

The climate of Hungary, while largely Continental in character, also shows important Oceanic influences, and to a lesser extent Mediterranean influences. Western parts of the country thus receive more annual precipitation (over 650 mm/25 in) than the Great Plains (less than 500 mm/20 in in parts of *Tiszantúl*). There are also more rain-days in the west and a smaller annual temperature range. In January all Hungary has an average temperature below freezing, with the north-east being the coldest part of the country, and in July all lowland areas have average temperatures of over 20°C/68°F, with the south-east being the hottest. Temperatures are lower and precipitation higher in the Central Range and the Alpine foothills than in adjoining lowland areas. The months with the highest rainfall tend to be May, June and July, but a second maximum occurs in October, especially in the south-west, reflecting Mediterranean influences. The accompanying table gives climatic statistics for selected stations and shows some of these regional variations. Thus, of the places listed, Debrecen, in the north-east, has the coolest winter and Szeged, in the south-east, the warmest summer. The rainfall total for Szeged should also be compared with that for Keszthely, in the moister west of the country.

Conditions can vary considerably from year to year, depending on the relative strength of Continental and Oceanic influences. Early summer drought occurs periodically and can lead to crop failure. Flooding can also be serious. Two periods of flood occur annually: the 'White Flood' in the early spring, when the rivers are in spate owing to snow-melt, and the 'Green Flood' of the early summer, related to rainfall and to the melting of Alpine snow. Flood hazards can be increased during the White Flood if drift ice from the upper Danube is impeded by conditions further downstream, where the thaw occurs later.

Until the 19th century Hungary's slow-moving rivers, with their gentle gradients, were largely unregulated. Rivers shifted their course frequently and disastrous floods were commonplace. Since the mid-19th century

TABLE 6

CLIMATIC STATISTICS · HUNGARY

Station	Average temperature January °C	°F	Average temperature July °C	°F	Average annual precipitation mm	in
Budapest	−0·8	30·6	21·9	71·4	615	24·2
Debrecen	−2·7	27·1	20·5	68·9	587	23·1
Eger	−2·3	27·9	20·5	68·9	587	23·1
Keszthely	−1·1	30·0	21·1	70·0	683	26·9
Mosonmagyaróvár	−1·7	28·9	20·3	68·5	599	23·6
Szeged	−1·3	29·7	22·3	72·1	566	22·3

rivers have been regulated by means of straightening and embanking, and as a result the incidence of serious flooding has been very greatly reduced, while at the same time land-reclamation schemes have enabled an extension of the cultivated area. In spring the Great Plain offers an interesting view from the air of water-filled cut-offs and small depressions, contrasting with swollen rivers sharply delimited by sinuous lines of tree-planted embankments.

Despite its relatively small extent Hungary shows a considerable variety of soil-types. The most fertile are the 'black-earth' soils, characteristically developed on the loess of the Trans-Tisza Plain, the southern part of the Interfluve and the Mezőföld of Transdanubia. Differing from these are the soils lying at a slightly lower level nearer to the rivers. Here are areas of fertile meadow soils, of alluvial origin, together with more recent and skeletal alluvial soils. Swamp soils are also fertile when reclaimed, as in the Rétköz. Specific conditions of hydrography and climate have led locally to the formation of *szik* soils, i.e. alkali (sodic) soils, such as the *solonets* soils of the Hortobágy and the saline *solonchak* soils on the low-lying left bank of the Danube (Plain of Solt). The sandy areas of the Interfluve have poor skeletal soils, but on the sands of the Nyírség more fertile rust-brown forest soils have developed.

Transdanubia (except the Mezőföld) and the Northern range, with their more humid conditions, have large areas of relatively fertile brown forest soils, with podzols in the mountains and in the hilly areas of the west. Rendzina soils occur in limestone areas of the Transdanubian and Northern ranges. In the Little Plain there are alluvial, meadow and swamp soils, with brown forest soils and podzols on the higher margins.

Land-Use (Fig. 25) and Farming

Owing to the high proportion of the land surface under cultivation, much of the natural vegetation of Hungary has been removed over time.

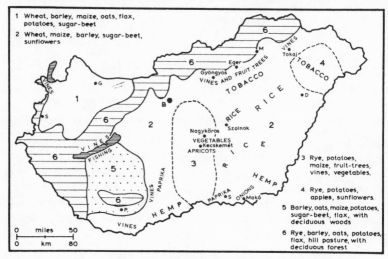

Fig. 25. Generalized land-use regions of Hungary

Thus the wooded steppe (*puszta*) of the Great Plain has virtually disappeared and such areas as remain are scarcely typical, being chiefly those where alkali soils prevail. Similarly the deciduous woodland of southern and western Transdanubia has been greatly depleted. Although cultivation has thus transformed the lowland areas of Hungary, forests and woods still account for about 14% of the country's area (a proportion twice as high as that of Great Britain). Even so Hungary needs to import much timber, especially softwoods; before the boundary changes at the end of the First World War these requirements could be easily met by her Carpathian forests. A large part of the tree-covered area is accounted for by the Central Range, which has extensive beech-forests, with oak occurring on the lower slopes, especially those that are south-facing. Oak- and beech-woods also occur in the Transdanubian hill country, and planted conifers appear in the Alpine foothills. In the Great Plain willow and poplar groves are found along the rivers, together with acacia plantations, introduced in order to stabilize embankments. The acacia has also been used for anchoring sand-dunes, especially in the sandy areas of the Interfluve, which still retain some natural growth of oak and birch. Conifers have also been used for this purpose. Poplars for cellulose production have been planted in some flood-plain areas.

Hungarian agriculture has changed considerably in the past hundred years. In the latter decades of the 19th century the cultivated area was greatly extended, partly at the expense of the *puszta* and its sheep flocks and partly by the reclamation of flood-plains as a result of drainage and river-control schemes. The growth of the railway network enabled Hungary to export large quantities of grain from the extended area of cultivation. In the sandy areas of the Interfluve and the Nyírség there was a veritable agricultural colonization, based on the development of phylloxera-free vineyards, orchards and vegetable growing. At the end of the Second World War large areas of Hungary's farmland were still owned by the aristocracy and the Church, despite partial redistribution in the 1920s, but by the land-reform measure of 1945 about one-third of the country changed hands in favour of the small peasants and landless labourers. Within a few years, however, collectivization measures were introduced and by the early 1960s these had been completed. In recent years irrigation has been very much extended in the Great Plain, especially in the area of the Tisza and the new Eastern Main Canal (1956), which crosses the Hortobágy. A Western Main Canal was to be completed in 1966. Crops of rice are now obtained from these areas and fish-ponds have also been created.

Grain farming is still the dominant theme, although it is true that maize–destined for livestock–has tended to increase at the expense of wheat, which no longer plays a significant role in the export trade. Drought conditions can periodically reduce grain output. Maize, wheat and barley are the leading cereals in the Great and Little Plains and the Mezőföld, and sugar beet and leguminous forage crops are also important. The rather more humid Little Plain also grows oats, flax and potatoes. In the other lowland areas the sunflower achieves prominence. Within the Great Plain there are two major areas where local soil conditions lead to important differences in the range of crops. These are the two sandy areas of the Interfluve and the Nyírség, where rye and potatoes are dominant. The hilly and mountainous zone, extending diagonally across the country from south-west to north-east, is also a distinctive land-use region, with considerable areas of deciduous forest and hill pasture in addition to crops of rye, barley, oats and potatoes, with some maize and wheat where conditions permit. Rather better conditions for agriculture prevail in the rolling country between Lake Balaton and the Mecsek Hills.

Superimposed on these broad zones are a number of special, localized crops. Rice cultivation in the Trans-Tisza Plain has already been referred to. Vines for table-grapes or wine-making are located in the following chief areas: Sopron, the north shore of Lake Balaton (Badacsony area), southern Transdanubia, the Interfluve, and the southern margins of the

Northern range. In this latter area the wines of Tokaj and Eger are especially notable. Hemp is grown in the far south of the country, tobacco in the Nyírség and in a zone between the Tisza and the Northern range. Apples and apricots are grown in the Nyírség and the Interfluve, Kecskemét in the latter being a renowned centre of apricot cultivation, while the Buda area is noted for its peaches. Nagykőrös is an important centre for vegetable growing (including tomatoes), while in the Szeged and Kalocsa areas paprika is a specialized crop. Makó is well known for its onions. The Jászság and the district around the capital are also vegetable-growing areas.

The large output of maize, together with smaller quantities of barley and rye, sustains large numbers of livestock, especially pigs. These show the highest density in Trans-Tisza, where also poultry farming is well developed. Sheep and cattle tend to have a more uniform distribution, although the former are better represented in hilly limestone areas and lowland areas of poor alkaline pasture, while dairy cattle are more typical of the Little Plain and south-west Transdanubia. Specialized high-value agricultural products today play an important role in Hungary's export trade and include quality wines, fresh, canned and deep-frozen fruit and vegetables, pork, dressed poultry, eggs, sunflower oil and sugar.

Industry and Mining

Industrial development was given a stimulus as a result of the *Ausgleich* of 1867 and various Acts for the encouragement of industry from 1881 onwards. Food-processing, mining and manufacturing had shown significant growth by the First World War and certain engineering products, such as agricultural machinery, railway rolling-stock and rivercraft, had achieved a high reputation. However, factory industry tended to be overwhelmingly located in the capital, Budapest. After the war Hungary lost important mining and metallurgical districts to Czechoslovakia and Rumania; on the other hand her economic separation from the rest of the former Habsburg territories, especially Bohemia, encouraged the home production of items, e.g. textiles, that such areas had formerly supplied.

Industry thus expanded between the wars and became more diversified, but much of the capital was foreign, and in the 1930s German economic influences became progressively stronger. Since the Second World War industry has been deliberately expanded and, while Budapest still accounts for over 40% of the total of industrial workers (compared with over 60 in 1938), there has been an attempt to set up new industries in the provincial towns, many of which had previously been stagnating or only growing slowly. As a result of the industrialization drive the percentage of the active population engaged in agriculture has fallen from about 50% in the 1930s to 35% (1960).

ENERGY SUPPLIES (Fig. 26)

Hungary's endowment of energy resources is insufficient for her growing needs, especially as regards black coal and petroleum. Even so her annual output of coal of all types, now reaching 31·5 million tons (1964), is over three times that of 1938, and she also produces some petroleum and natural gas.

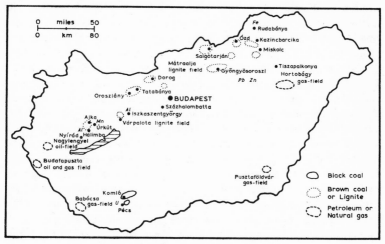

Fig. 26. Mineral exploitation in Hungary

Stretching diagonally across the country from Lake Balaton to the Sajó valley is Hungary's 'coal axis'. Here deposits of brown coal, and also lignite, are located within, or on the flanks of, the Transdanubian and Northern ranges. The chief brown-coal workings are near Dorog, Tatabánya-Oroszlány and Ajka, in the former area, and near Salgótarján (Nógrád county), Ózd and Miskolc-Kazincbarcika (Borsod county) in the latter. Total output reaches 22 million tons (1964) and consists of approximately equal outputs from the Transdanubian and Northern fields. In addition, there are small lignite fields near Várpalota and in the *Mátraalja* ('Matra-foot') area (total output 5 million tons). Output from the latter field is to be greatly expanded for thermal power generation. On the flanks of the Mecsek there are useful deposits of Jurassic black coal, some of coking quality, which are mined in the neighbourhood of Pécs and Komló (total output 4 million tons). The deficit in black coal requirements is made good by imports from Czechoslovakia, Poland and the Soviet Union.

In the hilly south-west of the country, in Zala county, are Hungary's oilfields, where exploitation by American interests began in the late 1930s. There are two chief areas—an older field near the Jugoslav border (Budafapuszta) and a newer field to the north (Nagylengyel). Total output was 1·8 million tons in 1964. The crude from the former is piped to small refineries near Budapest, Várpalota and Komárom (Szőny and Almásfüzitő), while petroleum from the latter field is refined locally at Zalaegerszeg. The new 'Comecon' oil pipe-line, entering the country through the Cserhát Mountains from Slovakia, and terminating at the Százhalombatta refinery downstream from Budapest (eventual annual capacity 6·5 million tons), will deliver far more oil than the Hungarian fields, however. Natural-gas deposits are exploited in south-west Hungary and newer fields have recently come into production in south-east Hungary and the Hortobágy, especially near the spa-town of Hajdúszoboszló. Gas is piped from the latter area to Budapest and to the chemical and metallurgical industries of the Miskolc region.

Electricity generation is almost entirely thermal in character, and power-stations are closely related locationally to the various coalfield districts. Natural gas, piped from Rumania, is used at the Tiszapalkonya station, near Miskolc, and Százhalombatta has an oil-fired station. Hydro-electric power generation is as yet very small and is chiefly accounted for by the post-war Tiszalök regulation dam on the Tisza. In the future, however, two schemes now being put into effect, in collaboration with Czechoslovakia, on the Danube between Bratislava and the gorge, at Gabčíkovo and Nagymaros, will lead to a substantial increase in hydro-power generation. Several barrages may also be built below Budapest, and in the future Hungary and Jugoslavia will jointly harness the Dráva and Mura. Nuclear power may also be developed, based on the uranium being mined near Pécs.

METALLURGY (Fig. 26)

While Hungary has a shortage of iron ore (not to mention coking coal) for her expanded iron and steel industry, she has, on the other hand, a large export surplus of bauxite and she also has ample supplies of manganese. The bauxite deposits occur on the flanks of the Bakony and Vertes Mountains in Transdanubia, and exploitation, originally chiefly for the German and Swiss markets, dates from the 1920s. Mining takes place near Iszkaszentgyörgy, Halimba and Nyírád. In the mid-1930s some conversion to alumina began to take place in Hungary itself and during the Second World War the production of aluminium began under the stimulus of the German war effort. Further expansion has occurred in the post-war period.

The present distribution of the industry is as follows: alumina plants at Mosonmagyaróvár (north-west of Győr) and Almásfüzitő (near Komárom), aluminium refineries at Tatabánya and Inota (part of Várpalota) and an alumina–aluminium complex at Ajka. There are also rolling-mills at Budapest and Székesfehérvár. Although much processing of bauxite and alumina thus takes place within Hungary, electricity costs are relatively high and increasing quantities of alumina are therefore being sent by way of the Danube and the Black Sea for conversion into aluminium at cheap hydro-power centres on the Volga in the Soviet Union. The metal ingots then return to Hungary for fabricating or export. Hungary also has a large export trade in bauxite and alumina to Austria, Czechoslovakia, East Germany and Poland. The output of bauxite, alumina and aluminium reached, respectively, 1,500, 250 and 57 thousand tons in 1964. About half of the bauxite and half of the alumina are exported (1964).

In the 18th century an iron industry developed in the Northern range, based on local ores and charcoal and using water-power for hammer-forges. Today there are two iron and steel centres in this district, both extensively modernized since the Second World War–Diósgyőr (now part of the city of Miskolc) and Ózd. These use the low-grade limonite of Rudabánya and imported Ukrainian ore and they depend also on Czech and Soviet coke. Both works use natural gas piped from the Horto-bágy and from Rumania for their steel furnaces. Near Ózd sheets are produced at Borsodnádasd. Further to the west there are cast-iron foundries and steel-fabricating works at Salgótarján, while on Csepel Island (Budapest) there are steel furnaces and tube-mills. In the mid-1950s there came into production the first stage of a new integrated plant on the Danube at Dunaújváros ('Danube-New-Town'), some 65 km/40 miles downstream from the capital. (This project had originally been destined for the Mohács area, but tension with Jugoslavia in the late 1940s led to a relocation.) A new settlement of over 40,000 has grown up in a rural setting on the high right bank of the river. Coking coal comes from the Pécs–Komló field and iron ore arrives by river from the Ukraine. Total Hungarian steel output reached 2·4 million tons in 1964, but 50% of coke and 80% of ore requirements have to be imported. Manganese ore is obtained from Úrkút in the Bakony. Hungary has few other metal ores in significant quantities, although there is a small output of lead-zinc ores from the Gyöngyösoroszi area in the Mátra.

OTHER INDUSTRIES

In view of the high proportion of cultivated land in Hungary, food-processing industries of many kinds are widespread and include grain and sunflower milling, sugar beet refining, fruit and vegetable processing, wine-making and meat-packing, including the production of salami. Until the Second World War non-food industries were, however, highly localized in Budapest, the mining and metallurgical districts of the Central Range and the towns of the Little Plain. This preponderance of the nation's industry in an area north of a line running from Lake Balaton through Budapest to Miskolc still exists in spite of the introduction of new industries into the towns of the Great Plain and southern Transdanubia, both large and small. Nevertheless, Budapest's share of the nation's growing industrial output is certainly being gradually reduced.

Engineering industries are well developed in certain fields, such as diesel and electric locomotives, railway rolling-stock, sea-going river-craft, floating cranes, turbines, radio, electrical and telecommunication equipment, electric lamps and agricultural machinery. The range of engineering products has been greatly extended since the Second World War (e.g. machine-tools, buses). The leading centre by far for engineering is Budapest, followed by Miskolc (heavy machinery, machine-tools) and Győr (rolling-stock). Székesfehérvár has a radio and television industry. Textile and clothing industries were poorly represented until the inter-war period. They became chiefly concentrated in Budapest and the towns of the Little Plain (Győr, Sopron, Pápa and Mosonmagyaróvár), but there have been post-war expansions in the south of the country, as at Kaposvár, Baja, Szeged, Békéscsaba and Hódmezővásárhely. Artificial fibres are made at Nyergesújfalu on the Danube upstream from Esztergom, and Kazincbarcika. The chemical industries show some association with the coal-mining, metallurgical and oil-refining districts. New fertilizer plants based on coal resources have been established at Várpalota, on natural gas at Tiszapalkonya and on natural gas and coal at Kazincbarcika ('Borsod' chemical complex). A joint Hungarian–Jugoslav phosphate plant is being built at Subotica, just over the southern border. Places on the River Tisza, such as Szeged and Szolnok, are also now becoming important chemical centres; water resources and river-borne raw materials are important locational considerations. Cellulose industries based on straw supplies have developed at Szolnok and Dunaújváros for similar reasons. The rubber industry has important concentrations at Nyíregyháza and Szeged. In the building materials industry there is a large concentration of cement works in the Dorog–

Tatabánya–Danube gorge area, close to limestone and coal. Miskolc is another centre of cement-making.

Distribution of Population and Chief Cities

The general distribution of population shows a fairly regular pattern. Although there is only a small agricultural population in parts of the 'mountainous' districts, there is compensation here in the form of mining and metallurgical centres. Indeed such major gaps as exist in the population pattern are related to certain infertile lowland areas, such as the Hortobágy and parts of the Interfluve. The location of the major provincial cities (Miskolc, Debrecen, Szeged, Pécs and Győr) shows a certain symmetry in that they are all situated near the borders of the country and form a semicircle surrounding Budapest, which is located in the north-central part of the country. There is an enormous difference in size and functions between them and Budapest, however, and one long-term aim of Hungary is to slow down the rate of growth of Budapest and increase that of the other cities in order to try to reduce this disparity.

The Great Plain differs significantly from the rest of the country as regards the details of population distribution and settlement patterns. Always less well populated than Transdanubia, it was subjected to serious depopulation during the Turkish period and the settlement pattern became reduced to one of large, widely separated villages. In the 18th century, after the Turkish withdrawal, the population began to build summer farmsteads (sing. *tanya*) in the surrounding districts and in many cases these became permanent in time. Settlement in the Great Plain thus typically consists of large agricultural villages and 'towns' with many thousands of inhabitants, surrounded by a scatter of tiny outlying farm hamlets–a combination of extreme nucleation and extreme dispersal of the agricultural population. The tanyas present problems for the provision of modern services and their liquidation thus often occurs as part of the collectivization policy. A similar development of scattered farmsteads occurred in the 19th century, when large areas of the Interfluve were settled for vine and vegetable growing. Another group of 'agricultural towns' is found in the Hajdúság near Debrecen. These date from the 17th century and they began as settlement colonies for the 'hajduk' (sing. *hajdú*), Protestant irregulars who had helped the Prince of Transylvania against both the Emperor and the Turks. Even today the towns of the Great Plain still contain a large agricultural element and such industries as exist are largely concerned with food-processing. Thus despite its poor representation of industry the Great Plain has as many 'towns' of over 20,000 inhabitants as the rest of Hungary.

The increased pace of industrialization and urbanization in recent decades, combined with the collectivization drive of the 1950s, has led to the intensification of a rural exodus that had already begun before the end of the 19th century. Old-established country towns have become centres of industry, and new settlements have also sprung up, such as Ajka, Dunaújváros (the largest), Kazincbarcika, Komló, Oroszlány, Tiszaszederkény (near Tiszapalkonya) and Várpalota. About 40% of the population is now urban, half of this proportion being accounted for by Budapest. The distribution of the leading cities and towns is shown in Fig. 27.

Fig. 27. Distribution of chief cities and towns in Hungary

BUDAPEST (1·90 m in 1963) (Fig. 28). As a municipality Budapest dates only from 1873, when Buda and Óbuda (Old Buda), on the west bank of the Danube, were united with Pest on the east bank. Each of the three constituent settlements has had a long history. In Roman times the north–south line of the Danube formed the frontier of the Empire, and the large city of *Aquincum*, superseding an earlier Celtic settlement, was built on the west bank of the river in the neighbourhood of present-day Óbuda. Downstream, on the plain across the river, the outpost of *Contra-Aquincum* was built on a site that later corresponded to the Inner Town (*Belváros*) of Pest.

In early medieval Hungary the royal seat was located successively at Esztergom, Székesfehérvár and Óbuda, but during the devastating Tatar invasion of 1241 Óbuda and Pest, the latter already an important commercial centre, were destroyed. After the Tatar withdrawal, King Béla IV

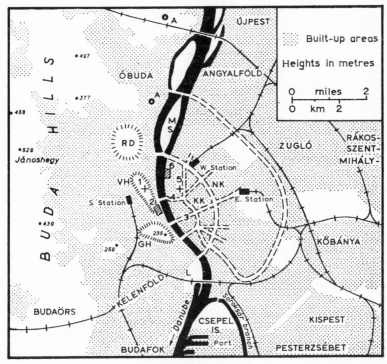

Fig. 28. Budapest

Key: A–Roman amphitheatre. **GH**–Gellérthegy (Gerard's Hill). **KK**–Kiskörút (Little Boulevard). **L**–Lágymányos. **MS**–Margitsziget (Margaret Island). **NK**–Nagykörút (Great Boulevard). **RD**–Rózsadomb (Rose Hill). **VH**–Várhegy (Castle Hill).

1. Matthias Church. **2.** Royal Castle. **3.** Belváros (Inner city of Pest). **4.** Suspension Bridge. **5.** St Stephen's Basilica. **6.** Parliament Building.

decided to utilize a long, narrow limestone ridge, to the south of Óbuda and lying almost opposite Pest, for the building of a more easily defensible royal settlement. Castle Hill (*Várhegy*) thus became the nucleus of a new Buda. The royal castle (rebuilt many times, almost completely destroyed in the Second World War and still being reconstructed) was located at the south end of the ridge, while the civil town developed to the north, dominated by the 'Matthias' or 'Coronation' church, where many kings were crowned between 1309 and 1916. The *Várhegy* is one of three limestone hills overlooking the west bank of the Danube, the others being Rose Hill (*Rózsadomb*) and the much loftier Gerard's Hill (*Gellérthegy*, 235 m/770 ft) towering above the river. These three are outlying members of the wooded Buda Hills, which form a semicircular range to the west of Buda. Today the hills are a popular recreation area, with villa development on the lower slopes. Further natural amenities of Budapest are the many thermal springs, related to faulting, that are chiefly found on the west bank of the Danube in Buda, and also on Margaret Island. Well known from Roman times onwards they are today used for swimming pools and therapeutic baths.

Between 1541 and 1686 Buda and Pest were held by the Turks and they took on an Oriental appearance. During this period (and afterwards until 1848) Pozsony (Slovak *Bratislava*) was the capital of free Hungary. The withdrawal of the Turks left the twin settlements devastated and depopulated, and rebuilding, largely in the Baroque style, did not gain momentum until the second half of the 18th century. Immigrant German speakers now formed a large element of the population.

In the 19th century growth became brisker in Pest than in Buda, owing to its more favourable level terrain. Here expansion proceeded northwards from the *Belváros* and also eastwards beyond the old walls. Under the stimulus of Count Széchenyi a permanent bridge, of a suspension type (the *Lánchíd*), was built across the river, replacing a pre-existing pontoon bridge. This bridge, the first of the eight now spanning the river, was completed in 1849 by the British engineer, Clark, who subsequently built a tunnel through the *Várhegy*, thus facilitating urban development on its far side.

In the latter decades of the 19th century the impressive Great Boulevard (*Nagykörút*), nearly 5 km/3 miles in length, was built along an old channel of the river. This boulevard encircled the Little Boulevard (*Kiskörút*) that had developed along the line of the former walls of Pest and the road to Vác running northwards. Today the area between the Great Boulevard and the Danube constitutes the administrative and commercial heart of Budapest. A third, outer boulevard has taken shape in the 20th century. A short underground railway line (the first on the Continent) was built in Pest in 1896. A new line (10 km/6 miles long), now under construction, will link Pest with Buda.

Budapest is by far the largest centre of industry in Hungary, accounting for over 40% of the total number of industrial workers. The growth of traffic on the Danube and the development of a railway network led to considerable industrial expansion from the middle of the 19th century onwards, with food-processing, clothing and other consumer-goods industries being prominent. In the present century there has been a marked development of engineering and metallurgical industries. The chief industrial zones lie well away from the central areas of Buda and Pest, and are as follows: (*a*) Angyalföld ('Angel-land') and Újpest

('New Pest') with metallurgical, engineering, electrical, leather and pharmaceutical industries, (b) Kőbánya ('Quarry'), Kispest ('Little Pest') and Pesterzsébet ('Pest Elizabeth') in the south-east, with manufactures of textiles, tractors, railway rolling-stock, chemicals, beer and food products, and (c) Csepel Island, with steel furnaces and various engineering industries (machine-tools, motor-cycles, lorries and sewing-machines). Industry is less well represented on the west bank, but there is a new zone of development in Lágymányos (electrical cables, telephonic equipment). The building of river-craft (up to 1,500 tons) takes place on Óbuda Island and across the river in Angyalföld. In the eastern suburbs of the city are the 'Ikarus' motor-bus works.

Despite the considerable destruction caused during the last winter of the Second World War, when all the bridges were destroyed, and the smaller-scale damage during the rising of October 1956, Budapest has now retrieved much of its former grandeur, and the view from *Gellérthegy* still offers one of the finest urban panoramas in Europe.

DEBRECEN (140,000) is an old route-centre situated in the fertile *Hajdúság*. To the west lies the *Hortobágy*. Like all towns of the Great Plain, it still retains an important agricultural function, but in recent years modern industries have been introduced, especially pharmaceutical products, furniture and ball-bearings. Debrecen has been a major stronghold of Calvinism since the 16th century, and the great church where the 1849 Declaration of Independence was made still overlooks the centre of the town.

MISKOLC (160,000) the chief town of the 'Borsod' industrial region, lies at the eastern margin of the Bükk Mountains and dominates the embayment formed by the junction of the valleys of the lower Hernád and Sajó. It is an important metallurgical centre, the Lenin iron and steel works being located to the west in Diósgyőr (now part of the city) up the small valley of the Szinva. In addition to a large heavy engineering industry there are also glass, cement, textile and food industries and there are brown-coal mines in the vicinity. The whole built-up area extends for several miles along the Szinva valley, with the newer districts of Miskolc proper reaching the plain of the Sajó.

PÉCS (127,000), situated at the southern foot of the wooded Mecsek Hills, is one of the most ancient towns of Hungary. It occupies the site of the Romano-Celtic town of *Sopianae*, and the present cathedral is built on the foundations of a Roman church. A university was first established in 1367. The exploitation of local coal deposits stimulated some industrial development in the 19th century, the best-known activity being the manufacture of ornamental glazed earthenware and tiles ('majolica'). There are leather, glove-making, engineering and brewing industries and uranium ore is mined to the west of the city. A mosque in the main square, later converted into a Catholic church, is a reminder of the period of Turkish occupation.

SZEGED (107,000), the chief city of the southern part of the Great Plain, lies on the left bank of the Tisza just below its confluence with the Maros. It has always been a leading commercial centre and water-borne traffic is still important. The town was devastated by floods in 1879 and was rebuilt according to a plan of concentric semicircular boulevards intersected by radial thoroughfares. The best-known products of Szeged are its foodstuffs, including salami and paprika, but the rubber and textile industries (cotton, hemp and jute) have recently increased in importance and new chemical and glass industries are also being developed.

Transport and Trade

The compact shape of Hungary, the presence of few physical barriers, and the fairly even distribution of the population have favoured the development of a good network of railway and road communications, although the standard of the latter is still rather below that of Western Europe. The railways converge markedly, indeed excessively, on Buda-pest, with the result that connections between the other cities tend to be poor. This great centrality of Budapest is not merely an effect of its sheer size, but is also related to the fact that the rail network was built in the second half of the 19th century when the city was the capital and commercial metropolis of a much wider area, embracing Slovakia, Transylvania, the Bánát and Bácska, and Croatia-Slavonia. After the First World War the Hungarian railway system was truncated by the superimposition of new frontiers.

Main lines radiate from Budapest to all the other chief towns and there are also a number of important international links. From Komárom and from Szob (above the Danube gorge) there are connections to Bratislava, leading on to Prague and Warsaw, while from Győr there are links to Vienna and Wiener Neustadt. Southwards there are lines through Székesfehérvár and Nagykanizsa to the ports of Trieste and Rijeka, and through Kiskunhalas to Subotica and Belgrade. Szolnok, on the Tisza, one of the most important railway junctions in Hungary, controls lines to Kiev through Debrecen and Nyíregyháza, and also lines to Arad and to Cluj in Rumania. In view of her geographical position Hungary uses Adriatic and Baltic ports for sea trade, as well as the Danube, and she handles a considerable amount of transit traffic (by rail, road and water) between Jugoslavia, Rumania and Bulgaria to the south and east, and Czechoslovakia, Poland and East Germany to the north. Electrification has been introduced on the busy northern lines from Budapest to Szerencs, east of Miskolc, and to the Austrian frontier (Hegyeshalom). Budapest also has domestic and international airway connections from its airport at Ferihegy, south-east of the city.

River communications are of very considerable importance, especially as these allow Hungary direct access by sea-going river-craft to the Black Sea. The whole length of the Danube (about 400 km/250 miles), most of the Tisza, and also the lower Körös are available for all-the-year navigation. The Sió is navigable for part of the year only. Most of the traffic goes upstream and includes Soviet iron ore (for Dunaújváros) and other raw materials from the Soviet Union, Bulgaria, Rumania and Jugoslavia, some of which continue upstream to Bratislava in Czechoslovakia. The largest river-port is that of Budapest (Csepel Island) and others on the Danube are at Győr, Komárom, Dunaújváros, Baja and Mohács, while on the Tisza Szeged and Szolnok are the most important. Budapest has a summer hydrofoil service to Vienna.

Before the Second World War Hungary's export trade was dominated by foodstuffs (grain, pigs, poultry, wine) and certain raw materials (especially bauxite), although some engineering products were becoming significant, and manufactures were the chief import. Nearly half the foreign trade turnover was with Germany and Austria and trade with the Soviet Union was negligible. Today Hungary's chief imports are raw materials (e.g. fibres, iron ore, non-ferrous metals and timber) and fuels (coal and petroleum), and manufactures account for well over half of her export trade. It may be noted that in some years wheat imports are now necessary. 70% of trade is with the other Socialist countries, 30% being with the Soviet Union, who is the leading supplier of fuels and raw materials. Trade with West European countries and with under-developed countries is increasing, however. Now that she has achieved a larger and more diverse infrastructure of basic industries, it seems likely that further economic growth will be related to exports of high-value manufactures, especially engineering products, and high-value foodstuffs (fruit, vegetables and animal products).

Chapter 7

JUGOSLAVIA · JUGOSLAVIJA

Introduction

Jugoslavia is roughly oblong in shape and extends from north-west to south-east. It is bordered by Italy and Austria to the north-west, Hungary to the north, Rumania to the north-east, Bulgaria to the south-east, and Greece and Albania to the south. The Adriatic coastline forms most of the long south-western boundary, but Jugoslav Macedonia, in the far south, is separated from the sea by Albania and Greece, and in the north-west Slovenia is partly screened by the Trieste salient of Italy. The longest distance from north-west to south-east (along a line passing through Ljubljana, Sarajevo and Skopje) is about 950 km/600 miles, and the maximum width, from the Hungarian frontier city of Szeged to the mouth of the Neretva, is about 400 km/250 miles. The straight-line length of the Adriatic coast, from Trieste to the Albanian border, is over 600 km/375 miles. At a distance of 150–200 km/100–125 miles across the Adriatic lies the peninsula of Italy.

While the sea constitutes an obvious natural frontier, the land boundaries of the country only occasionally coincide with natural features. The southern part of the border with Italy in fact partitions the town of Gorica (Italian *Gorizia*) and also almost encircles Trieste. Further north part of the frontier with Austria coincides with the lofty Karavanke range of the Alps. The border with Hungary and with the Rumanian part of the Banat runs through the almost featureless Pannonian Plain and crosses the southward-flowing Danube and its great tributary, the Tisa. The Drava, another tributary, forms the boundary line with Hungary for part of its length, however. East of Belgrade the Danube enters its winding gorge section (the *Đerdap*), cut into the Carpathians, and here the river coincides with the Rumanian boundary. The Bulgarian and Greek frontier districts correspond to a large extent with mountainous country, but the upper Nišava basin lies in Bulgaria and that of the upper Strumica in Jugoslavia, while the River Vardar is crossed by the Greek frontier only about 60 km/35 miles above its outflow into the Aegean Sea near Thessaloníki. The border with Albania likewise follows mountain ranges for most of its length, although it also passes through Lakes Prespa, Ohrid and Skadar. From the latter the border follows the River Bojana to the sea.

184

Jugoslavia, or the 'Kingdom of the Serbs, Croats and Slovenes', as it was officially called until 1929, came into existence at the end of the First World War, when the independent Kingdom of Serbia, together with the tiny neighbouring Kingdom of Montenegro, united with other South Slav territories hitherto forming part of the defeated Habsburg Empire of Austria–Hungary (Fig. 29b). 'Jugoslavia' means the land of the South Slavs, i.e. the Serbs, Croats, Slovenes, Macedonians, the Mohammedan Slavs of Bosnia and Hercegovina, and the Montenegrins (who are basically Serb in origin). Strictly speaking the Bulgarians are also 'Jugoslavs', but the longstanding mutual antipathy between them and the Serbs, which has waned only very recently, has precluded union. In a brief period of rapprochement after the Second World War some form of union was seriously envisaged, however.

The chief language of Jugoslavia is Serbo-Croat; this is written in the Roman alphabet by the Croats and in the Cyrillic by the Serbs. Both are written phonetically and transcription from one to the other follows simple rules. In spite of a large measure of 19th-century standardization important dialectal differences remain, however; even so, most Serbo-Croats speak the 'Štokavian' dialect (itself having three sub-dialects). The 'Kajkavian' dialect of Serbo-Croat is spoken in the Zagreb region and the 'Čakavian' on the Dalmatian islands. Other dialects are spoken in those areas bordering on Bulgaria and Macedonia. Serbo-Croat is also spoken in Montenegro (Cyrillic alphabet), Bosnia and Hercegovina (both alphabets) and the Vojvodina (both alphabets). Slovene, which also has several dialects, ranks as a separate language (using the Roman alphabet), but it has close connections with Serbo-Croat. Macedonian (Cyrillic alphabet), which may be regarded as transitional between Serbo-Croat and Bulgarian, has been elevated to the status of a separate language only since the Second World War, but the Bulgarians have customarily regarded it as a Bulgarian dialect.

In south-west Serbia and parts of Macedonia there is a large Albanian (*Šiptar*) population, speaking a language that is generally considered to be a survivor of the old pre-Roman languages of the Balkans. In the Vojvodina there are, in addition to Serbs, many Hungarians (Magyars), together with Croats, Slovaks and other groups. There are also Rumanians in Serbia in the area between the Morava and the Timok. Before the Second World War there were about half a million German speakers. They occurred in small pockets in Slovenia, and in the towns of Croatia, but they were most numerous in the Vojvodina, where many were farmers. The majority of them migrated, or were expelled, to Germany at the end of the war, however, and their place was taken by land-hungry settlers from impoverished areas in the Dinaric ranges. The number of Rumanians also declined and the number of Hungarians showed little change, a result in both instances of wartime or post-war population shifts. Turks are found in the south, especially Macedonia, while a Bulgarian minority is found near the Bulgarian border. The Turkish population has been reduced by post-war migration to Turkey.

The breakdown of the various Jugoslav ethnic groups at the census of 1961 was as follows: Serbs 7·8 millions (42%), Croats 4·3 (23%), Slovenes 1·6 (9%), Macedonians 1·0 (6%), Montenegrins 0·5 (3%) and 'Undefined Jugoslavs' (i.e. in effect, the Mohammedan Jugoslavs of Bosnia and Hercegovina) 1·3 (7%). Thus only about 16·5 millions (89% of the total population) were Jugoslavs in the strict sense. The other chief groups were Albanians 0·9 million (5%), Hungarians 0·5 (3%) and Turks 0·2 (1%), followed by Slovaks (86,000), Bulgarians (63,000) and Rumanians (61,000). There were also much smaller minorities of Ukrainians (chiefly in the Vojvodina), Gypsies, Vlachs (Macedonia), Italians (Istria), Czechs (Slavonia), Germans and Russians (émigrés). Non-Jugoslavs thus together totalled 2·0 millions, or 12% of the population (this figure including 0·2 million belonging to other Slav groups– Czechs, Slovaks, Bulgarians, Ukrainians and Russians). The greater part of the pre-war Jewish population (79,000) was exterminated by Germans during the war and some of the survivors emigrated to Israel.

Religious differences are also important. The Croats and Slovenes are traditionally Roman Catholic, while the Serbs, Macedonians and Montenegrins are traditionally Orthodox. In Bosnia and Hercegovina there is a large body of Mohammedan Jugoslavs. Most of the Albanians are also Mohammedans, and most of the Hungarians are Catholics. Although the impact of Marxism has been to weaken the observance of religion, important cultural differences still persist.

Since the Second World War Jugoslavia has had a federal system of government (albeit under a one-party Socialist system), in order to satisfy the desire for autonomy by the various constituent territories. Although there are close linguistic affinities among the South Slav peoples, strong religious, cultural and economic differences still existed after union in 1918, as a result of their widely differing historical experience during many centuries, and an over-centralized administration between the wars led to inter-regional tensions. Such differences still survive, although with diminishing force. The federal system also recognizes the rights of the non-Slav minorities, especially the Albanians and the Hungarians, who constitute a large element in the two Autonomous Regions of *Kosovo-Metohija* and the *Vojvodina* respectively.

The Federal Socialist Republic of Jugoslavia (population 19·3 millions in 1964) consists of six constituent republics, as follows (Fig. 29a).

Fig. 29. Constituent republics of Jugoslavia (*a*) and territorial growth of Serbia, Montenegro and Jugoslavia (*b*)

(a) SERBIA (*Srbija*) (7·9 millions, capital Belgrade), comprising *Serbia proper* (4·9 millions) and two Autonomous Regions–the *Vojvodina* (1·9, capital Novi Sad), and *Kosovo-Metohija* (1·1, capital Priština), often abbreviated to *Kosmet*. The *Vojvodina* has a very mixed population, dominated by Serbs and Hungarians, the other peoples including Croats and Slovaks. Territorially the Vojvodina consists of Bačka, together with the Jugoslav part of the Banat (the remainder being in Rumania) and most of Srem (Symria). *Kosovo-Metohija* is largely populated by Albanians. *Metohija* broadly corresponds to the plain of the White Drim, and *Kosovo* refers to the Kosovo Polje ('Blackbird Field'), drained by the Sitnica, a tributary of the Ibar.

(b) CROATIA (*Hrvatska*) (4·3, capital Zagreb), including Slavonia and Dalmatia, and also Međimurje and part of Baranja, which both formed part of Hungary proper before 1918, and most of the Istrian peninsula, with Rijeka, which were Italian before 1945.

(c) BOSNIA AND HERCEGOVINA (*Bosna i Hercegovina*) (3·5, capital Sarajevo), a territory of mixed populations, including Mohammedan Jugoslavs, Serbs and Croats. Bosnia takes its name from the Bosna river (although the Vrbas and Una basins are also important), while Hercegovina, a smaller territory to the south, largely corresponds to the Neretva basin.

(d) SLOVENIA (*Slovenija*) (1·6, capital Ljubljana), corresponding largely to the old Austrian province of Carniola and the southern part of Styria, together with Prekomurje, part of Hungary before 1918, and the upper Soča valley and the northern part of the Istrian peninsula, both Italian before 1945.

(e) MACEDONIA (*Makedonija*) (1·5, capital Skopje), that is to say the major (Jugoslav) part of it, since historically Macedonia also includes the Struma valley of Bulgaria and the Thessaloníki area of northern Greece.

(f) MONTENEGRO (*Crna Gora*) (0.5, capital Titograd, formerly called Podgorica, which was destroyed in the Second World War). 'Montenegro' is the Venetian-Italian rendering of the area's Jugoslav name, 'Crna Gora', i.e. 'Black Mountain'.

The boundaries of the Republics and the Autonomous Regions do not neatly coincide with ethnic boundaries since there is considerable inter-mixture of the population, and in some instances historical boundaries are deliberately observed. In Croatia, for instance, there are 0·6 million Serbs, chiefly located near the Bosnian border. The economic expansion of Jugoslavia since the Second World War has also produced a substantial migration of labour. Thus Slovene technical specialists may be found in the underdeveloped south, and unskilled southerners can be found working in relatively advanced Slovenia. Outside the limits of Jugoslavia there are small minorities of Slovenes in Italy and Austria, Serbs in the Rumanian Banat, and Macedonians in Bulgaria and Greece. Émigrés who left the country at various times for economic or political reasons are found in many countries. In recent years many Jugoslavs have been officially permitted to take up employment in West European countries and their remittances are a useful source of foreign exchange.

Historical Background

Before the Roman period the territory of modern Jugoslavia was inhabited chiefly by the Illyrians, with the Thracians occupying large areas in the east. Greek trading colonies existed on the Adriatic coast and Celtic peoples were dominant to the north. After intermittent Roman expeditions from the 3rd century B.C. onwards, conquest took place at the beginning of the Christian era. Most of Jugoslavia became *Illyricum*, but the Danubian plains to the north were part of *Pannonia*, and Serbia was part of *Moesia Superior*. In the far south was *Macedonia*. The area underwent considerable Romanization and many Illyrians rose to high office, five of them becoming Emperor. Roads were built, metal ores were mined and cities flourished, such as Emona (Ljubljana), Naïssus (Niš), Salona (near Split), Scupi (Skopje), Singidunum (Belgrade), Sirmium (Sremska Mitrovica) and Siscia (Sisak). A large Roman amphitheatre survives at Pula. When the Empire was divided at the end of the 4th century the partition line ran in a north–south direction across the country, from the lower Sava to the Montenegrin coast. Later this was to coincide broadly with the boundary between the spheres of influence of the Roman and Byzantine ('Orthodox') churches.

In the 5th and 6th centuries the area was overrun by the barbarians, including the Goths, Huns and Avars. In the late 6th and early 7th centuries they were followed by the Slavs, who had spread southwards from their presumed homeland north of the Carpathians. In time they absorbed the surviving Romanized peoples, although small groups of their descendants, the so-called 'Vlachs' (or 'Mavrovlachs'), still exist to this day, especially in southern Serbia and Macedonia. A district of Serbia is still called *Stari* (i.e. 'Old') *Vlah*. On the Dalmatian coast Imperial rule was maintained for several centuries, however. The Albanians, to the south, are thought to represent the descendants of Illyrian tribes who escaped both Romanization and Slavonicization. The Slavs themselves consisted of three main groups, the Serbs, Croats and Slovenes, and such early differences as existed were further accentuated by the fact that the Serbs were converted to Christianity from Byzantium, and thus became adherents of the Eastern Orthodox Church, while the Croats and Slovenes were converted by the Roman Church. The peoples of Jugoslavia were not formally united until 1918, however, and so their history up to that time is essentially a history of the various component territories.

SERBIA, Montenegro, and adjacent parts of Macedonia and Bosnia–Hercegovina were populated by Serb settlers, who became organized under their local chiefs or 'župans'. In the late 9th century they were converted to Christianity as a result of the Byzantine missionary activity initiated by the brothers Cyril and Methodius, who also introduced the earliest form of the Cyrillic alphabet. The Serb territories were for long periods under Byzantine rule, but for a time they fell partly within the First Bulgarian Empire, and in the 10th and 11th centuries powerful rulers–Časlav and Bodin–were temporarily able to achieve a substantial degree of consolidation and independence. An independent Macedonia broadly corresponding to the western parts of the First Bulgarian Empire, flourished under Samuel in the late 10th and early 11th centuries. Ohrid, it may be noted, was the seat of the Bulgarian Patriarch at this time.

By the 12th century the most powerful district of Serbia was *Raška*, largely corresponding to the Ibar and Lim basins, where Stephen Nemanja became ruler in 1169. He was able to annex *Zeta* (Montenegro), and his son, St Sava, became Archbishop of a Serbian Church with its eventual headquarters at Peć. Cultural and economic progress, as well as territorial expansion, was achieved by subsequent rulers of the dynasty and in 1346, Stephen Dušan, the greatest of the line, was crowned as Emperor in Skopje. His territories included Macedonia and Albania and, later, Epirus and Thessaly (in northern Greece). The Second Bulgarian Empire had already been humbled in 1330 after resisting Serbian expansion. After his death, in 1355, Dušan's Empire collapsed into a number of petty states, as a result of which Turkish penetration into the Balkans was facilitated.

The Turks, who had already obtained a European foothold before Stephen Dušan's death, defeated a league of Balkan Christian armies in 1389 on the Kosovo Polje. By then Macedonia was already occupied. This tragic defeat, which inspired many Serbian folk-ballads, made possible the long Turkish occupation that lasted until the 19th century. Northern Serbia, extending up to the margin of the Pannonian Plain, did not fall under complete Turkish control until the middle of the 15th century, however. One effect of the Turkish advance was a movement of refugee Serbs northwards and westwards into southern Hungary, Bosnia and Montenegro.

In the earlier period of the Turkish occupation relatively efficient government was exercised, although there was certainly discrimination against the Christian peasantry (*raya*). In Macedonia considerable

Turkish settlement took place and there were also Turkish estates ('čifliks'). Later on, and particularly from the 17th century onwards, oppression increased, together with corruption and heavy taxation. This worsening was partly due to inadequate central control over local rulers and over the powerful Janissaries, a 'corps d'élite' for long recruited by means of a periodic tribute of Christian boys. Greek influence was also becoming obnoxious; the Serbian patriarchate at Peć was placed under the Greek patriarch at Constantinople in 1766, and Greek was introduced into the churches.

At the end of the 17th century Habsburg forces liberated Hungary and even pressed southwards into Serbia for a time. By the Treaty of Karlovci (German *Karlowitz*) in 1699, the Habsburg Empire expanded up to the lower Sava approximately, but the Banat was not regained until 1718, by the Treaty of Požarevac (German *Passarowitz*). Between 1718 and 1739 Austria also occupied Belgrade and northern Serbia. Thereafter the Habsburg boundary with the Turkish Empire remained stable, running along the Danube–lower Sava line and then encircling the salient of Bosnia to the west. Inside the Habsburg boundary was the 'Military Frontier', where peasant settlers held land under the Crown in return for military duties. Many Serbian refugees found a new home in these areas, including parts of Croatia and southern Hungary, and settlers were also drawn from other areas of the Habsburg territories. In the Banat and Bačka particularly there came into being a mosaic of agricultural villages, each speaking its own language. Amongst the Serbian settlers there were large numbers from the south-west, especially the present 'Kosovo-Metohija' area. A large migration movement from here was organized by the Patriarch of Peć in the 1690s. Their place was eventually filled by immigrant Albanians. Initially the settlers in southern Hungary were promised the right to have their own governor or 'vojvoda'–hence the origin of the name 'Vojvodina'. Until the liberation of Serbia itself, beginning in 1817, the Serbs of the Vojvodina played an important part in preserving the national tradition.

There was a rising in northern Serbia in 1787 and again in 1804. The latter, led by Kara ('Black') George, was successful, but in 1813 Turkey re-established control. A further rising in 1815, led by Miloš Obrenović, resulted in autonomy for the Pashalik of Belgrade, i.e. northern Serbia (the *Šumadija*, together with areas to the east and west), under Miloš as prince. Further territory was gained in 1833 (Fig. 29b). Alexander Karadjordjević, son of Kara George (whose murder in 1817 had been attributed to Miloš), became ruler in 1842 after Miloš and his son had abdicated. The Obrenović line was restored in 1859.

In 1878, at the conclusion of the Russo–Turkish War, Serbia gained the Niš area by the Russian-sponsored Treaty of San Stefano. At the same time a large, autonomous Bulgaria was to be set up which was to include Macedonia, but the Western Powers, alarmed at the advantage this might give to Russia, succeeded in having the size of Bulgaria reduced and thus Turkey was allowed to retain Macedonia (Treaty of Berlin). Serbia obtained a further award of territory, however (Fig. 29b). Austria–Hungary occupied Bosnia–Hercegovina and the adjoining Sanjak of Novi Pazar, a wedge of territory lying between Serbia and Montenegro (and partly corresponding to old Raška). Serbia was recognized as completely independent, and it thus became a Kingdom in 1882. The last Obrenović was assassinated in 1903 and the Karadjordjević line, in the person of Peter I, was restored. A long violent feud between the two dynasties thus came to an end.

Serbia in the early 20th century was a state that had achieved considerable economic and constitutional progress, but it was anxious to gain access to the sea through Turkish-held Macedonia or Albania, and at the same time there was strong feeling in favour of the liberation of Macedonia, Bosnia–Hercegovina and the Vojvodina, and of union with these and independent Montenegro to form a large South Slav state, which might also include the Croats and Slovenes. Macedonia in particular was seething with revolt against Turkey and also with communal strife amongst its various national groups.

Austria–Hungary was concerned at Serbia's increasing strength, her friendship with Russia and France, and her suspicious sympathy with fellow-Slavs under Habsburg rule. She showed her displeasure in the 'Pig War' of 1906, when she placed a high duty on livestock exports from Serbia, whose trade, of geographical necessity, was largely with, or through, Austro–Hungarian territories. In 1908 she formally annexed Bosnia–Hercegovina, thereby ending the fiction of a temporary military occupation. At the same time she withdrew from Novi Pazar, however.

In 1912 Serbia, in alliance with Bulgaria, Montenegro and Greece, made war against Turkey, and by the Treaty of London (1913) they obtained most of what still remained of Turkey-in-Europe. Austria and Italy supported Albanian independence, however, thus blocking Serbian access to the sea. But the victorious powers could not agree over the division of Macedonia; in particular there was a territorial overlapping of the expansionist claims of Serbia and Bulgaria. The two medieval Bulgarian Empires had both included Macedonia, as also had Dušan's Serbian Empire. Moreover, the Bulgarian ecclesiastical exarchate, authorized by Turkey in 1870, embraced Macedonia. Bulgarian forces attacked those of Serbia and Greece, and, following a Bulgarian defeat, Serbia obtained the greater part of Macedonia, together with the Kosovo polje, and partitioned the Sanjak with Montenegro (Treaty of Bucharest, 1913). As a result Serbia almost doubled in size (Fig. 29b).

MONTENEGRO corresponds approximately to the territory once known as *Zeta*, which broke away from Serbia after the death of Dušan. It included the Zeta basin, the lowlands around Lake Skadar and part of the Adriatic coast. The small district around Mount Lovćen, including the town of Cetinje, was able to maintain a fierce but often precarious independence as an area of refuge after the Turkish conquest of the Balkans. It boasted the earliest printing press in Jugoslavia by the end of the 15th century. From 1516 to 1852 it was ruled by 'vladikas' (bishops), the succession being hereditary (from uncle to nephew) after 1697. From the early 18th century onwards it received periodic subsidies from Russia. In 1852 the offices of ruler and bishop were separated and in 1859 an international commission delimited the border with Turkey. A kingdom was declared in 1910. As an ally of Serbia Montenegro gained additional territory from Turkey by the Treaties of Berlin (1878) and London (1913) (Fig. 29b). Proposals for a form of union with Serbia were being discussed in 1914.

The SLOVENES, occupying the upper Sava basin, and also the upper Drava and Mura basins to the north and the Soča basin to the west, were converted to Christianity from the West in the 8th century and their lands, falling under Frankish rule, became marchland territories of the Holy Roman Empire. In the 13th and 14th centuries these came under Habsburg rule. The Slovene language, which was in danger of being submerged by German, was stimulated by the Reformation in the 16th century, but there followed the Counter-Reformation and further Germanization. A new impetus to Slovene nationalism took place when much of Slovenia and large parts of Croatia and Dalmatia became the 'Illyrian Provinces' of the Napoleonic Empire in 1809. The local language was encouraged and many reforms took place. Austrian rule was restored after Napoleon's Russian defeat, but the so-called 'Illyrian Movement', fostering South Slav cultural and political nationalism, persisted. Nevertheless, like the Czechs at this time, the Slovenes aimed at autonomy rather than complete independence.

CROATIA, converted, like Slovenia, to the Roman Church, emerged as a separate entity in the early 10th century under Tomislav. It included the greater part of the Adriatic coast and much of Bosnia, but there is some doubt about its precise limits to the north in Slavonia. Two centuries later, in 1102, it came under the Hungarian crown and the two countries thereafter remained in association until 1918. Bosnia eventually broke away, and the coast came under Venetian control in the early 15th century after a protracted struggle between Venice and Hungary.

The Adriatic trading cities had retained much of their Latin culture and, moreover, their interests lay with the Mediterranean world rather than with the interior, but with the passage of time they became more Slav in character. One city, Dubrovnik (Italian *Ragusa*), maintained its independence but became nevertheless a centre of South Slav culture.

After the defeat of Hungary in 1526 at the battle of Mohács large parts of Croatia and Slavonia were lost to the Turks and what remained came under Habsburg rule, together with western Hungary. Certain areas formed part of the Austrian 'Military Frontier'. In 1699, by the Treaty of Karlovci, most of the remaining parts of Croatia and Slavonia were regained and the Military Frontier was then extended eastwards along the Sava. Dalmatia remained under Venice until 1797, when Napoleon extinguished the Venetian state, and Dubrovnik also lost its independence at Napoleon's hands in 1805. These coastal areas and other parts of Croatia were later included in his 'Illyrian Provinces', and a stimulus was thereby given to Croat nationalism. With the defeat of Napoleon Habsburg rule was reinstated in Croatia and Dalmatia was annexed.

Anti-Hungarian feeling became acute at the time of the Hungarian national revolution of 1848–9. Jelačić, the native Governor of Croatia, helped to defeat the Hungarians with South Slav troops, in the hope of gaining from Vienna the autonomy that revolutionary Hungary refused to grant. In 1867, Hungary, including Croatia–Slavonia, obtained equality with Austria within the Empire, and in 1868 the *Nagodba* between Hungary and Croatia gave the latter a limited degree of autonomy under its old-established Parliament, the 'Sabor'. During the 19th century the 'Illyrian Movement' gained ground. Eminent amongst its champions were the poet and scholar, Gaj, and Bishop Strossmayer, who founded at Zagreb both a South Slav Academy of Science and Art and a University.

In the years before the First World War Croat national aspirations lay in two directions. Some Croats favoured a large, independent South Slav state, while others favoured the 'Trialist' solution, whereby the South Slavs of the Habsburg Empire would form a third political unit equal in status to both Austria and Hungary.

BOSNIA and HERCEGOVINA lie between Catholic Croatia and Orthodox Serbia and Montenegro and in the middle ages they were an area of religious competition not only between Catholic and Orthodox influences but also between both of these and the *Bogomil* heresy. The Bogomils may be described as 'fundamentalists' or 'Puritans' who scorned both Eastern and Western Christianity and indeed rejected parts of traditional Christian belief. Bosnia first appeared as a separate political entity at the end of the 12th century under Kulin. After passing under Hungarian rule for a time it emerged again in the 14th century, absorbed *Hum* (later Hercegovina) to the south, and under Stephen Tvrtko seemed likely to supplant the Serbian Empire, but the disaster of Kosovo curtailed expansion. Turkish occupation followed after the middle of the 15th century. In the meantime Hum had briefly become the Dukedom ('Hercegovina') of St Sava.

The Bogomils apparently regarded the Mohammedan Turks as a lesser evil than their Christian brethren. Indeed, many Bosnians were converted to Islam and as a result they were able to retain their lands; their descendants, although Jugoslav in speech, sometimes tended to be more fanatical than the Turks. Christian revolts in the 19th century culminated in that of 1875, the suppression of which was one of the causes of the Russo–Turkish War of 1877–8. By the ensuing Treaty of Berlin Austria–Hungary occupied Bosnia and Hercegovina, and in 1908 she annexed them. Despite much economic progress after 1878 the people–Mohammedans, Orthodox Serbs and Catholic Croats–were not reconciled to Habsburg rule. In June 1914 the Archduke Francis Ferdinand, heir to the throne, and his wife, were assassinated in Sarajevo by Princip, a young Bosnian Serb. Accusing Serbia of complicity, Austria presented an ultimatum and shortly afterwards declared war–thus setting in motion the various European alliances and so precipitating the First World War.

The movement for South Slav unity and independence gathered momentum during the war, although Serbia and Montenegro were both overwhelmed and suffered very heavy loss of life. The Declaration of Corfu (1917), made by Serbia and a Jugoslav Committee from the Habsburg territories in London, aimed at union under the Serbian monarchy. This aim was eventually supported by the Western Powers and in December 1918 the Kingdom of ₍the Serbs, Croats and Slovenes was proclaimed. To Serbia and Montenegro were added Slovenia, Dalmatia and Bosnia–Hercegovina from Austria (by the Treaty of St Germain, 1919), and Croatia–Slavonia and the Vojvodina from Hungary (by the Treaty of Trianon, 1920). The new country also made an agreement with Italy (Treaty of Rapallo, 1921), acknowledging the latter's annexation of Trieste, Istria, some Adriatic islands and the mainland town of Zadar (Italian *Zara*). Italy had been promised these areas, and more, by the Western Allies, as the price of her entry into the war (secret Treaty of London, 1915). In 1924 Italian rule was also recognized over Rijeka (Italian *Fiume*), the former seaport of Hungary, after a long dispute. Jugoslavia obtained its suburb of Sušak, however, with some port facilities. Altogether about half a million Jugoslavs found themselves transferred from Austria–Hungary to Italy. In the extreme south of

Carinthia, in Austria, a plebiscite was held in the area of mixed German and Slovene population, but the voting was in favour of Austria. From Bulgaria (Treaty of Neuilly, 1919) Jugoslavia gained several frontier districts. Fig. 29b shows these changes.

Between the two World Wars no other new state of Europe was faced with the problem of welding together such a number of diverse territories with such varying levels of cultural and economic development. Internal politics were marred by sharp differences between the Serbs and Croats. Many Serbs regarded the new state as merely an extension of the Serbian Kingdom. The constitution of 1921 was of a centralist kind, but the Croats and other groups favoured a federal system. A crisis was reached when Radić, leader of the powerful Croat Peasant Party, was shot in Parliament in 1928. The following year King Alexander took over the government and dissolved the parties. In an attempt to eliminate Serbian hegemony and induce a single national loyalty he changed the name of the country to 'Jugoslavia' and replaced the old historical territories by nine large provinces. A less liberal constitution was introduced (1931), but much legislation of a practical nature was achieved. Alexander was assassinated in Marseille in 1934. His brother, Prince Paul, became Regent and retained the system of a 'managed' Parliament and government. In 1939 an agreement was finally reached by which Croatia gained her autonomy.

In the international field Jugoslavia was a member, with Czechoslovakia and Rumania, of the anti-Hungarian 'Little Entente' (1921) and also of the Balkan Entente (1934), with Greece, Rumania and Turkey. Serbia's friendship with France was also maintained by Jugoslavia. In 1937 agreements were made with Italy and Bulgaria, with whom relationships had hitherto not been cordial. However, Jugoslavia's security was soon to be undermined. With the German annexation of Austria in 1938 and the Italian annexation of Albania in 1939 the two 'Axis' powers drew geographically closer. Strong economic links with Germany had developed after the Great Depression of the early 1930s. In 1940 Italy invaded Greece. Bulgaria, Hungary and Rumania joined the 'Axis' alliance in 1940–1 and by March 1941 Jugoslavia was encircled. Prince Paul's government then also adhered, but it was immediately overthrown by a military coup with popular support, and the young king, Peter II, was declared of age. Retribution followed; Belgrade was heavily bombed and the country was invaded from several sides by German forces. Germany, Italy, Hungary and Bulgaria all annexed territory and Croatia (now awarded Bosnia–Hercegovina) and Serbia became puppet states. The extremist government of Croatia, led by Pavelić, was notorious for its atrocities, particularly against its Orthodox Serb minority.

The mountainous terrain of much of Jugoslavia permitted the operation of guerrilla forces. Initially resistance was under the command of the Serbian royalist general, Mihajlović, but subsequently a larger, rival force, with left-wing leanings, took shape under 'Tito' (Josip Broz), a Croat Communist. Allied support was transferred to his 'partisans', who had obtained control of large areas of the country by the end of the war. Tito and his associates were thus able to assume power without needing the physical presence of Soviet forces that was so necessary in most other countries. War deaths totalled 1·7 millions, representing one of the highest proportionate losses suffered by any country. A Federal People's Republic was instituted after the holding of 'single-list' elections in 1945. Private industry and commerce were nationalized. The Roman Catholic Church (whose leading personality, Archbishop Stepinac of Zagreb, was imprisoned on a charge of wartime collaboration) was restricted in its activities. By the Italian Peace Treaty of 1947 Jugoslavia gained most of the Soča (Italian *Isonzo*) valley, the Istrian peninsula, Rijeka, Zadar and several Adriatic islands (including Cres, Lošinj and Lastovo), but Trieste, which Jugoslavia coveted, was made a free territory. In 1954 an agreement was reached with Italy over the partition of Trieste, Italy regaining the city itself (Zone A) and Jugoslavia incorporating a rural area to the south (Zone B).

In June 1948 Tito incurred the displeasure of Stalin by refusing to submit more closely to the Soviet Union, and Jugoslavia was dramatically expelled from the 'Cominform' (effectively, the Soviet bloc). His defiance was followed by an economic boycott, accompanied by sabrerattling, that lasted for several years. As a result Jugoslavia received large amounts of economic and military aid from the West during the 1950s. Another result was the eventual collapse of the left-wing rebel forces in Greece, who had been supported from Albania, Bulgaria and Jugoslavia. Internally the breach was not without its repercussions: collectivization of the land was abandoned in 1953 and a decentralized system of partial self-government in nationalized enterprises was evolved, in contrast to the rigid methods of the Soviet Union. Since the mid-1950s there has been a very gradual rapprochement with the Soviet Union and other Socialist countries of East-Central Europe, but without any surrender of Jugoslavia's 'non-aligned' policy. In 1963 the country officially became a 'Federal Socialist Republic' under a new constitution. New schemes of economic liberalization began in 1965.

The Land (Figs. 30, 31, 32)

Basically there are three dominant elements in the structural geography of Jugoslavia–the ancient massif of Macedonia and southern

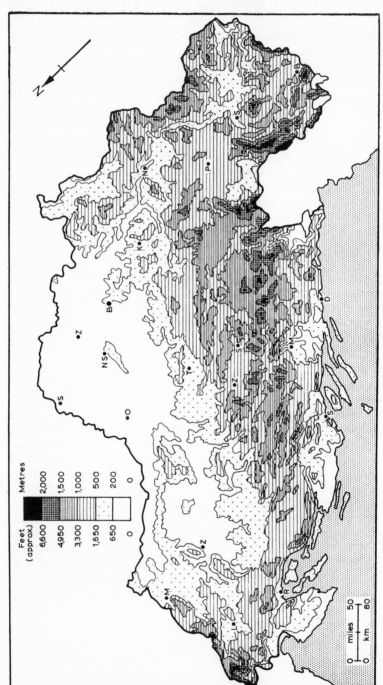

Fig. 30. Relief of Jugoslavia

Serbia ('Rodopi Massif'), the various ranges of Tertiary fold-mountains, and the Tertiary depressions, including the southern part of the vast Pannonian (Hungarian) Basin, constituting the extensive northern low-lands of Jugoslavia. The Pannonian Basin resulted from the foundering and submergence of Hercynian elements that were encompassed by the Alps, the Carpathians and the Dinaric ranges, while the Rodopi Massif, on the other hand, although fractured, persisted as a resistant wedge flanked by the fold-mountains of the Balkan peninsula. In Jugoslavia the Tertiary fold-mountains extend across the country from the Austrian and Italian borders to those of Albania and Greece, while in the north-east a further group forms a link between the Rumanian Carpathians and the Stara Planina of Bulgaria.

In the north-west of Jugoslavia ranges of the Eastern Alps stretch from west to east across northern Slovenia, gradually falling in height eastwards and southwards. Triglav, the highest peak in the whole country (2,863 m/9,400 ft), is situated in the extreme north-west in the Julian Alps. To the east, on the Austrian border, are the Karavanke range and the Kamnik and Savinja Alps. These impressive ranges, consisting predominantly of Triassic limestones, present a truly 'Alpine' appearance, with their jagged peaks (more than a dozen of over 2,500 m/ 8,200 ft), glacial lakes and U-shaped valleys (e.g. that of the upper Sava). Further east is the lower, granite range of Pohorje. South of these ranges is a foothill zone that also includes several large depressions, especially those of Ljubljana and Kranj (Sava valley), Celje (Savinja) and Maribor and Ptuj (Drava). East of Ljubljana the Sava has cut a gorge section through limestone hills (Carboniferous and Triassic).

South of the Julian Alps are the northernmost ranges of the Dinaric system, which, with its well-marked north-west to south-east trend-lines, stretches with increasing width towards Albania and the Rodopi Massif. Here some ranges have north-east to south-west or north–south trend-lines and merge into the Pindhos zone of Greece. The Dinaric zone consists of numerous hill and mountain ranges, set in parallel fashion, with minor intervening furrows and plateaux. Denudation has often reduced the ranges to rather flat-topped ridges and rounded eminences, but their sides are often steep. Much of the Dinaric zone is over 600 m/ 2,000 ft above sea-level, with considerable areas over 1,500 m/5,000 ft. In Bosnia–Hercegovina and Montenegro many summits exceed 2,000 m/ 6,550 ft in height and some show signs of past glaciation. The rivers, draining either to the Sava or to the Adriatic, are deeply incised and show a 'trellised' pattern, consisting of longitudinal and transverse elements. The frequently gorge-like character of the valleys often makes transport conditions difficult, but at the same time possibilities are

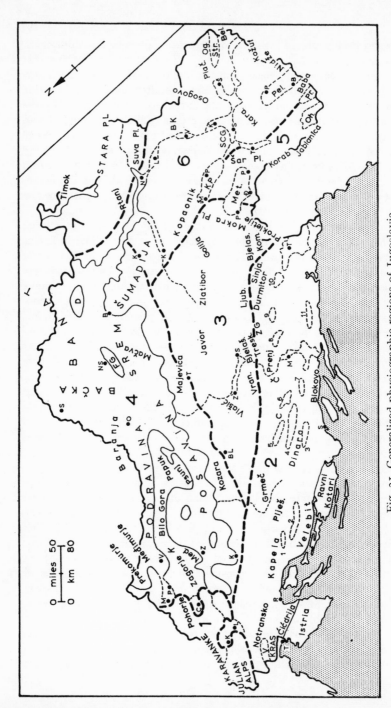

Fig. 31. Generalized physiographic regions of Jugoslavia

N.B. Pecked lines enclose the more important depressions or indicate valley routeways.

offered for hydro-electric power barrages, although porous rock conditions can present difficulties.

Within a belt extending for 60 to 100 km/35 to 60 miles inland from the Adriatic Sea limestones are dominant (chiefly Cretaceous, but also Jurassic and Triassic in part), and it is here that the Dinaric ranges are renowned for their development of 'karst'. This is the German word for the 'Kras' district of Slovenia, consisting of bleak bare limestone country just behind Trieste. Here and elsewhere in the Dinarics chemical erosion by solution of the pure, massive limestones has produced characteristic features that now enjoy the generic description of 'karstic'. A leading feature is the frequency of sub-surface drainage, so that arid conditions and sparse vegetation are also typical over wide areas despite the often high rainfall. Dry valleys are also common.

Typical erosional features include the large hollows known as *doline* (sing. *dolina*) and *uvale* (sing. *uvala*), the latter usually considered to be the result of the coalescence of adjacent *doline*. Such surface streams as exist often begin as *vrela* (sing. *vrelo*), i.e. springs, and they may well disappear again by means of *ponori* (sing. *ponor*), which are deep, shaft-like openings often leading to underground caverns. Intermittent streams disappearing in this way are known as *ponorice* (sing. *ponorica*).

Also typical are the extensive, flat-floored and steep-sided depressions known as *polja* (sing. *polje*). They usually reflect the geological structure, i.e. they are elongated, follow a north-west to south-east direction, and are flanked by the long flat-topped ridges known as *planine* (sing. *planina*). Intermittent streams disappear into *ponori* in the floor of the *polje* or into caverns at the base of the wall of the *polje*. The latter are called *jame* (sing. *jama*). During the rainy winters a *polje* may become flooded, since the *ponori* cannot accommodate the increased flow of water. Drainage tunnels through the Pleistocene alluvium that partially blocks the *ponori* can eliminate such flooding, however. In the summer the *polja* are dry and can be used for cultivation. The longest of the *polja* are those of Lika and Livno (each about 70 km/45 miles in length). The former is

Key to major units: 1. Alpine zone. **2.** Karstic Dinaric zone. **3.** Non-karstic Dinaric zone. **4.** Pannonian Plains and Hills. **5.** Pindhos zone. **6.** Rodopi zone. **7.** Fold Mts of NE. Serbia.

Key to minor units: BK Besna Kobila. **Bel** Belasica. **Bjelas** Bjelasica. **Bjelaš** Bjelašnica. **C** Cincer. **Č** Čvrsnica. **D** Deliblato dunes. **FG** Fruška Gora. **K** Kalnik. **KP** Kosovo Polje. **Kara** Karadžica. **Kom** Komovi. **Ljub** Ljubišnja. **M** Medvednica. **Met** Metohija. **Og** Ogražden. **Oh** Ohrid. **Pel** Pelagonia. **Plač** Plačkovica. **Plješ** Plješevica. **Pr** Prespa. **SCG** Skopje Crna Gora. **Sinja** Sinjajevina. **Stru** Strumica. **Tresk** Treskavica. **V** Vipava valley. **Vran** Vranica. **ZG** Zelengora.

Key to major karstic *polja*: **1.** Gacka. **2.** Lika. **3.**Sinj. **4.** Livno. **5.** Glamoč. **6.** Duvno. **7.** Imotski. **8.** Nevesinje. **9.** Gacko. **10.** Nikšić. **11.** Popovo.

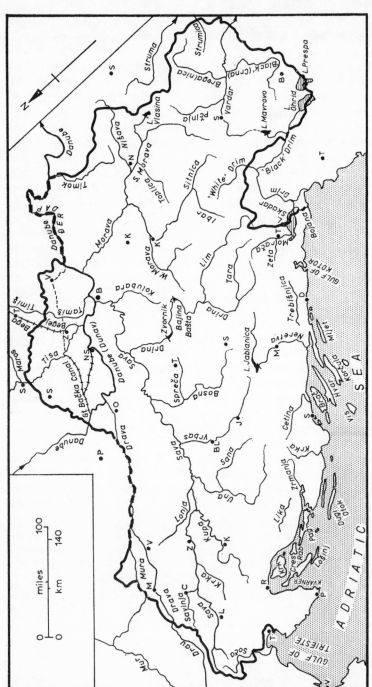

Fig. 32. Drainage of Jugoslavia

drained by the intermittent river of the same name. Inland from Dubrovnik is the well-known Popovo ('priest's') *polje* (40 km/25 miles), drained by the intermittent Trebišnjica. In conclusion it must be pointed out that the Jugoslav words used in karst terminology are often common words that are also used in more general contexts. Thus *polje* means a field or plain, usually of limited extent, and the word is used for virtually any kind of basin or depression. *Dolina* means a valley or dell, and *planina* can apply to any range of hills or mountains.

The coastal region (*Primorje*, i.e. 'sea-side') is a classic example of 'drowning'. A rise in sea-level in Quaternary times led to partial submergence, with the result that the present coastal area is characterized by islands and promontories of an elongated character, while the coastline itself often consists of bleak, bare mountains rising abruptly from the sea (e.g. Velebit and Biokovo). There is thus no coastal plain, and even beaches are rare, except in Montenegro. The lower courses of the deeply incised rivers have also been drowned (Zrmanja, Krka, Cetina) and on the Montenegrin coast there is the magnificent, winding Gulf of Kotor with its steep sides. Access from the sea to the interior is therefore difficult. The lower Neretva valley is an exception, however; here the river has built up a delta and, moreover, there are tracts of lowland (some being karstic *polja*) extending inland as far as Mostar. In the far south the Drim (Albanian *Drin*) has also built a delta, which is traversed by the Bojana, draining Lake Skadar. In two important areas the Dinaric coastlands consist of low platforms rather than mountain ranges. These are the Istrian peninsula west of a line from Trieste to the Kvarner straits and the Ravni Kotari ('Level Districts') promontory between the Zrmanja and Krka. Wide bands of soft Tertiary rocks alternate with the limestone in these areas.

The non-karstic Dinaric ranges, with their forests, pastures and abundant surface water, stretch north-westwards in a tapering fashion from the Rodopi Massif towards the neighbourhood of Karlovac. They are formed to a large extent of lower Triassic rocks, but there are also exposures of Carboniferous rocks. Both consist of sandstones and shales rather than limestones. There are also large outcrops of schists and serpentines, and Cretaceous limestones occur locally. Between Sarajevo and Zenica there is a zone of soft Tertiary rocks excavated by the Bosna.

Northern Jugoslavia forms part of the Pannonian Basin. Quaternary deposits of varying character cover monotonous plains that are bordered on the south by Tertiary rocks overlying the margins of the Eastern Alps, the Dinaric ranges, and the fold-mountains of north-east Serbia. Tertiary deposits also cover large areas of the *Šumadija*, the hill-country south of Belgrade, where underlying Cretaceous deposits in their turn conceal the northernmost extremity of the Rodopi Massif. Between the *Šumadija* and the mountains of north-east Serbia is the wide embayment of the lower Morava, leading southwards to the corridors of the Western and Southern Morava rivers.

The plains stretching north of Belgrade and approximating to the Vojvodina, are the lowest part of the Pannonian Basin, where the Sava, Drava, Tisa and Tamiš join the Danube, which then flows eastwards to pass through its gorge into the lower Danubian plains of Rumania and Bulgaria. There are considerable differences in the type of superficial deposit. There are low loess platforms, with intervening tracts of alluvium, which are often marshy near the 'slow-moving rivers with their many cut-offs, and there are also areas of sand-dunes, as near Deliblato, north-east of Belgrade. River-control schemes dating from the 19th century have done much to reduce flood dangers, and sandy areas have been planted with acacia. Certain areas have their own regional names: thus the *Banat* is the area lying north of the Danube and east of the Tisa (stretching into Rumania), *Srem* (Syrmia) lies between the Sava and the Danube, *Mačva* between the Sava and the Drina, *Baranja* (extending into Hungary) lies between the Danube and the Drava, and Bačka between Danube and Tisa. There is also the low hill range of Fruška Gora, near Novi Sad, which is an old Hercynian 'island' partly covered by later deposits.

The line of the Fruška Gora is continued westwards by a similar group of hills, covered on their flanks by Tertiary deposits, that separate the wide valley of the Sava from that of the Drava. This group includes the Papuk–Psunj hills of Slavonia, linked to the Kalnik, Medvednica and Zagorje ranges by the low, narrow Bilo Gora. The Gorjanci range, across the Sava, is of Triassic limestone, however. The rivers Drava and Sava, whose plains are known respectively as the *Podravina* and the *Posavina*, resemble those of Vojvodina in that they have only a slight gradient, are liable to flood, and show much development of cut-offs along their marshy courses. North of Varaždin are the two districts lying on either side of the Mura, known as *Međimurje* and *Prekomurje*.

The eastern two-thirds of Serbia, together with Kosmet and Macedonia, correspond to the Rodopi Massif and to its flanking ranges, in particular the fold-mountains of north-east Serbia on the one hand and the Prokletije–Mokra and Šar Planina–Korab ranges on the other. These two latter groups both contain a number of mountains rising to over 2,500 m/ 8,200 ft and some show evidence of glaciation in the past. The Rodopi Massif, which extends eastwards and southwards towards the Aegean, is an ancient bloc, consisting chiefly of crystalline rocks, but in Tertiary times there were also outpourings of volcanic rock, especially andesites, e.g. east of Skopje. Relief features include high mountain ranges, such as Kopaonik, Karadžica, and those on the Bulgarian and Greek frontiers (all rising in places to over 2,000 m/6,550 ft), lofty plateaux and a number of faulted Tertiary depressions. The latter are important for settlement and communications. A series of them, lying in a north–south direction, is followed by the rivers Morava and Vardar (Greek *Axios*). These depressions are often linked by gorge sections. Other depressions are those of the upper Strumica, upper Vardar (*Polog*), Pelagonian Plain (drained by the Crna Reka, i.e. 'Black' river), and Lakes Ohrid and Prespa. These depressions were submerged in Tertiary times and it is possible that there may have been a connection between the Aegean Sea of that time and the waters of the Pannonian Basin. Lying between the Šar Planina on the south and the Prokletije–Mokra and Kopaonik mountains on the north are the two large depressions of Metohija and the Kosovo polje, drained by the White Drim and Sitnica respectively.

Finally there are the fold-mountains of north-east Serbia, consisting mainly of Cretaceous, old crystalline, and Tertiary volcanic rocks. To the east are the lowlands of the Timok valley and of the south bank of the Danube below its gorge, while in the south is the gorge-and-basin route up the Nišava valley to the Dragoman Pass leading to Sofia.

Climate and Soils

A striking feature of the climate of Jugoslavia is the contrast between the 'Mediterranean' characteristics (moist, mild winters with long, hot, dry summers) of a narrow zone along the Adriatic coast and the 'Continental' conditions (cold winters, hot summers, and a very moderate rainfall, chiefly falling in the spring and early summer) of the interior lowlands. The mountainous areas lying between the Adriatic coast and the interior lowlands are noted for their high rainfall, however, especially in the karstic zone, and temperatures are greatly affected by altitude. The abrupt fall in winter temperatures inland from the coast is notable.

In January few parts of non-coastal Jugoslavia have average temperatures above freezing, but on the coast the figures range from 4°C/39°F in Istria to 9°C/48°F in the far south. In the summer there is no such marked difference, all lowland parts of the country having average July temperatures of over 21°C/70°F, with the Adriatic coastlands and the basins of southern Jugoslavia having temperatures of over 24°C/75°F. In the Alpine, Dinaric and Rodopi zones local temperatures vary greatly according to altitude and aspect.

Annual precipitation totals range from over 2,500 mm/100 in in the Julian Alps, the Kapela and Velebit ranges and the mountains of Montenegro to under 650 mm/25 in in the Vojvodina and the valleys and depressions of the Morava and Vardar basins. In the mountains over-looking the Gulf of Kotor the figure exceeds 5,300 mm/210 in (the highest in Europe) and in some parts of southern Macedonia falls to 430 mm/17 in. In the Adriatic coastlands and their mountainous hinter-land autumn and winter is the period of maximum precipitation. At this time depressions move south-eastwards down the Adriatic. Local winds are also important, especially the bitterly cold and violent *bura*, coming from the north and north-east, and the damp, warm *jugo* (*široko*) from the south-east.

The interior plains have their maximum precipitation in the spring and summer, related chiefly to the passage of depressions and to con-vectional rain respectively. The winters are drier, although snow-cover may last for three months. In the south-eastern Vojvodina a keen wind from the south-east, the *košava*, lends added severity, while in the Vardar region there is the cold, northerly *vardarac*.

The accompanying table, giving climatic statistics for a number of towns, shows some interesting regional differences. Ljubljana, Rijeka and Titograd, located close to areas of very high rainfall, may be compared with Belgrade, Novi Sad and Skopje, with their much drier continental conditions. The mild winters of Rijeka, Dubrovnik and Titograd may be compared with the cooler conditions of Ljubljana and Sarajevo, in their interior upland basins, and of towns in the interior lowlands. In the summer the latter are, however, hotter than Ljubljana and Sarajevo. In the north Zagreb, being closer to maritime influences, has a higher rain-fall than Novi Sad and Belgrade. In the south Titograd, in a near-coastal basin, has warmer and moister conditions than the Skopje basin, separated by mountain ranges from the influences of the Adriatic and the Aegean. In the extreme south of Macedonia, in the lower Vardar and Strumica valleys and the Pelagonian Plain, conditions become moister, however, and winters are slightly milder.

Soils vary considerably owing to regional differences in parent rock, climate and past vegetation. In the karstic areas of the Adriatic coastal region the solution of limestone has left pockets of residual red soil called *crvenica*, often known under its Italian name of 'terra rossa'. Although initially deficient in humus, it is often the basis of cultivation on terraced hillsides or in depressions within the karst. In the Alps, the remainder of the Dinaric zone, and the ranges of the Rodopi Massif leached soils, including podzols, are dominant, but there are also wide areas of skeletal mountain soils at the higher levels and on steep slopes. Locally dark 'Alpine Meadow' soils may form, giving good summer pasture, and in limestone areas *rendzinas* (carbonate soils) can be found. In the Vojvodina and adjoining parts of the Drava and Sava plains, fertile black earths

TABLE 7

CLIMATIC STATISTICS·JUGOSLAVIA

Station	Average temperature January °C	°F	Average temperature July °C	°F	Average annual precipitation mm	in
Belgrade	−0·2	31·6	22·7	72·9	687	27·1
Dubrovnik	8·9	48·0	24·7	76·5	1,272	50·1
Ljubljana	−1·4	29·5	19·7	67·5	1,618	63·7
Novi Sad	−1·2	29·8	23·0	73·4	613	24·1
Rijeka	6·2	43·2	24·1	75·4	1,854	73·0
Sarajevo	−1·2	29·8	19·8	67·6	920	36·2
Skopje	0·5	32·9	24·5	76·1	477	18·8
Titograd	5·4	41·7	27·1	80·8	1,733	68·2
Zagreb	0·6	33·1	22·2	72·0	925	36·4

(*chernozems*) have developed on the Quaternary deposits, particularly loess, as a result of steppe-like conditions in the past. In the *Šumadija* and the valleys and depressions of Serbia and Macedonia there are relatively fertile brown forest soils, together with the darker *smolnica* ('pitch') soils, usually considered to have developed on lacustrine clays. Alluvial soils, often of great fertility, are found along the main rivers and in the larger depressions, including most karstic *polja*. Saline soils may be found locally in areas of aridity, as in the Vojvodina and the Vardar basin.

Land-Use (Fig. 33) and Farming

The natural vegetation of most of Jugoslavia is forest, and despite clearances in the past more than a third of the country's area remains forested today, although the quality of the tree-cover varies considerably. About 70% is deciduous in character.

Along the Adriatic coast 'Mediterranean' vegetation, adapted to hot, dry summers, is typical, including pines (Aleppo and Black) and the brushwood often known as *macchia* or *maquis* (Serbo-Croat *makija*), consisting of evergreen shrubs, such as juniper, holm oak, broom and laurel. In interior Jugoslavia three broad zones can be distinguished, according to altitude. The high mountains carry coniferous trees (pines and spruce), the hills (up to about 700 m/2,300 ft) carry oak-woods, with other deciduous trees, while an intervening zone is typified by beech-woods. The oak-woods also descend to the Pannonian Plains and thin out into wooded steppe in the Vojvodina, where thickets of willow, poplar and alder are also found along the rivers. Over wide areas of the country the original cover has been removed (as in the *Šumadija*, which means

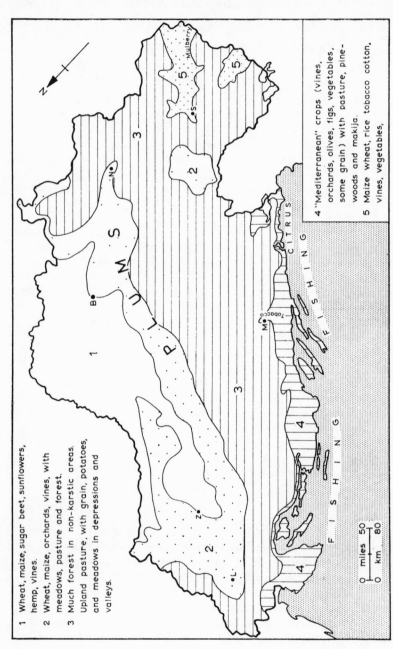

1 Wheat, maize, sugar beet, sunflowers, hemp, vines.

2 Wheat, maize, orchards, vines, with meadows, pasture and forest.

3 Much forest in non-karstic areas. Upland pasture, with grain, potatoes, and meadows in depressions and valleys.

4 "Mediterranean" crops (vines, orchards, olives, figs, vegetables, some grain) with pasture, pine-woods and makija.

5 Maize wheat, rice tobacco cotton, vines, vegetables,

Fig. 33. Generalized land-use regions of Jugoslavia

'forested area'). Oak- and beech-woods still survive locally, however. Over-grazing by sheep and goats has had serious effects and has encouraged soil erosion, especially in southern areas of the country. Deciduous brushwood, known as *šibljak*, has often replaced deciduous forest after its removal.

Despite depletion and variable quality the forests of Jugoslavia are a very important resource, especially as timber and timber products form a large item in the export trade. Slovenia, northern Croatia (including Slavonia), Bosnia and western Serbia are the chief areas of exploitation. Saw-mills and factories producing lumber and such products as plywood, fibreboard, veneers and furniture are located at a number of centres, both in the forested areas and at towns in the Drava and Sava valleys. The traditional rafting of logs still continues on some of the rivers, especially the Drina.

Jugoslav farming is largely carried out by small independent peasants. A land-reform measure of 1919 had the effect of abolishing estates and most large farms, and a second measure of 1945 virtually eliminated medium farms as well. Land in the Pannonian lowlands farmed by the evicted German-speaking community was also redistributed. Collectivization was pursued between 1948 and 1953, but in the latter year the drive was halted and collective farms already set up were allowed to be dissolved. Collectivization had proved highly unpopular, even though in some areas (e.g. Serbia) there had existed until the 19th century the institution of the *zadruga*, a type of extended-family farming unit. However, a ceiling of 10 hectares/25 acres was placed upon the individual ownership of land. The average size of holding is very much lower than this (about 4 hectares/10 acres). A small number of collective farms still exist and there are also over 2,000 agricultural co-operatives of individual farmers, but these together account for only about 10% of the cultivated area. The remainder is distributed amongst some 2·6 million private holdings, whose efficiency varies very greatly, depending partly on natural conditions and partly on the standard of husbandry.

As a result of the unfavourable environment in much of the upland area less than 60% of the country's surface is farmed, and of this only about a half is under cultivation. The most productive zone consists of the Pannonian lowlands, and especially the Vojvodina. This area, concentrating on maize and wheat, together with industrial crops such as sugar beet, sunflowers and hemp, provides a large food surplus which in some years is now adequate to meet the substantial deficit in the rest of the country. Periodically drought can reduce output, however. Flanking this zone is the Tertiary hill country, stretching from sub-Alpine Slovenia to the *Šumadija* and the Morava valley. Here arable crops are less significant and there is a much higher proportion of meadow, pasture and forest. Vineyards and orchards are also important, the famous Serbian and Bosnian plums being largely used for *šlivovica*, i.e. plum brandy, although prunes are also produced.

The mountainous areas of the country are dominated by forest and by upland grazings of considerable importance, although in the karst country bare rock surfaces are frequent. In the valleys and depressions grain crops (including barley, maize, oats and rye) and potatoes are often grown and hay gathered from meadows. In the large basins and open valleys of Macedonia, however, the shorter winters and long, hot summers permit the growth of a number of special cash crops such as tobacco, cotton, rice, early vegetables, melons and poppies (for drugs), in addition to wheat, maize and vines. Irrigation is essential in most instances, however, and a great drive is being made to increase the output of such crops. The mulberry is also grown in the lower Vardar valley. Further north climatic conditions are not so favourable in the Kosmet plains and here farming is similar to that in the hill margins of the Pannonian lowlands. On the Adriatic coast, with its Mediterranean climate, figs and olives can be grown, and in the far south oranges. Vines and fruit-trees are also important. Tobacco is grown in the Neretva valley of Hercegovina, while in its lower, marshy section vegetable cultivation has expanded in recent years. Fishing takes place in the Adriatic and there are a number of coastal canneries.

Amongst livestock sheep are dominant and almost as numerous as cattle and pigs together. Sheep are chiefly found in the karstic areas of the Dinaric ranges and in Serbia and Macedonia. Cattle are widespread, but pigs tend to be concentrated in the Pannonian lowlands and the Morava valley, where maize is fed to them, and in Slavonia and the *Šumadija*, where acorns from the residual oak forests are a traditional part of their diet. The transhumance of sheep and cattle from valleys and basins to upland summer pastures is still a feature in many areas.

Industry and Mining

Industry was rather poorly represented in Jugoslavia before the Second World War and, moreover, it was disproportionately concentrated, owing to historical reasons, in the north and especially in the north-west, i.e. Slovenia and the adjoining Zagreb region of Croatia. In the rich Vojvodina food industries were important. The southern areas of the country, including karstic Croatia, Bosnia–Hercegovina, Montenegro, Kosmet and Macedonia, were rich in natural resources–metal ores, coal, hydro-power, timber–but although these were being developed the pace of industrial growth was too slow to absorb surplus rural manpower and to narrow the very wide gap in living standards that existed between the north and the south. In Bosnia–Hercegovina the Austrian occupation had certainly not been without some economic benefit. Kosmet and Macedonia, on the other hand, had been liberated from Turkish rule only in 1913 and were even more retarded.

In the inter-war period there was some state stimulation of industry, but not always in the most needy areas; engineering industries, for instance, were deliberately encouraged in northern Serbia, including Belgrade. Since the Second World War there has been a great expansion of industry and mining, and the volume of production in the early 1960s was six times that of the late 1930s. During this period the proportion of the working population engaged in agriculture fell from about 75% to about 55%. Despite an official policy of canalizing more investment to the south there are still large inter-regional differences in living standards. *Per capita* income in Slovenia (with less than one-third of its population engaged in agriculture) was three times that of Macedonia in 1964. Indeed, the very capital equipment needed by the south has of necessity to be produced largely in the north, with the result that existing engineering industries there have had to be expanded and new ones developed.

ENERGY SUPPLIES (Fig. 34)

There are a number of widely-distributed deposits of brown coal and lignite, but black-coal resources are small and imports are necessary. There are also petroleum deposits in the Pannonian Basin, but these are not adequate for the country's growing needs. In contrast, however, there is a large hydro-power potential, second in Europe only to that of Norway.

Black coal is mined in three chief areas: the Raša area of Istria (the most important), the Timok basin (near Zaječar) and in the Ibar basin. Total output (1·3 million tons in 1964) has shown little change in recent years. Brown coal (10·7 m tons) and lignite (17·5 m tons) are mined in the following chief areas: the Sava gorge district of brown-coal mining, to the east of Ljubljana (Trbovlje–Hrastnik and Senovo); Velenje in the Celje basin (lignite); scattered lignite workings north of Zagreb; Tuzla–Banovići (both brown coal and lignite) and Zenica–Kakanj–Breza (brown coal) in central Bosnia; the Kolubara valley and Kostolac fields in northern Serbia (lignite); the Aleksinac and Senje fields in north-east Serbia (brown coal); the Kosovo polje (lignite); and near Mostar, in Hercegovina (brown coal). There are a number of other smaller fields. Since the Second World War the rate of expansion has been greatest in Bosnia and in Serbia, so that Slovenia, the leading pre-war producer, has now been overtaken by both, despite a large increase in its own output.

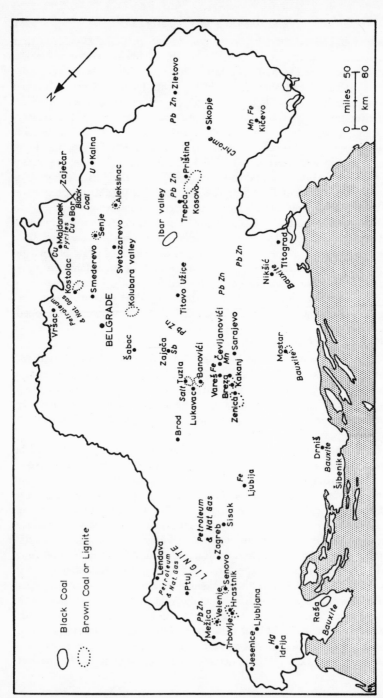

Fig. 34. Mineral exploitation in Jugoslavia

Jugoslavia's petroleum and natural gas fields lie on the margins of the Pannonian Basin in three chief areas: the Mura–Drava lowlands (Lendava field), the Sava lowlands east of Zagreb (Stružec, near Sisak, being a leading producer), and the Vršac district of the Banat. The output of crude petroleum (1·8 million tons in 1964) (most of which at present comes from the Sava field) is refined at Sisak and Bosanski Brod. A refinery is also being built at Pančevo, near Belgrade. Imported petroleum is refined near Rijeka.

Well over half the country's electricity is generated by hydro-power, reflecting the favourable natural conditions prevailing in upland Jugo-slavia. Several small hydro-power stations were built in Slovenia, Dalmatia and Bosnia before the First World War and others were added in the inter-war period. Since the Second World War, however, there has been a very great increase in capacity, involving the construction of larger-size stations. The general distribution at present is briefly as follows. Slovenia has a number of stations in the upper Soča, Sava and Drava valleys, the Drava being by far the most important. On the Adriatic coast there are stations near Rijeka and on the rivers Krka and Cetina in the neighbourhood of Šibenik and Split, and also on the Trebišnjica near Dubrovnik. In Montenegro there are schemes on the Zeta and Morača. In Bosnia–Hercegovina there are large stations at Jablanica, on the Neretva, and at Zvornik and Bajina Bašta, on the Drina. At Jajce the Vrbas and its tributary, the Pliva, are utilized. Electro-chemicals (calcium carbide) have, in fact, been made at Jajce since before the First World War. Two modern stations are now in use. In Macedonia Lake Mavrovo has been created by impounding the head-streams of the Radika, a tributary of the Black Drim, for hydro-power purposes. There is also a scheme on the Black Drim itself. In south-east Serbia Lake Vlasina has been created by damming the upper part of the river of the same name. In western Serbia there are hydro-power schemes on several rivers, including the western Morava and the Bistrica, a tributary of the Lim.

Jugoslavia has a large programme of hydro-power development, which includes the joint project with Rumania involving a barrage across the Danube in the Iron Gate gorge. This will provide each country with a power-station with a capacity of about 1 million kW (see Chapter 9). The increasing availability of relatively cheap hydro-electric power will enable Jugoslavia to expand electro-metallurgical and electro-chemical industries and also to export increasing quantities of current to her neighbours. Thermal power-stations are chiefly found in the coalfield areas and the northern plains, and the gradual development of a national network has enabled these to be integrated with the hydro-power stations. Long-distance connections between the latter are also useful, since the Slovenian and Dalmatian rivers have their greatest discharge in summer and winter respectively, and they therefore complement each other.

METALLURGY (Fig. 34)

The country has a generous endowment of metal ores, including considerable resources of iron ore, but supplies of coal for making metallurgical coke are extremely small indeed, only blending coal being available. Jugoslavia is the largest European producer of copper, lead and antimony, and also stands high as regards the output of zinc, chrome, bauxite and mercury. Manganese and pyrites are also important.

The exploitation of non-ferrous metal ores was largely in foreign hands before the Second World War. After the war these interests were nationalized. Output has expanded and an increased proportion of the ores is now refined within the country. Copper ores (52,000 tons metal content in 1964) are mined in north-east Serbia near Bor and Majdanpek. Electrolytic refining takes place at Bor. The copper is rolled at Sevojno (Titovo Užice) and cables are made at Svetozarevo. Iron pyrites are also exploited in the copper-mining district.

Lead and zinc ores (101,000 and 45,000 tons by metal content in 1964) are mined in the Kopaonik Mountains (e.g. at Trepča), at Mežica in the upper Drava valley, at Zletovo in eastern Macedonia, and at places in northern Serbia and northern Montenegro. Refining takes place at Šabac and Celje (zinc) and Trepča and Mežica (lead).

Bauxite (1964 output 1·3 million tons) is exploited in a number of districts in the Adriatic coastlands. A large part of the output is exported, but a growing domestic aluminium industry also exists (35,000 tons in 1964). A plant was set up at Lozovac, near Šibenik, before the Second World War, followed more recently by a rolling mill at Ražine. There are newer plants in Slovenia, at Moste (Ljubljana) (alumina only) and Kidričevo (Ptuj), the latter being the most important in the country. Rolling takes place at nearby Slovenska Bistrica. A new aluminium complex is also to be built at Titograd in the future. Mercury is obtained at Idrija in western Slovenia (597 tons in 1964) and antimony is mined at several places in western Serbia (2,700 tons metal content). Uranium occurs in the Stara Planina and is mined at Kalna.

The iron and steel industry is still rather small, but has grown very considerably since the Second World War. There are ample reserves of good-quality ore in Bosnia, at Ljubija and other places in the Sana valley, and at Vareš, the latter being the more important. Vareš is a small smelting centre for foundry pig-iron. Recently lower-grade, phosphoric ores have been opened up near Kičevo, in Macedonia. In Slovenia, which has a long tradition of iron-working, steel furnaces were built in the late 19th century at Jesenice, Ravne (upper Drava) and Štore (near Celje). Jesenice became an integrated plant in the inter-war period, using Bosnian ore, while the two others specialize in electric steel. There are also integrated plants at Sisak (tubes being a speciality) and Zenica (the largest steel producer). These have both developed as a result of government plans dating back to the 1930s. Bosnia had a medieval tradition of iron-working, but modern iron works were not initiated until the 1890s under Austrian auspices at Zenica. North-west of Sarajevo there is a new blast-furnace plant for foundry pig-iron at Ilijaš. Smederevo, on the Danube downstream from Belgrade, has steel furnaces, and in Montenegro electric steels are made at Nikšić with Bosnian pig-iron. This new plant, using local hydro-electric power, was built largely to aid the economic development of Montenegro. The same applies to the large new integrated plant being built at Skopje, which will use Macedonian ore. The Jugoslav iron industry depends heavily on imports of coking coal (chiefly from the USA and the USSR), which are blended with some domestic coal in coke-ovens at Zenica and Lukavac (near Tuzla). Some iron ore is also imported. In 1964 the output of home iron ore reached 2·3 million tons, while the figures for pig-iron and steel production were, respectively, 1·0 and 1·7 million tons. Ferro-alloys are made at Šibenik and Tetovo.

Manganese ore is mined at Čevljanovići, in Bosnia, and near Kičevo (total output 18,000 tons in 1964) and large amounts of chrome ore (88,000 tons) are obtained from the Skopje region (especially from the Šar Planina and Skopje Crna Gora), making Jugoslavia the second largest producer in Europe after Albania.

OTHER INDUSTRIES

Since the Second World War the output and range of Jugoslav industry has widened greatly, especially in the field of engineering, which still tends to be located in the north, however. The electrical engineering industry is particularly concentrated in the north-west, e.g. at Ljubljana (turbines), Maribor, Kranj (telecommunications), Zagreb (generators) and Karlovac. In Serbia there are electrical industries in Belgrade, Novi Sad and Niš (radio). The vehicle industries are located at a number of centres, including Kragujevac (assembly of 'Fiat' cars), Belgrade's satellites of Rakovica and Zemun (tractors), Priboj, in south-west Serbia (buses), Maribor (lorries), Vogošća, near Sarajevo (scooters), and Koper, in Istria (motor-cycles and assembly of 'Citroen' cars). Locomotives and wagons are built at Slavonski Brod and wagons at Smederevska Palanka (north of Kragujevac). Shipbuilding takes place at Pula, Rijeka and Split. Machine-tools are made at Železnik (Belgrade) and Zagreb.

The textile industries are well dispersed but still show something of their former concentration in Slovenia (e.g. Maribor) and western Croatia (e.g. Varaždin), but there has been a marked tendency for new factories to be built in the south, often close to areas of cotton production. Loznica (near Zvornik) is a leading producer of artificial silk and a nylon industry is being developed at Prizren. Footwear manufacture is likewise well distributed, although an important centre is Borovo (near Vukovar in the Vojvodina), where a Bat'a factory was set up in the inter-war period. Food-processing tends to be located in the rich arable areas, especially the Pannonian lowlands (sugar-beet refineries, grain and sunflower-oil mills, meat-packing). Tobacco factories are found in the tobacco-growing areas of the south and also in the northern cities. There is fish-canning on the Adriatic coast. Chemical industries include plastics (Split), petrochemicals (Zagreb), sulphuric acid (non-ferrous metal smelting centres), and fertilizers (Prahovo, on the Danube below the gorge, Kosovska Mitrovica, Šabac, Subotica and Pančevo, near Belgrade). Tuzla has chemical industries related to its salt deposits and coke-ovens. There are also chemical works based on the Velenje lignite field in Slovenia. Cement works are chiefly located in limestone areas and there is an important concentration near Split.

Distribution of Population and Chief Cities

Since more than half the Jugoslav population is still engaged in agriculture, it is not surprising that the general pattern of population distribution should broadly reflect the productivity of the land. As a result there is a wide zone of higher than average density stretching from west to east through Pannonian Jugoslavia and then extending southwards through the *Šumadija* and up the valleys of the Morava basin. Within this zone the most fertile areas are not always the most densely populated; thus higher densities are found in the Tertiary hills than on the adjacent plains of the Drava and Sava, which are still marshy in places or only recently drained. In the Vojvodina low densities occur in areas liable to flood or where sand-dunes exist.

Some of the highest rural densities are found in sub-Alpine Slovenia and the hill-country to the north of Zagreb (*Zagorje*). Here, significantly, rural life was much less affected by Turkish inroads than most other parts of Jugoslavia. Such fairly high rural densities, combined with substantial urban and industrial development (which, in Slovenia, often also affects the villages), has led to the existence of a north-western populous region, embracing Ljubljana, Karlovac, Sisak, Zagreb and Maribor. There is then some thinning-out of population along the Drava and Sava corridors until the Vojvodina is reached. Here villages are exceptionally large and compact; many are, in fact, 'colonization villages', dating from the 18th century after the Turkish retreat from the old Hungarian territories. Another feature is that the towns often have a strong agricultural element. South of Belgrade the *Šumadija* hillcountry, largely deforested within the last two hundred years, supports a considerable rural population, but of a less nucleated character, and there are also a number of growing industrial towns in the valleys of the Morava basin. There is thus a second populous region in the north-east, lying beyond a line that curves south-eastwards from Osijek to Niš. The two populous regions of the north-west and the north-east correspond to the two leading cultural and industrial 'core areas' of modern Jugoslavia. It is rather surprising that there is no intervening town of more than 30,000 inhabitants along the Sava routeway (370 km/230 miles long) linking their two chief cities, Zagreb and Belgrade. Some towns along this route, such as Sisak and the twin towns of Bosanski and Slavonski Brod, are now growing as industrial centres, however.

Dinaric Jugoslavia, between the Tertiary hills of the Pannonian fringe and the Adriatic coast, is rather thinly peopled, in both its karstic and non-karstic zones. In the former the *polja* often stand out as 'islands' of relatively dense population, villages being characteristically located on their dry margins, while in the latter isolated lumbering, mining and metallurgical communities increase local densities. The coastal region, extending from Trieste to Lake Skadar and including the islands, is better populated than its karstic hinterland. The population is often highly concentrated, however, and is largely dependent on maritime activities or tourism. The more populous areas include Istria and the Rijeka district, Ravni Kotari with Zadar and Šibenik, and the Dubrovnik–Kotor and Split districts. In the south of the country, in Kosmet and Macedonia, there are often striking differences in density between the mountainous areas and the basins and plains, although it is also true that the latter themselves vary considerably in density, as a result of differences in the degree of agricultural utilization. The distribution of Jugoslav towns with more than 20,000 inhabitants is shown in Fig. 35.

As industrial development increases so the proportion living in towns also increases; by 1964 this was 28%. Regional rates of population growth vary very considerably, as a result of differences in culture, hygiene and living standards. Thus, largely owing to a higher birth-rate, natural increase in the south is about twice as high as in the north. In

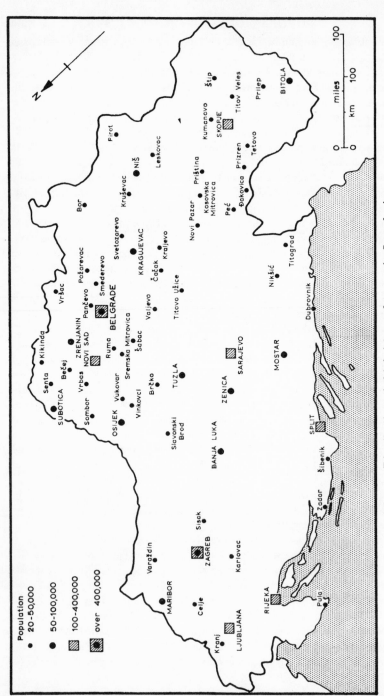

Fig. 35. Distribution of chief cities and towns in Jugoslavia

spite of this the infant death-rate in Kosmet and Macedonia is four times that for Slovenia, which is close to the West European level.

BELGRADE (*Beograd*) (703,000 in 1965), the federal capital of Jugo-slavia and also capital of Serbia, has had a turbulent history as one of the most important fortress cities of Europe. The city (Fig. 36) is built on a

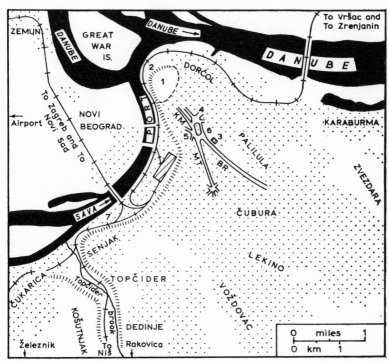

Fig. 36. Belgrade

Key: 1. Upper fortress (Gornji grad) and Kalemegdan Park. **2.** Lower fortress (Donji grad). **3.** Parliament Building. **4.** Republic Square (Trg Republike). **5.** Terazije. **6.** Marx and Engels Square (Trg Marksa i Engelsa). **7.** Fair.

KM Kneza Mihajla. **MT** Maršala Tita. **BR** Bulevar revolucije.

flat-topped ridge that juts northwards from the *Šumadija* into the Pan-nonian Plain. The average height of the city above sea-level is 140 m/ 460 ft. The Danube, flowing from north-west to south-east, delimits this ridge on the north and east, while its tributary, the Sava, flowing from the south-west, delimits it on the west. The north-western end of the ridge forms a promontory overlooking the confluence, and it has carried a fortified settlement since prehistoric times. In the 1st century A.D.

Belgrade was the Romano-Celtic *Singidunum*, guarding the northern frontiers of the Roman Empire. With the collapse of Roman rule it was overrun by the various waves of barbarian invaders, including the Slavs, and later came under Bulgarian and Byzantine control. In the course of time its population became predominantly Serb in character and the city took the name of *Beograd*, i.e. 'white city'. During the middle ages, owing to its geographical location, it was often in dispute between the Serbs and the Hungarians. In the early 15th century Belgrade briefly became the capital of the northern, free, part of Serbia, during the Turkish advance, but it was then ceded to the Hungarians, who successfully resisted Turkish sieges in 1444 and 1456. Finally it was taken by the Turks in 1521.

In 1688 it was captured by Habsburg forces and held by them for two years. It was again occupied between 1717 and 1739 (when the fortress was rebuilt) and 1789 and 1792. Kara George held the city between 1806 and 1813, and although the rising of 1815 led to Serbian autonomy, the Turkish garrison did not finally leave until 1867. It should be noted that between 1739 and 1918 Belgrade lay just across the boundary of the Habsburg Empire. The city was heavily damaged by Austrian bombardments during the First World War and by German air attacks in the Second.

In 1914 Belgrade, with under 100,000 inhabitants, was the frontier capital of a small but vigorous state, the Kingdom of Serbia. It had grown rapidly in the 19th century, but after the creation of Jugoslavia in 1918 it received a new impetus, and further growth has taken place since 1945. The old part of the city includes the fortress area, containing a small park still called by its Turkish name of 'Kalemegdan' ('town-field'), succeeded southwards by what was formerly the walled-in town. Republic Square marks the entrance to one of the former gates. The heart of the modern city extends from Republic Square and Prince Michael Street (*Kneza Mihajla*) to *Terazije* and Marx and Engels Square, and thence along the two thoroughfares of 'Marshal Tito' and 'Revolution Boulevard' (following the old road to Byzantium). East of the old fortress the district of Dorćol, occupying the area sloping down to the Danube, was formerly a Turkish quarter. To the east and south-west of the city are the hilly wooded parks of Zvezdara, Topčider and Košutnjak.

Belgrade is an important focus of water and land traffic. It is the leading inland port of the country. The quays for barge traffic lie at the foot of the steep bank leading down to the Sava. Here also are the main railway facilities, giving connections up the Sava and Morava valleys and northwards into the Pannonian Basin.

The city has numerous industries, including food, timber and textiles.

The chief concentration of industry lies to the east of the city on the right bank of the Danube. Some important industrial concerns are in outlying areas, however, such as Zemun, further up the Danube, and Rakovica (tractors) and Železnik (machine-tools), south of the city. In recent years Novi Beograd (New Belgrade) has begun to take shape. This is an area of new government buildings and residential blocks lying across the Sava on an alluvial tract between Belgrade and Zemun. Its population will eventually reach about a quarter of a million.

LJUBLJANA (183,000), the capital of Slovenia, occupies the site of the Roman town of *Emona* and is strategically situated in a gap between the Ljubljana Plain, lying to the north and drained by the upper Sava, and the former Ljubljana Marsh, to the south, drained by its tributary the Ljubljanica. This little river flows through the old, Baroque, part of the town, lying at the foot of the citadel, and continues northwards to join the Sava. Ljubljana, commanding routes using its Tertiary depression (290 m/950 ft above sea-level), has always been an important traffic centre. Here the railway line from Munich and Salzburg to Zagreb and Belgrade crosses the line from Vienna and Maribor to Rijeka and Trieste. Local hydro-electric power and coal deposits were already promoting industrial development before the First World War. Today Ljubljana has a wide range of industries, in which engineering (heavy electrical equipment, cycles, typewriters) is well represented.

NOVI SAD (126,000), capital of the Vojvodina Autonomous Region, lies on the north (left) bank of the Danube. Across the river is the fortress of Petrovaradin, beyond which the Fruška Gora hill-range rises to the south. Although then under Habsburg rule, it was the most vigorous centre of Serb culture during the 18th and early 19th centuries. It lies on the Budapest–Belgrade railway, and the Little Bačka Canal here joins the river. There is a considerable volume of water-borne traffic, including grain, and food industries are notable.

RIJEKA (116,000), the leading seaport of Jugoslavia, lies at the head of the Gulf of Rijeka and is shielded from the open sea by the large islands of Cres and Krk. Behind the town the land rises to the karstic hills of the interior. Its name, meaning 'river' in both Serbo-Croat and Italian (*Fiume*), indicates its location at the mouth of the Rječina ('little river'). The old harbour was situated in its small delta, but in the late 19th century a series of basins was built immediately to the west behind a mole. At this time Rijeka flourished as the port of Hungary, but trade slackened between the two World Wars, when it was partitioned between Italy and Jugoslavia (the latter controlling the eastern suburb of Sušak and the delta, with one modern basin). Rijeka is an important centre of shipbuilding and marine engineering and also has port-processing industries. Westwards, across the bay, is the resort of Opatija, while further along the coast, to the south, are Kraljevica (shipbuilding) and Bakar (port for bulk carriers) in a small bay. There are railway connections to Ljubljana and Zagreb, and a spur from the Zagreb line reaches Sušak by means of a spiral tunnel. Rijeka was declared a free port in 1964.

SARAJEVO (223,000), capital of Bosnia–Hercegovina, is located where a gorge cut by the little river Miljacka opens out westwards into the Sarajevo Plain (height above sea-level 530 m/1,750 ft), drained by the upper Bosna. The old town is built on the slopes near the gorge, while the newer districts have grown up on the flatter land. The 'townscape' of Sarajevo is extremely mixed, ranging from the mosques and rambling 'Turkish' houses, with balconies and courtyards, in the old quarters, to the ornate public buildings of the Habsburg period and the tall residential blocks of recent years. Sarajevo lies on the railway, following the Bosna and Neretva valleys, that links the Sava valley to Ploče and Dubrovnik on the Adriatic coast, and it is also connected to the Morava basin. There are food, tobacco and timber industries and many craft-trades survive (e.g. carpets and metalware). Vogošća to the north-west and Hrasnica to the south-west have new engineering industries.

SKOPJE (230,000), capital of Jugoslav Macedonia, is situated on the River Vardar near the western margins of a Tertiary depression. Known as *Scupi* in Roman times, it has always been an important traffic node, controlling the Morava–Vardar route and routes to the Kosovo polje and the Polog depression. It lies on the Belgrade–Thessaloníki railway line and is also connected to Belgrade by a parallel route following the Ibar. The old town, parts of which still retain an oriental appearance, lies on the north (left) bank, while the new town lies on the opposite bank. There are food and tobacco industries and a large new iron and steel works will be completed by the late 1960s. The city suffered heavy damage in the earthquake of 1963.

SPLIT (114,000), the second seaport of the country, lies in a small embayment cut into a promontory that terminates in the headland of Marjan. The Emperor Diocletian built a large palace here (c. 300 A.D.). Behind the promontory, in Kaštela bay, was the ancient trading city of *Salona*. When this was destroyed by the Avars the citizens took refuge within the walls of the palace, and this unusual type of urban settlement has survived as the core of the modern city. In the 20th century additional port facilities have been developed in Kaštela bay, where there are also shipyards and cement and chemical (plastics) factories. A chain of small settlements extends westwards along the bay to Trogir, lying behind the island of Čiovo, and eastwards along the coast to Omiš, producing a tenuous conurbation about 40 km/25 miles in length. Rising steeply in the background are the limestone massifs of Kozjak and Mosor, while seawards lie the islands of Brač and Šolta. Since 1925, when a rail link was completed to Zagreb, Split has shown considerable growth as a port, industrial town and tourist centre.

ZAGREB (503,000), capital of Croatia, had its origins in two medieval settlements situated on small neighbouring eminences overlooking the northern margins of the Sava flood-plain (*Turopolje*). Behind them rose the wooded Medvednica range. *Kaptol*, with its cathedral, was an ecclesiastical settlement, while across a small stream was *Grič*, the civil town. In the 18th century there was much rebuilding in the Baroque style, while in the 19th century the town expanded southwards on to the flood-plain, and a new town of squares and public buildings developed between *Ilica*, the west–east thoroughfare at the foot of the old town, and the railway station lying towards the river. In the 20th century development has proceeded eastwards and westwards, while since the Second World War a new east–west thoroughfare has been built between the station and the Sava. Across the river, where a new residential city is being built, are the buildings of the internationally important Zagreb Trade Fair (established 1909). Zagreb has many varied industries and in recent years a large electrical engineering industry has developed. There is also a new chemical industry based on local supplies of petroleum and natural gas. There was serious flooding of the Sava in 1964.

Transport and Trade

The physiography of upland Jugoslavia presents considerable difficulties for internal transport. Moreover, political fragmentation before 1918 meant that the railway system did not develop in a coherent manner, while wide regional differences in the level of economic development resulted in great variations in the density of the network. The density was highest in the Pannonian lowlands, especially the Vojvodina, then forming part of Hungary. In Bosnia the Austro–Hungarian administration had developed a system of narrow-gauge lines after 1878. Interwar Jugoslavia was thus faced with the need for the integration and amplification of her railways. Significant improvements included the further development of the main railway axis of the country as an international route linking Austria and Italy, via Ljubljana, Zagreb, Belgrade and Niš, to Bulgaria and Greece. This route forms an arc following the Sava and Morava valleys, with Thessaloníki being reached by the valley of the Vardar and Sofia by way of that of the Nišava, a tributary of the Morava. Several new links were made, including one between Zagreb and the ports of Split and Šibenik. Zagreb had been part of Hungary before

1918 and was therefore connected only to the Hungarian port of Rijeka. Split and Šibenik were in Austrian-administered Dalmatia. A connection was also made between Sarajevo and the Morava valley and between Nikšić in Montenegro and the Sarajevo–Dubrovnik line. In Serbia the old Turkish railhead at Kosovska Mitrovica was joined to Kragujevac, thus providing some relief for the Belgrade–Skopje line.

Since the Second World War further projects have been completed, including a line in Montenegro from Nikšić to Titograd and the port of Bar, a line from the new port of Ploče, at the mouth of the Neretva, to the Sarajevo–Dubrovnik line, and a line from Bihać to Knin, along the Una valley, which gives a second connection between Zagreb and both Split and Šibenik. New lines have also been built in Bosnia, Kosmet and Macedonia. In the former a number of narrow-gauge lines have been converted to standard gauge, including the main route linking Sarajevo to the Sava valley, and conversion is now taking place between Sarajevo and Ploče. Other schemes in progress include a line from Valjevo to Titograd, following the Lim and Morača valleys, which will connect Belgrade to Montenegro by a direct route for the first time, and a line connecting the port of Zadar to the Zagreb–Split line. Over 2,000 km/ 1,250 miles of additional track were laid between the end of the war and 1960. Despite many improvements, only a relatively small part of the present mileage is of double track, however, and the conversion of the more important narrow-gauge lines is not yet completed. Electrification, which is now proceeding on the main lines (and has been completed between Rijeka and both Ljubljana and Zagreb), will enable the over-strained railway system to be more intensively utilized.

The railway pattern consists of the main axis indicated above, with a number of domestic and international routes branching from it, the more important being: (a) Ljubljana to Trieste and Rijeka (via Pivka), (b) Ljubljana to Maribor, Graz and Vienna, (c) Zagreb to Rijeka, (d) Zagreb to Split (two routes), (e) Zagreb to Budapest, (f) Vrpolje, in the Sava valley, to Sarajevo and thence to Ploče, Dubrovnik and Montenegro, (g) Niš to Sofia, (h) Belgrade to Novi Sad, Subotica and Budapest, and (i) Belgrade to Vršac and thence to Rumania. North of the west–east line following the Sava valley there is a parallel line of lesser importance, following that of the Drava, while to the south there are some other west–east routes, such as that from the Una valley to the Timok valley (via Sarajevo) and that from Peć, near the Albanian border, to Niš. In the far south there is an alternative route from Skopje to Thessaloníki by way of Titov Veles, Prilep and Bitola.

Road traffic is increasing, although surface conditions frequently leave much to be desired. The 'Brotherhood and Unity' motor road is now completed, extending from Slovenia to Macedonia and running near to the main railway axis. At Niš a new road branches off to the Bulgarian frontier. The new 'Adriatic Highway', from Istria to Montenegro, has greatly improved communications between the coastal towns, hitherto more easily connected by sea. It is being extended inland to Skopje. These new highways will also aid the tourist traffic. Domestic air travel is also increasing, especially between Belgrade and the capital cities of the constituent Republics. The Adriatic tourist centres of Dubrovnik and Split have a considerable air traffic in the summer months. Belgrade has an international airport at Surčin, west of the city, and Zagreb and Ljubljana also have a number of international flights.

Inland waterways are of substantial importance in the Pannonian lowlands, especially for the transport of agricultural produce. Here the Danube, Tisa, lower Drava and the Sava downstream from Sisak are navigable for craft of up to 1,000 tons. Smaller boats can use the Great and Little Bačka canals and the Begej canal. The Danube–Tisa canal, now under construction, will also be used for drainage and irrigation purposes. On the Sava it is planned to extend the head of navigation to Zagreb. Belgrade is the major focus of waterway traffic and other leading river-ports include Novi Sad, Sisak and Vukovar.

The leading seaport is Rijeka, which had been developed as the port of Hungary before 1914. After the First World War the greater part of it came under Italian rule and, being politically cut off from its hinterland, it tended to stagnate. Since its transfer to Jugoslavia after the Second World War it has revived considerably. Next in importance is Split, followed by Šibenik, the new port of Ploče, Dubrovnik (Gruž), and Pula, the former Austro–Hungarian (later Italian) naval base in Istria. Bar will become a convenient port for Belgrade when railway connections and modern harbour installations are completed, and Zadar will also benefit by being linked to Zagreb. Koper, south of Trieste, is also being expanded. About 60% of Jugoslavia's foreign trade is conducted by sea, largely through her own ports, although Thessaloníki is also used to some extent. Some transit traffic to and from Hungary and Czecho-slovakia passes through Rijeka.

Jugoslavia's foreign trade has expanded both in volume and scope since the Second World War. Foodstuffs (including tobacco), ores and timber are still leading exports, but manufactures now account for over 40% of the export trade. Moreover, an increasing proportion of the primary commodities undergoes processing of some kind before being exported. On the other hand grain imports are sometimes necessary to supplement home supplies and black coal is also an essential import, while the rapid pace of industrial development requires large imports of machinery. Over half the foreign trade is with Western Europe and North America, especially the former, and about a quarter is with the Soviet bloc countries, with whom economic collaboration has greatly increased in recent years after the estrangement of the late 1940s and 1950s. The rest of her foreign trade is chiefly with less developed Near Eastern and tropical countries, where Jugoslav enterprises now often gain contracts for the supply of capital equipment. The export of ships is also significant. Tourist receipts are a very important item in the balance of payments, the number of foreign visitors reaching over 2 millions in 1964. The most popular areas are the Slovenian Alps, Istria and the Gulf of Rijeka, the Split district, and Dubrovnik and the Montenegrin coast. Clearly Jugoslavia has triumphed over her post-war difficulties, and the intensive capital investment of recent years, together with a foreign trade policy that is remarkably flexible for a Socialist country, has led to a vigorously expanding economy. On the other hand it is true that the various steps towards greater economic freedom have often been accompanied by short-term crises of adjustment.

Chapter 8

POLAND · POLSKA

Introduction

Modern Poland is a compact state that is almost square-shaped, with sides over 600 km/400 miles in length. The south-western corner is truncated, however, by Czechoslovakia. The country is bordered on the north-east and east by the Soviet Union, on the south by Czechoslovakia, and on the west by East Germany ('German Democratic Republic'). In the north the Baltic coastline is some 400 km/250 miles long. At either end are the two great bays – the Bay of Pomerania (*Zatoka Pomorska*) and the Bay of Gdańsk (*Zatoka Gdańska*), which are shared with East Germany and the Soviet Union respectively.

Poland's land boundaries adhere partly to natural features. On the west the border with East Germany follows the Odra (German *Oder*) and its tributary the Lusatian Nysa (*Neisse*). In the extreme north, however, the boundary runs well to the west of the lower Odra, to leave the left-bank port of Szczecin in Poland, and then crosses the Szczecin Lagoon (*Zalew Szczeciński*) and the island of Uznam separating it from the Bay of Pomerania. In the north-east the boundary with the Soviet Union shows a similar anomaly in that it bisects the Vistula Lagoon (*Zalew Wiślany*) and the Vistula Spit separating it from the Bay of Gdańsk. Inland the boundary with the Soviet Union pursues an almost straight west–east course through the former (1939) German province of East Prussia, and then turns southwards. Apart from a middle section, where the River Bug is followed for about 250 km/150 miles (and a short section in the extreme south-east where the River San is followed), the eastern border does not conform to any major natural features.

By contrast, the southern border with Czechoslovakia coincides with the Carpathians in the east and the Sudets (*Sudety*) in the west. The border does not, however, always follow summits and watersheds and thus there are many minor anomalies. Moreover, between these two ranges the border cuts across the upper Odra drainage basin and also the broadly coincident Upper Silesian coal-basin. Although there were disputes between Poland and Czechoslovakia concerning part of this area, both after the First World War and on the eve of the Second, the fact remains that the southern frontier has, in general, enjoyed remarkably long periods of stability, especially when compared with Poland's eastern and western frontiers, which have undergone numerous changes over time. The Carpathian frontier has existed for nearly a thousand years, and separated Poland from Hungary until 1918, when Slovakia broke away from the latter to become part of the new state of Czechoslovakia. The Sudets separated Bohemia from Poland in the early middle ages, but between the 14th and 18th centuries the Polish province of Silesia was politically associated with Bohemia across the mountains. The frontier role of the Sudets was restored again when Prussia seized Silesia from Bohemia's Austrian rulers in 1741.

The present eastern and western frontiers bear a close resemblance to

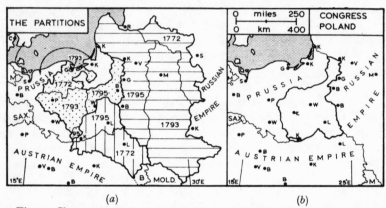

(a)　　　　　　　　　　　　　　　　(b)

Fig. 37. Changes in the boundaries of Poland–the Partitions, 1772–1795 (a) and the 'Congress' Kingdom, 1815 (b)

those of the early Polish state in the 11th and 12th centuries. Thereafter there was a gradual easterly shift of Poland (see *Historical Background* below). In 1772, 1793 and 1795 Austria, Prussia and Russia carried out the three Partitions of Poland, resulting in the country's disappearance from the map of Europe until 1918 (Figs. 37a and 38a). The German invasion of Poland in 1939, marking the outbreak of the Second World War, was followed by a new partition, as a result of the invasion from the east by Russia shortly afterwards. The territories taken by Russia were overrun by German forces after their attack on Russia in 1941. The effect of Russia's defeat of Germany in 1945 was that eastern Poland was retained by the Soviet Union, who, with the agreement of the Western allies, handed over to Polish administration the southern half of East Prussia, together with Pomerania and Silesia, all integral parts of Germany in 1939 (Fig. 38b). The German population was expelled and Polish settlers moved in. It was in this manner that the Polish state was restored to its approximate geographical extent of the early middle ages. Most of the German minority of pre-war Poland was also repatriated.

Poland lost 45% of her pre-war territory to the Soviet Union and although she gained large areas from Germany the net effect was a reduction of one-fifth in territory. One-third of the area of contemporary Poland consists of pre-war German territory. The population of 31·5 millions (1965) has not yet regained the 1939 level of 35 millions (living on a larger area) but the national density of population is higher. The population had fallen to 24 millions by 1947, as the result of heavy war casualties (about 6 millions killed, including most of the Jewish population of over 3 millions), the loss of the eastern territories and their Byelorussian and Ukrainian populations to the Soviet Union, and the

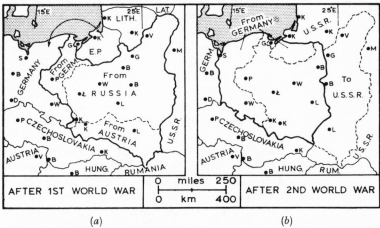

(a)   (b)

Fig. 38. Changes in the boundaries of Poland–after the First World War (a) and after the Second World War (b)

fact that many wartime émigrés, especially members of the armed forces in the West, decided not to return home at the end of the war. A high rate of natural increase has subsequently brought the population up to its present level.

In view of the changes mentioned above, the total population of the minorities is now very much smaller (453,000 in 1963) than before the war. The chief groups are Byelorussians (165,000) and Ukrainians (180,000) who have chosen to identify themselves with Poland. In addition there are very small minorities of Gypsies, Jews, Lithuanians, Russians and Slovaks. Amongst the Polish population itself distinctive characteristics are retained to some extent by the Silesians, many of whom speak a dialect formerly known as *Wasserpolnisch* when they were under German rule, and the Kashubians, a small community in eastern Pomerania, whose speech is sometimes regarded as a separate language.

There are large numbers of Poles living outside their native land, either as a result of emigration in the past for economic or political reasons, or because of boundary changes with the Soviet Union. Estimates vary between 6 and 10 millions. About half are in the United States, and there are also large groups elsewhere in the Americas, in Argentina, Brazil and Canada. In 1959 about 1·3 million Poles were living in the Soviet Union, not only in those areas transferred from Poland, but also in parts of Soviet Asia, to which they had been deported after 1939. Over the Czechoslovak border some 70,000 Poles live in the Karviná–Těšín district of the Ostrava coalfield. In Western Europe the largest group is in France (over half a million), but Great Britain, Western Germany and Belgium also have substantial minorities. Indeed there are few countries in the world where Polish immigrants cannot be found; conversely there are few families in Poland who are not in touch with members or friends living abroad.

Historical Background

In the Dark Ages the Vistula and Odra basins were inhabited by West Slavonic tribes, and place-name evidence shows that Slavonic settlement once extended at least as far west as the Elbe. Thus the name of the German city of Leipzig is derived from its Slavonic name of *Lipsk* (an adjectival form of *lipa*–a lime-tree). By the middle of the 10th century a strong state had appeared in the territory, drained by the Warta, lying between the Vistula (*Wisła*) and the Odra and later known as 'Greater Poland' (*Wielkopolska*). Its first recorded ruler, Mieszko I, of the Piast dynasty, accepted Christianity in 966 and thus obtained Papal recognition. Neighbouring areas gradually came under the rule of Mieszko and his successor, Bolesław I ('The Brave'), including 'Lesser Poland' (*Małopolska*), corresponding to the upper Vistula basin, Mazovia (*Mazowsze*), Pomerania (*Pomorze*, i.e. 'sea-side') and Silesia (*Śląsk*). In 1000 an Archbishopric was established at Gniezno, east of Poznań, the chief town of Greater Poland, and in 1025 Bolesław was crowned king.

This early unity proved to be temporary, however, owing to internal separatism and periodic strife with the Empire and Bohemia. Bolesław III ('Wrymouth') briefly succeeded in consolidating the country again, but he arranged that after his death (1138) his territories should be split amongst his four sons, with the elder as supreme prince, and in time further sub-division occurred. In 1181 Pomerania submitted to the Emperor and although its status thereafter underwent a number of changes it remained alienated from the rest of Poland, with the exception of 'Gdańsk Pomerania'. This separation was facilitated by the fact that the German state of Brandenburg began a policy of eastward expansion and, conquering the marshy Noteć–lower Warta district (*Neumark*), it isolated western Pomerania from contact with *Wielkopolska*. Shortly afterwards the foundations were laid for another German penetration when the ruler of Mazovia invited the Knights of the Cross (Teutonic Knights) to subdue and convert the heathen Prussians, who dwelt in the morainic lake country to the north of Mazovia between the Vistula and the Niemen (Russian *Neman*). The Knights, a military-religious order recently returned to Europe from the Crusades, launched their campaign about 1230. By the end of the century their task was completed, but the Order now proved unwilling to recognize Polish overlordship and, moreover, had begun a policy of expansionism.

The 13th century was also punctuated by the devastating Tatar invasions, particularly that of 1241. German colonists were already being invited to settle by feudal and ecclesiastical authorities and the effect of the Tatar invasion was to intensify this trend. Urban centres with initially strong German elements were thus established or re-established in the 13th and 14th centuries, usually on the basis of the Magdeburg Law (the model for municipal self-government in Central Europe). The period of internal disunity ended with the coronation of Władysław I ('The Short') in 1320, but even so not all the provinces had been brought under control: Silesia had come under Bohemian overlordship and Gdańsk Pomerania and Kujawy were in the hands of the Knights. Kazimierz (Casimir) III ('The Great'), his son, continued the policy of consolidation. Kujawy was returned by the Knights and Mazovia submitted, but the loss of Silesia to Bohemia was formally recognized in 1335. On the other hand new territorial gains were made to the south-east, and in this way the town of Lwów, later to be an important centre of Polish culture, was acquired, and also command of the trade routes from the Black Sea to the Baltic and Western Europe.

Casimir built up a strong central authority and a code of law. Trade and culture flourished; the University of Kraków was founded in 1364, and Casimir is said to have 'found a country of wood and left a country of stone'. Dying in 1370 he was the last of the Piast dynasty and was succeeded by his nephew, Louis of Hungary. The marriage of the latter's daughter, Queen Jadwiga, to Władysław Jagiełło, Grand Duke of Lithuania (1386), represented an attempt of the Polish nobility to gain further influence to the east and to obtain assistance against the Teutonic Knights, who were a menace to both countries. Lithuania was then a vast state that consisted not only of its small heathen homeland near the Baltic but also large parts of modern Byelorussia and the Ukraine to the south. Although full union with Poland did not occur until much later, Polish culture was now able to penetrate eastwards, Wilno eventually becoming an important Polish city. In 1410 the Poles and Lithuanians, in alliance with the Russians, decisively defeated the Knights at the Battle of Grunwald (Tannenberg), south-west of Olsztyn. After further warfare Poland regained large areas from the Knights by the Peace of Toruń (1466). Gdańsk Pomerania, Toruń and Warmia (German *Ermland*) were regained. Moreover, the Order recognized Polish suzerainty and was restricted to the territory that it had originally colonized.

The 16th century has been called the Golden Age of Poland. The economy prospered, the Renaissance expressed itself in architecture, culture and science (Copernicus was a Pole who had studied in Kraków), the Polish language developed as a literary medium, and Protestantism enjoyed toleration. A national Parliament of two Houses had emerged by this time, consisting of the Senate (the landed aristocracy, or 'magnates') and the *Sejm*, representing the powerful large class of 'gentry' (*szlachta*). Mazovia became fully incorporated into Poland in 1526 and Poland and Lithuania were formally united in 1569 (Union of Lublin). One effect of the union was to bring the Ukraine under direct Polish rule; large Polish estates developed there, and the Uniate Church was created (1596), whereby the Orthodox Church acknowledged the supremacy of Rome while retaining its own liturgy.

On the other hand the death of the last ruler of the Jagiełło line in 1572 led to a system of elected kings. Poland became in effect a 'royal republic' and her rulers were henceforward chosen either from the magnates or from foreign royal houses, with results that were to lead to internal dissension and to external entanglements. Thus in 1655-6 Poland was ravaged by a Swedish invasion at a time when her king was of the Swedish Vasa dynasty, and in the early 18th century Poland was drawn into the Northern War against Sweden, owing largely to the ambitions of the Elector of Saxony, who had become King of Poland. Russia, one of the anti-Swedish allies, was now able to begin to exert influence over Poland–a striking turn of events when it is realized that only a century previously Poland had been able for a short time to gain control of the Moscow Kremlin. In 1667 Russia obtained the easternmost borderlands of the Polish–Lithuanian territories (including Smolensk and Kiev) after an anti-Polish rising led by the Cossacks. Polish military might was not yet dimmed, however, for in 1683 King John Sobieski defeated the Turks outside Vienna and thereby precipitated their withdrawal from Hungary.

In the 18th century the growing menace of Russia was accompanied by that of Prussia. In 1701 the Dukedom of Prussia, the lay survival of the territory of the Teutonic Knights, was united with Brandenburg to form the new Kingdom of Prussia. Brandenburg had already (1648) absorbed most of Pomerania, and the Szczecin area became hers in 1720. With the seizure of Silesia from Austria in 1741 Prussian territory now adjoined Poland on both the north and the west. It was on Prussian initiative that the first Partition of Poland was carried out in 1772. Prussia took the lower Vistula area ('West Prussia'), except Gdańsk, thus bridging her territories along the Baltic, and she also took Warmia. Austria, advancing from her common border with Poland, took the southern part of the country, while Russia took areas in the east. The ease with which the partitioning was carried out was as much a reflection of Polish weakness as of the growing might of her three neighbours. Some of the Polish magnates and the *szlachta* in general had resisted the development of a strong central authority. Another source of weakness was that the transactions of the *Sejm* could be nullified by the operation of the notorious *liberum veto*, whereby a single deputy could veto a majority decision.

The shock of the partition stimulated reformist tendencies. Schemes of public education were launched, and economic progress was encouraged. Eventually a standing army was authorized. The culmination of these trends was the May constitution of 1791, inspired by French ideals and abolishing the *liberum veto* and providing for an hereditary constitutional monarchy. This measure antagonized some of the magnates, who then invited Russian intervention. The outcome was the Second Partition of 1793, whereby Russia took large areas of Byelorussia and the Ukraine, and Prussia took Greater Poland and Gdańsk. In 1794 Kościuszko led an unsuccessful campaign against the Russians and the following year the Third Partition, by Russia, Prussia and Austria, resulted in the complete disappearance of what was, for its time, one of the most democratic states in the world.

The hopes of Polish patriots eventually came to rest on Napoleon Buonaparte. He formed a Polish Legion, mostly from captured Poles in the Austrian army, and it fought in his campaigns. In 1806 France defeated Prussia, and parts of Prussian Poland then became the independent Duchy of Warsaw by the Treaty of Tilsit (1807). With the subsequent defeat of Austria in 1809 the Duchy's area was further enlarged. Napoleon's defeat in Russia led to the downfall of the Duchy, however.

The Congress of Vienna (1815) set up the so-called 'Congress Kingdom' of Poland, a semi-autonomous state with the Russian Tsar as monarch, and also a free, neutral city-state of Kraków (Fig. 37b). Prussia retained the lower Vistula and Greater Poland, however, although certain concessions to the Poles were to be made in a Grand Duchy of Poznań. Austria retained southern Poland ('Galicia'), while Russia retained Lithuania, Byelorussia, and that part of the Polish Ukraine not included in Austrian Poland.

From 1815 until 1830 the Congress Kingdom showed considerable vigour. Industry, mining and education were deliberately fostered. In 1830 an anti-Russian rising took place in Warsaw that developed into a Polish-Russian war, but the following year the Poles were defeated and the Kingdom was virtually incorporated into the Empire. Many eminent Poles fled to Western Europe, chiefly France, including Chopin and the writers Mickiewicz and Słowacki. The last remaining island of Polish liberty, the city of Kraków, was occupied by Austria in 1846 after a peasant rising in southern Poland. Further risings occurred in 1848 in Prussian Poland and in 1863 in Russian Poland, where also the Russian revolution of 1905 had repercussions.

During the 19th century and up to the First World War each of the three parts of Poland received a distinctive imprint from its conqueror. The Prussian areas, including the ancient Polish provinces of Pomerania, Greater Poland and Silesia, enjoyed the highest level of economic development, with a good railway network, well-ordered towns and a fairly prosperous countryside, although in some areas Polish peasants were evicted in favour of Germans. Polish culture was suppressed, however, and there was a determined Germanization policy. In the Austrian areas the countryside remained rather backward, but Germanization was less intense and Kraków and Lwów had flourishing Polish universities. In the Russian areas economic development tended to lag behind that of the Prussian areas (although the rapid growth of Warsaw and Łódź was notable) and here also national self-expression was impossible. In all parts of Poland the pace of economic development was insufficient to match the rising population and as a result there was much emigration after the mid-19th century to the industrial areas of Germany and to the Americas, especially the USA. There was also an annual migration of agricultural workers to Germany for the harvest, while many Polish engineers and other specialists exercised their talents in distant parts of the Russian Empire.

During the First World War the three partitioning powers each promised Poland the freedom that they had hitherto denied her, and later President Wilson included the independence of Poland amongst his Fourteen Points. The new Poland that emerged at the end of the war after the collapse of the three powers was immediately faced with frontier questions. In the west and north Poland regained, in general, her boundaries of 1772, but Gdańsk (*Danzig*) became a Free City within the

Polish customs area. Plebiscites were held in parts of Silesia and East Prussia and as a result industrial Upper Silesia was partitioned between Poland and Germany in 1922. To the east Polish forces under the pre-war Socialist revolutionary, Piłsudski, became engaged in a war with the Soviet Union over the old Polish territories in Byelorussia and the Ukraine. The Western Powers had, however, recommended a provisional boundary, based mainly on linguistic grounds, that largely excluded them (the 'Curzon Line'). By the Treaty of Riga (1921) Poland broadly regained the eastern boundary that she had had after the Second Partition. Poland also forcibly obtained the Wilno (Vilnius) area from newly-independent Lithuania and as a result the two countries remained estranged until shortly before the Second World War. The new Poland thus included important minorities of Ukrainians (Ruthenians), Byelorussians, Germans and Lithuanians, who together constituted more than a fifth of the population. In addition there were many Jews, particularly in the towns of the former Russian areas.

The welding together of the three parts of Poland presented a number of transitional problems and there was also the question of rural over-population and land-hunger, especially in the south. A land-redistribution measure of 1925 was only partly effective and the Great Depression of 1929–34 had serious effects. On the other hand the Polish coal industry, taking advantage of the British coal strike of 1926, won valuable foreign markets. The building of the new port of Gdynia was also a notable inter-war achievement. In the years immediately before the Second World War a number of industrial projects were being developed under state auspices in the overpopulated south-central part of the country (now the south-east), where metallurgical, engineering and armaments industries were to be located away from the German frontier in a new 'Central Industrial Region'.

Politically Poland suffered instability in the years immediately after the First World War. In 1926 Piłsudski ushered in a system of semi-authoritarian rule that lasted after his death (1935) until the Second World War. A new constitution of 1935 replaced the more liberal one of 1921. Poland attempted to secure her frontiers by signing non-aggression pacts with Germany and the Soviet Union in the 1930s, but in the event these were to prove valueless.

In the spring of 1939 Hitler began a 'war of nerves' against Poland, demanding the incorporation of Danzig (admittedly a change favoured by its largely German population) and extra-territorial transit facilities through the adjacent 'Polish Corridor' separating East Prussia from the body of Germany. In August negotiations for a defence pact between Britain and France, Poland's guarantors, and the Soviet Union broke down, and instead the world was astounded by an agreement between Germany and the Soviet Union, which, it later transpired, implicitly envisaged a new partition of Poland. Germany invaded Poland from three sides on September 1st, and Britain and France, while declaring war, felt themselves unable to offer military help. The Soviet Union invaded Poland from the east shortly afterwards, annexing the areas concerned to its Byelorussian and Ukrainian Republics. The Wilno area was given to Lithuania, herself destined to be absorbed by the Soviet Union a year later. Part of German-occupied Poland was incorporated into Germany, many Poles being evicted, and the rest (*General Gouvernement*) was placed under a Governor at Kraków.

A broadly-based Polish government-in-exile was set up, first in France and then in London, and Polish forces fought in the Allied cause under General Sikorski. After Hitler's invasion of the Soviet Union in 1941 there was a rapprochement between the émigré government and the Soviet government and large numbers of Poles on Soviet territory, including interned soldiers, were allowed to go to the West and fight in the Allied armies. In 1943, however, the Soviet Union broke off relations with the London government because of the latter's request that the Red Cross should investigate mass graves found by the Germans near Smolensk and suggested by them to be those of missing Polish officers captured in 1939 by the Soviet Union. More basic differences related to the future eastern frontiers of Poland and the nature of the future régime if Poland were liberated. The Soviet Union installed a friendly provisional government of its own choosing at Lublin in July 1944, as its armies gradually pushed back the Germans. When the Red Army approached Warsaw the Polish underground Home Army initiated a rising against the local German forces, but its crushing after several weeks of fighting led to the organized destruction of the city by the Germans and also to the collapse of the Home Army, which, if victorious, would possibly have challenged the Soviet Union's military control of Poland.

The Yalta conference of the Allied Powers early in 1945 approved an eastern boundary of Poland similar to the Curzon Line and it was also anticipated that Poland would receive territorial compensation from Germany in the north and west. The Lublin government was to be widened by the introduction of members of the London government, but although Mikołajczyk took advantage of this offer he subsequently felt obliged to flee the country in 1947. By the Potsdam Agreement of the Allies (August 1945), after the defeat of Germany, Poland was authorized to administer those parts of 1939 Germany lying east of the rivers Oder (Odra) and Neisse (Nysa), with the exception of northern East Prussia (under Soviet control), together with the former Free City of Danzig. At the same time Poland was authorized to transfer Germans to the Allied Zones of Occupation. While the Potsdam Agreement had the effect of permitting the *de facto* annexation of German territory by Poland the final boundaries of Germany still remain to be formally defined by a German Peace Treaty. Eastern Germany recognizes Polish annexation of the territories, but Western Germany does not.

Poland thus reverted to the approximate boundaries that she enjoyed at the time of Bolesław III at the beginning of the 12th century, with the addition of half of East Prussia. Within the territories lost to the Soviet Union were two leading centres of Polish culture–Lwów and Wilno. Most of Pomerania and Silesia had been thoroughly Germanized over the centuries, although a considerable Polish minority remained in Upper Silesia and there were also some Poles in southern East Prussia. Over one million persons of Polish origin thus remained in these 'Recovered Territories' after the eviction of the Germans. New settlers arrived from other parts of Poland, and about $1\frac{1}{2}$ million Poles were transferred here from the former eastern areas of Poland annexed by the Soviet Union. Other settlers were drawn from about 200,000 Poles returning from Western Europe, including some members of the Armed Forces and also miners and their families who had emigrated to France between the wars. By 1950 about 4 million newcomers had settled in the territories and a high rate of natural increase has led to rapid population growth. Thus by 1970 the population of the Recovered Territories (including Gdańsk) will probably have regained the pre-war figure of about 8·9 millions.

In addition to these dislocations resulting from boundary changes it must be remembered that Poland suffered the highest rate of war deaths compared to total population experienced by any country in the Second World War. The educated classes, in particular, were very severely depleted. Many other Poles suffered imprisonment or uprooting from their homes by either Germany or the Soviet Union. Devastation of towns and factories was widespread. In the Recovered Territories the Soviet Union dismantled a number of industrial plants for her own use.

The post-war left-wing government quickly carried out a land-redistribution measure and also nationalized all large enterprises. It gradually consolidated its power under the leadership of the Polish United Workers' Party (in effect, the Communist Party). The 1947 elections were considered suspect by the Western Powers. In the late 1940s and 1950s the régime became harsher, the Catholic Church was persecuted and its leader was imprisoned, and living standards suffered as a result of a rapid industrialization programme. In 1952 the Polish People's Republic was inaugurated, based on a new constitution. After riots in Poznań in the summer of 1956 the régime entered a period of crisis. In October Gomułka, a 'national' Communist, who had been ousted by his colleagues in 1948 and later imprisoned, took over the government, which now pursued a more liberal course. The collectivization drive was abandoned, greater liberty of expression was allowed, the Catholic Church regained much of its freedom and a limited degree of small-scale private enterprise was permitted. Some emigration to the West by Poles and by members of the residual German minority was permitted, and the Soviet Union facilitated the repatriation of many Poles still living within her borders. Between 1956 and 1959 the two movements totalled 345,000 and 250,000 respectively.

Economically Poland has been transformed since the Second World War into an industrial-agricultural state and most of the massive wartime damage has been made good. Certain basic problems remain, however. The rapid rate of population growth poses the task of generating enough employment opportunities to absorb large numbers of school-leavers. There is also the problem of increasing the food and forage output to reduce the need for imports. Politically there still remains the problem of reconciling a fervently Catholic nation to Marxism-Leninism, the 20th-century atheistic philosophy of one of its old enemies.

The Land (Figs. 39, 40, 41)

There is a marked contrast between the physiography of the northern two-thirds of Poland and that of the southern third. The former is a vast zone of plains and low hills, where the surface is essentially one of glacial drift. These cover Tertiary rocks chiefly, but an anticline extends diagonally across central and northern Poland, from the Kielce area to the west Baltic coast, and thus makes accessible the underlying Permo-Triassic salt domes of the Inowrocław area and Jurassic iron ores north of Łódź. Beneath Warsaw there is a large artesian basin providing a water supply from Cretaceous rocks. In the south of the country there are a number of well-marked major regions, consisting of mountain or upland areas of varying origin and adjacent or intervening lowlands. Here, too, are glacial deposits, but the main outlines of the relief are related to the solid geology.

In the south-west, on the Czechoslovak border, are the Sudet Mountains (*Sudety*), of Hercynian age, which form the outer ramparts of the Bohemian Massif. They consist of old crystalline rocks, together with much less extensive outcrops of sedimentary rocks of Carboniferous, Permian and Mesozoic age. The Alpine earth movements led to uplift, faulting and fracturing, and the removal of much of the sedimentary

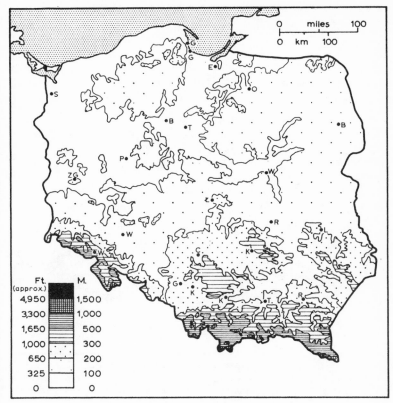

Fig. 39. Relief of Poland

cover from uplifted portions has resulted in the exposure of ancient erosion surfaces. Significantly one of the ranges is known as the Góry Stołowe ('Table Mountains'). These much-fragmented mountains, drained by tributaries of the Odra, contain a number of basins, notably those of Kłodzko and Jelenia Góra. The Carboniferous rocks are coal-bearing in the vicinity of Wałbrzych. Six summits reach a height of over 1,000 m/ 3,300 ft, including Śnieżka ('Snowball') (1,603 m/5,260 ft) in the Karkonosze (Giant Mountains). Metal ores and water resources for textile industries have been important factors in economic development.

Adjoining the foothills of the Sudets is the Silesian Plain, a Tertiary depression covered with Quaternary deposits that is drained, from southeast to north-west, by the Odra. In the upper Odra district the large Carboniferous basin of Upper Silesia, extending southwards into Czechoslovakia, lies beneath the Tertiary cover and is partly exposed in the

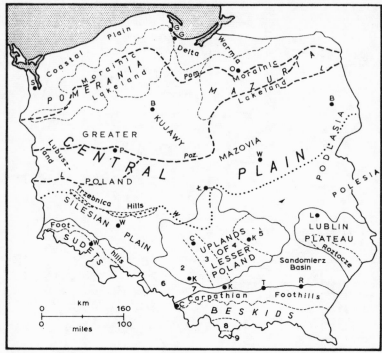

Fig. 40. Generalized physiographic regions of Poland (and regional names)

Key: 1. Łódź Plateau. **2.** Silesian Upland. **3.** Częstochowa–Kraków scarplands ('Polish Jura'). **4.** Nida depression. **5.** Holy Cross Mts. **6.** Racibórz basin. **7.** Oświęcim basin. **8.** Nowy Targ (Podhale) basin. **9.** Tatras.

Stages of retreat of ice-sheets: Pom. – Pomeranian, **Poz.** – Poznań. **L** – Leszno, **W** – Warta.

Katowice area. The Upper Carboniferous rocks contain one of Europe's leading coalfields. Eastwards and northwards the coal-basin is overlooked by rising ground (*Silesian Upland*) consisting of Triassic limestones. Further east the Triassic hills are succeeded by Jurassic scarplands (350 m/1,150 ft to 500 m/1,650 ft), running approximately from Częstochowa to Kraków and sometimes known as the 'Polish Jura'. Then follows a synclinal depression developed in Cretaceous rocks and drained by the Nida. Eastwards again are the Holy Cross Mountains (*Góry Świętokrzyskie*), in the neighbourhood of Kielce. Here a lofty peneplaned Hercynian massif, consisting of Lower Palaeozoic rocks, rises to 611 m/ 2,000 ft in the *Łysogóry* ('Bald Mountains'). On the eastern and northern flanks are, successively, outcrops of Triassic, Jurassic and Cretaceous rocks, the latter extending eastwards to become the Lublin Plateau,

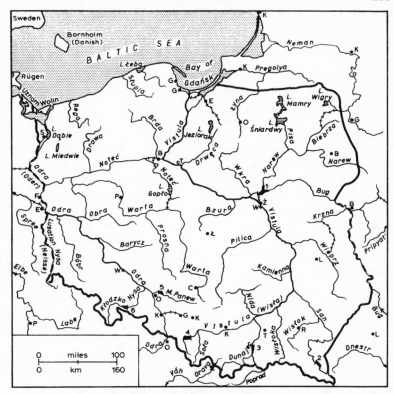

Fig. 41. Drainage of Poland

Key to major reservoirs: 1. Dębe (Zegrze). **2.** Myczkowce and Solina. **3.** Rożnów. **4.** Goczałkowice. **5.** Turawa. **6.** Otmuchów.

beyond the south–north gap cut by the Vistula, and north-westwards to become the low Łódź Plateau, which merges into the Central Plain. The entire area from the Polish Jura to the Vistula is known as the Uplands of Lesser Poland (*Wyżyna Małopolska*). The Lublin Plateau (200 m/650 ft to 400 m/1,300 ft), which may be regarded as a transitional region between Lesser Poland and the Russian Platform (more appropriately known as the 'Black Sea' or 'Ukrainian' Platform), is sharply delimited on its south-western side by the broad ridge-feature known as the *Roztocze*.

Southern Poland also includes a part of the Western Carpathians, most of which, however, lie in Slovakia. By far the greater part of the Polish Carpathians consists of the Beskids (*Beskidy*) and their foothills, which extend northwards to a line running approximately through

Cieszyn, Tarnów and Rzeszów. The Beskids consist of Cretaceous material, including flysch and limestones, overlain by Tertiary flysch. Several summits exceed 1,000 m/about 3,300 ft, the highest being Babia Góra (1,725 m/5,650 ft) in the Western Beskids. Within the well-dissected Beskids there are a number of basins, such as those of Żywiec, Nowy Sącz and Krosno, and also the large west–east longitudinal depression of Nowy Targ (*Podhale*). This is succeeded to the south, in a small salient of Polish territory, by the Tatra Mountains (*Tatry*), most of which lie in Slovakia. Four of their towering, glaciated peaks, of crystalline rocks, reach heights of over 2,000 m/6,560 ft, the highest being Rysy (2,499 m/8,200 ft). A number of mountain passes give access through the Carpathians to the valleys and basins of Slovakia.

Within the triangle formed by the Lublin Plateau, the Carpathians and the Uplands of Lesser Poland is the Sandomierz basin, drained by the Vistula and its tributary, the San. This is a structural depression filled with Tertiary sediments. Natural routeways lead out of the basin in easterly and westerly directions–to the upper Dnestr valley, in the Ukraine, by way of the Przemyśl Gate, and to the shallow Oświęcim basin on the upper Vistula above Kraków, respectively. From the latter a very low plateau-watershed gives easy access to the Racibórz basin in the upper Odra valley and thence north-westwards to the Silesian Plain. From the Oświęcim basin there is also unrestricted passage south-westwards to the Ostrava coalfield of Czechoslovakia and thence, by way of the Moravian Gate, to the Moravian Corridor. These east and west passage-ways at the foot of the Carpathians owe much to the work of ice and of escaping waters that were ponded back when ice-sheets blocked. drainage northwards.

Southern Poland was affected in the past by both mountain glaciers and continental ice-sheets advancing from the north. Cirques are in evidence in the Tatras and morainic deposits lie at their foot. The Karkonosze were also glaciated, but to a much smaller extent. In the Antepenultimate (Elster/Mindel or 'Kraków') period of glaciation the ice-sheet extended as far as the Sudets and the Carpathians, but most of its deposits have been either removed or much modified. Much more evidence survives of the Penultimate (Saale/Riss or 'Central Polish') ice-sheet. This extended as far as the Sudets, the Uplands of Lesser Poland and the Lublin Plateau. The important 'Warta' stage of its retreat is indicated by a discontinuous line of terminal moraines well to the north of the position of furthest advance. These include the Trzebnica Hills, which delimit the Silesian Plain on the north. Glacial and fluvio-glacial deposits and water- and wind-borne deposits derived from these therefore mask the solid geology of large parts of southern Poland. Thus in

Silesia and the Sandomierz basin there are contrasting areas of sands, glacial till and loess, the latter presumably blown under periglacial conditions from areas of deposition further north. Sandy tracts are particularly widespread in the northern part of the Sandomierz basin, where also marshy conditions occur in the neighbourhood of the Vistula–San confluence. On the surrounding slopes of the Uplands of Lesser Poland, the Carpathian foothills and the Lublin Plateau there are loess deposits. These are particularly extensive in the latter region.

In central and northern Poland there is a continuous mantle of glacial and fluvio-glacial deposits dating chiefly from the last glaciation (Vistula/Würm or 'Baltic'), but also partly from the Penultimate, especially in the east of the Central Plain. The deposits consist predominantly of terminal moraines, with sandy outwash-spreads in front of them and areas of glacial till in the rear. This simple arrangement has often been blurred, however, e.g. by periglacial action. The three most important moraines are those marking the 'Leszno', 'Poznań' and 'Pomeranian' stages of retreat. The moraines of the last-named, which merge in the north-east with those of the other two, present the most impressive relief features.

Melt-waters from the retreating 'Vistula' (German *Weichsel*) ice-sheet drained away laterally in a westerly direction. In doing so they produced within the sandy outwash-spreads great shallow east–west valleys that today often contain marshes and sand-dunes. These are known as *pradoliny* (sing. *pradolina*), meaning 'ancient valleys'. The corresponding term '*Urstromtäler*' (sing. *Urstromtal*) is used for these features in Germany. So characteristic are the *pradoliny* of the Central Plain that it is sometimes called the 'Land of the Great Valleys' (*Kraina Wielkich Dolin*). The two best-developed *pradoliny* are: (i) Warsaw–Berlin (Lower Bug–R. Bzura–Middle Warta–R. Obra–R. Odra–R. Spree) and (ii) Toruń–Eberswalde (north-east of Berlin) (R. Noteć–Lower Warta).

The present drainage pattern of Central Poland shows only partial use of the *pradoliny*; the rivers and streams following them may be called 'misfits', since they are, of course, much smaller in volume than the original melt-waters. Pre-glacial south–north drainage directions have reasserted themselves to an important extent, especially in the case of the lower Vistula and lower Odra, which have both breached the 'Pomeranian' moraine belt. Owing to the gentle tilt of the land to the west, as well as northwards to the Baltic, the present rivers often show a characteristic alternation of south–north and east–west portions. As a result there is a trellised or gridded pattern of valleys dissecting the glacial drift into rectangular blocks. The far south-east of the Central Plain deserves separate mention. Here, near the Soviet frontier, are the

Polesian Marshes, which adjoin the Pripyat' (Polish *Prypeć*) Marshes, lying beyond the frontier. Historically the Marshes were a thinly-peopled zone separating the areas settled by the Poles and the Byelorussians.

In the rear of the Leszno moraine the drift cover is pitted by numerous lakes and marshy depressions, often originating as sub-glacial channels or kettle-holes. The local term 'lakeland' or 'lakeside' (*pojezierze*) is often applied. In northern Poland, in Pomerania and Mazuria, the number and size of lakes become particularly impressive within, and on the margins of, the great ridges of terminal moraines associated with the 'Pomeranian' stage. In the Pomeranian and Mazurian 'Lakelands' these morainic hills (sometimes called the 'Baltic Heights') are over 125 m/400 ft high. South-west of Gdańsk a height of 329 m/1,080 ft is reached (Wieżyca) in the picturesque 'Kashubian Lakeland', while in Mazuria the hills reach 309 m/1,000 ft near the Soviet frontier (Szeskie Wzgórza) and 312 m/1,025 ft south-west of Olsztyn (Dylewska Góra).

Between the northern morainic hills and the Baltic Sea there is a coastal plain, largely consisting of glacial till. The plain becomes pinched out, however, at several places, including Gdynia, where there are low morainic cliffs. Immediately to the east is the Vistula delta, parts of which are below sea-level. The coastline itself is remarkably smooth, owing to accretion in shallow water as a result of long-shore drift in an easterly direction. Here there are lagoons lying behind dune barriers. In Gdańsk Bay there are two great spits—Hel Spit, protecting the port of Gydnia, and the Vistula Spit, which almost closes the Vistula Lagoon. At the mouth of the Odra the large islands of Wolin and Uznam separate the Szczecin Lagoon from the open sea. Sandy beaches provide the basis of a growing holiday traffic at places on the Baltic coast.

Climate and Soils

Poland is a land of transition where both Continental and Oceanic influences are felt. In January the average temperature in all parts of the country is below freezing-point, but there is a distinct fall from west to east (excluding the mountain regions of the south). In summer maritime influences have much less effect on the pattern of isotherms and there is thus a slight rise in temperature from north to south. July temperatures in lowland areas are almost everywhere over 17·0°C/62·5°F. Coastal and mountain areas have lower temperatures, however. Near Tarnów, in the south, the average reaches 19·0°C/66·0°F.

In general the summer months have a greater precipitation than the winter, although on the coast this difference is less marked. Annual precipitation in lowland areas varies from about 500 mm/nearly 20 in to about 700 mm/27·5 in, according to location. The lowest totals occur in the middle and lower Vistula region within the triangle Gdańsk–Warsaw–Poznań. In the Sudets and the Tatras figures rise to well over 1,000 mm/40 in.

The accompanying table of climatic statistics for various towns shows a number of regional differences. Szczecin and Wrocław, in the west, have slightly moister conditions than Białystok and Lublin, in the east, and also have winters that are rather less cold. In the summer there is little difference in temperature. Lidzbark, in the morainic hills of Mazuria, not far from the Baltic, has a smaller temperature range than Białystok, further inland in the eastern part of the Central Plain, and also has a greater precipitation. The figures for Zakopane, the resort centre at the foot of the Tatras, show the effect of altitude on precipitation and temperature. It will be noted that Kraków, in a westward-facing gap between the Uplands of Lesser Poland and the Beskids, has a higher rainfall than the other lowland places listed.

TABLE 8

CLIMATIC STATISTICS · POLAND

Station	Average temperature January		Average temperature July		Average annual precipitation	
	°C	°F	°C	°F	mm	in
Warsaw	−2·9	26·8	18·6	65·5	530	20·9
Białystok	−4·1	24·6	18·4	65·1	522	20·6
Kraków	−2·5	27·5	18·8	65·8	721	28·4
Lidzbark	−3·3	26·1	17·0	62·6	634	25·0
Lublin	−3·5	25·7	18·4	65·1	551	21·7
Szczecin	−0·9	30·4	18·3	64·9	561	22·1
Wrocław	−1·1	30·0	18·8	65·8	592	23·3
Zakopane	−4·9	23·2	14·7	58·5	1,122	44·2

Sandy deposits, variously consisting of glacial outwash, morainic hills or more recent fluviatile material, cover considerable areas of northern and central Poland, as well as certain areas in the south. There are also wide tracts of glacial till, itself often rather sandy. The resultant soils, developed on clayey sands and sandy loams under a cover of coniferous forest, are podzols and thus are rather acid and deficient in humus. In some areas, with free drainage and a former deciduous cover, brown forest soils have developed on the glacial till. Heavier and more fertile soils are found in the reclaimed marshlands (*Żuławy*) of the Vistula delta and in alluvial tracts near the rivers. Locally there are also areas of rich black fen-soils. These are found in Kujawy particularly, and also to the south-east of Szczecin.

In the south of the country fertile soils have developed on the loess deposits. In the Silesian Plain these are often brown forest soils, but on the loess of the Lublin Plateau and of the southern flanks of the Uplands of Lesser Poland 'black-earths' (chernozems) have also developed in certain areas, and where loess does not mask the limestone of these two districts there has also been a development of carbonate, i.e. 'rendzina', soils (Polish *rędzina*). The Sandomierza depression, where sandy glacial deposits are widespread, has soils similar to those of central and northern Poland. In the higher parts of the Sudets and the Carpathians mountain soils of a skeletal character succeed podzols and brown forest soils.

Land-Use (Fig. 42) **and Farming**

About one-quarter of the surface-area of Poland is forested, chiefly by conifers. Beech and oak are the leading deciduous trees, the former being

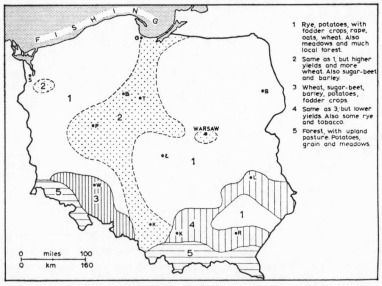

1 Rye, potatoes, with fodder crops, rape, oats, wheat. Also meadows and much local forest.

2 Same as 1, but higher yields and more wheat. Also sugar-beet and barley.

3 Wheat, sugar-beet, barley, potatoes, fodder crops.

4 Same as 3, but lower yields. Also some rye and tobacco.

5 Forest, with upland pasture. Potatoes, grain and meadows.

Fig. 42. Generalized land-use regions of Poland

prominent in the Baltic coastlands and the lower parts of the Beskids, where there is also an admixture of conifers. In the higher parts of the Beskids there are stands of spruce. In the Tatras this zone is succeeded by dwarf pine and then by Alpine meadow. On morainic hills and sandy wastes birch- and pine-woods, with heathland, are common. Many of the forests are, in effect, managed plantations, but the proportion of natural cover, particularly in the east of the country, is, nevertheless, substantial. Ruthless depletion took place during the two World Wars. While there are extensive areas of forest in the Carpathians and the Sudets these are by no means dominant in the general distributional pattern. Thus there are large tracts of forest in part of the northern morainic belt, in the Sandomierz depression, in rural Upper Silesia, in the lower Noteć–Warta interfluve, in the Białystok area, and near the East German border in Lower Silesia and Lubusz-land. Such areas are usually known as *bory* ('coniferous forests') (sing. *bór*) or *puszcza* ('primeval forest'). In the *puszcza* of Białowieza, south-east of Białystok, wild bison are protected in a special reservation. Commercial felling occurs in all the main forest areas, with timber-working industries being found in a number of local centres. Bydgoszcz, with its waterway connections, is a leading timber-handling town. Kostrzyń has a large cellulose and paper industry. Piotrków and Radomsko (south of Łódź) are notable furniture centres. Sawn timber, matches, plywood, furniture and fibreboard are exported.

In spite of the indifferent quality of soils over large parts of Poland 51% of the surface area is under arable cultivation (1962); this represents over three-quarters of the total area of farmed land (65% of Poland). Cereals account for 57% of the arable area, rye alone accounting for 31%. Potatoes cover a further 19% of the arable area. Rye and potatoes thus together account for one-half of the arable area. Poland is the second largest producer of both in the world after the Soviet Union.

Polish farming is predominantly under small-scale private ownership. A land-reform measure after the First World War reduced large estates to some extent, and expropriation after 1945 released further land for redistribution, especially in west-central Poland. Here and in the Regained Territories, from which German farmers and landlords had been evicted, estates and large farms were often kept intact as state farms, however, rather than broken up for peasant cultivators. About one-third of the appropriated area was treated in this way. Today state farms number about 6,500 and occupy 12% of the farmed area. Collectivization was begun in the early 1950s, but the changes in the régime in 1956 led to a halting and reversal of the process, so that today the land operated by collective farms (about 1,500) is little more than 1% of the total. The number of private farms is 3·6 millions, covering 86% of all agricultural land. Only 11% of the farms are over 10 ha/25 acres in size, but these cover 33% of the area. Only 36,000 private farms of over 20 ha/50 acres survive. Since 1959 the government has stimulated the formation of voluntary 'agricultural circles', which are co-operatives broadly similar in principle to those of Western Europe. Only rarely do they involve the communal cultivation of land, their chief role being to hire out tractors and other machinery to their members, to act as agencies for various state-assisted facilities, and to undertake the joint purchase of fertilizers, seeds, etc.

The regional pattern of land-use is a relatively simple one. On the rather sandy soils of the north and the Central Plain cropping is dominated by rye and potatoes, with oats and wheat occupying a very subordinate place. Oats are relatively more important in the extreme north-east of the Baltic coastlands, however. Fodder crops and rapeseed (colza), cultivated for its oil, are also grown, and flax achieves some importance in the north-east of the country. Interspersed with the cultivated fields are patches of meadow and forest, the latter covering wide areas locally, as has been indicated. Within the rye–potato zone there are certain districts where crop yields are higher, on average, where wheat has considerable emphasis and where barley and sugar beet are also grown. The main area embracing these districts extends southwards up the Vistula from its delta and then stretches westwards to the Poznań district and eastwards and southwards in the direction of Warsaw and the Upper Silesian complex respectively, both of which have considerable market-gardening belts. Within these more favoured districts there is often a higher proportion of heavier and more fertile soils of deltaic, alluvial or fen origin. A similar area, related to fen soils, occurs south-east of Szczecin. Moreover, the fact that these districts lay within Germany up to 1914 led to soil and drainage improvements and to a good standard of husbandry, expressed in higher yields, even on sandy soils. In addition, the average size of farm tends to be distinctly above the national average. In the Regained Territories of the north and north-west the post-1945 settlers found mainly sandy and sandy-loam soils that had been considerably improved by generations of German farmers and estate-owners (*Junkers*) and here, too, the size of farms tends to be above the average. As a result the two voivodships (provinces) of Szczecin and Zielona Góra have better yields of rye and potatoes than the eastern parts of the rye–potato zone (e.g. Białystok). Even so, the standard of husbandry varies considerably, according to the origins of the post-1945 settlers.

In the south-west and south-east there are the two main regions of loess soils (and others of good quality). In the former, in the Silesian Plain, wheat and sugar beet are dominant, together with barley, potatoes and fodder crops. Here again the farms of the new Polish settlers tend to be of above average size. The south-eastern loess area, with similar crops, consists of a zone of either hill or plateau country enclosing the sandy and partly wooded Sandomierz depression, where the rye–potato combination is more typical. Holdings are small in these loess areas and often excessively fragmented. Wheat yields tend to be not only below those for the Wrocław and Opole voivodships (Silesian Plain), but also below those for the Gdańsk, Bydgoszcz and Poznań voivodships, and, indeed, the national average itself. Except in Lublin voivodship sugar beet yields are also lower. In the Carpathian and Sudet Mountains and their foothills the proportion of forest and grass increases, but grain, potatoes and clover are cultivated where natural conditions permit.

Pigs are the most numerous form of livestock and they show the greatest density in the Central Plain. Cattle show some concentration in the Silesian Plain and the Carpathian zone. Sheep are third in importance and tend to have their greatest density in the higher, south-central part of the Central Plain and the adjoining northern margins of the Uplands of Lesser Poland, as well as in the eastern part of the Central Plain (where fallowing still persists). Horses are still numerous (and are responsible for much fodder consumption), but are slowly declining as mechanization gradually proceeds.

The rapid growth and accompanying urbanization of Poland's population since the Second World War, its increasing purchasing power and its shift in taste towards white bread all place a strain on domestic food supplies, even though output is increasing. Large wheat imports are now usually necessary, from North America or the Soviet Union. On the other hand exports of certain quantities of high-value products are carefully maintained, such as eggs, bacon, ham, butter, sugar and vodka (chiefly from potatoes). Crop and livestock yields, although now rising owing to the increased application of fertilizers and the introduction of improved strains, are still rather low by north-west European standards. The peasants themselves are better off than ever before and the standard of rural amenities has also risen (e.g. as regards electrification and housing). Part-time cultivation combined with factory employment is becoming more frequent. Although the threat of collectivization has receded, the farming community still tends to regard the régime with distrust. Certain quotas of output are bought on a contract basis by the government at fixed prices, but the free market is quite large.

Sea-fishing, both in the Baltic and in the Atlantic and the North Sea, is carried out from Gdynia and Szczecin and some of the smaller ports. However, despite a recent increase in its fishing fleets Poland cannot yet be said to rank as one of the major fishing countries of Europe.

Industry and Mining

Modern industry dates from the end of the 18th century and the early decades of the 19th. At this time a stimulus to industrial development was given by the government of independent Poland and later, to a more important extent, by that of the Congress Kingdom. In Silesia the Prussian government was active in developing coal-mining and metallurgy. The partitioning of Poland had the unfortunate effect of placing the country within three separate economies that were to undergo considerable change by the outbreak of the First World War. For each of the three partitioning powers its Polish territories were geographically marginal, however, and obviously, therefore, 19th-century industrial development lacked coherence. Except in the German areas capital was scarce, so that industrial development in Austrian and Russian Poland, especially the latter, often relied on foreign capital, chiefly French and German. Immigrant Germans, many of whom became polonized, were often active in commercial and industrial endeavour, as also were the Jews.

After the reconstitution of an independent Poland in 1918 certain industries were severed from their traditional markets in other parts of the partitioning countries, e.g. the textile factories of former Russian Poland and the coal mines of the Polish part of former German Upper Silesia. In the latter area the partitioning (1922) between Poland and Germany created special problems. The new boundary interfered with electricity and water supplies, the journey to work, and the operation of numerous enterprises. For a transitional period of fifteen years, however, a special joint commission had the task of ensuring that vital interrelationships should not be too abruptly broken. Nevertheless disengagement was encouraged by both countries. Firms were broken up in some instances and American capital was important in the reorganization of Polish Upper Silesia.

In the 1930s the Polish government introduced a plan for a 'Central Industrial Region', broadly coincident with the Vistula–San–Carpathians triangle. The early stages of this plan–to establish new engineering and defence industries away from the western and eastern frontiers and to absorb surplus rural population–were overtaken by the outbreak of the war in 1939.

Since the Second World War rapid industrial development on a very much greater and more comprehensive scale has been a deliberate policy of the government. But first much wartime destruction of plant had to be made good. Since the early 1950s Polish industry has grown at an impressive rate, despite much early overstraining of the economy and cutting back of consumption. The iron and steel, engineering and chemical industries have been particularly stressed. The food, textile and other consumer goods industries, after early neglect, have been re-equipped and rationalized in many instances. As regards the location of industry the policy has been to moderate further growth in Warsaw, Upper

Silesia, Łódź and the other leading cities and to introduce new industrial employment into the smaller towns, especially those with surplus labour in their rural hinterlands.

ENERGY SUPPLIES (Fig. 43)

Poland contains, in the Upper Silesian basin, one of the leading bituminous coalfields of Europe, both in terms of current output

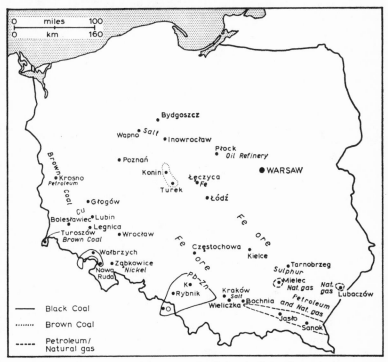

Fig. 43. Mineral exploitation in Poland

(114·2 million tons in 1964) and accessible reserves (about 85,000 million tons at a depth of less than 1,000 m/3,300 ft). Poland is the sixth largest producer of bituminous coal in the world and has the highest *per capita* output after Great Britain. She is also a prominent exporter of coal. In addition to the output of the Upper Silesian field there is a much smaller output from the geologically separate Lower Silesian field, lying in the Sudets (3·2 million tons in 1964). There is also a growing output of brown coal, but the country is only very moderately endowed with petroleum, natural gas and hydro-power potential.

The Upper Silesian coalfield is a vast basin of Upper Carboniferous age, lying mainly in southern Poland but also extending for some distance over the Czechoslovak frontier into the Ostrava–Karviná area of northern Moravia and Czech Silesia (Fig. 44). The basin forms a rough triangle with its apex lying south of Ostrava and with Tarnowskie Góry and Kraków being situated just beyond the other two 'corners'. The north-western and south-eastern sides of the triangle have distances of about 120 km/75 miles, while the shorter, north-eastern side is about 80 km/50 miles long.

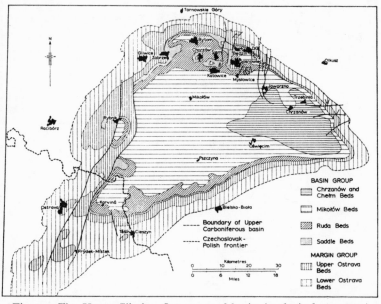

Fig. 44. The Upper Silesian–Ostrava coal-basin (geological structure)

The Polish part of the basin is situated on the low, rolling watershed area between the Odra and Vistula drainage systems, the small rivers Kłodnica, Bierawka and Ruda flowing westwards to the Odra, and the Czarna ('Black') Przemsza and its tributary, the Brynica, flowing southwards to form the Przemsza after joining the westward-flowing Biała ('White') Przemsza (Fig. 45). The Przemsza then continues southwards to join the upper Vistula in the marshy Oświęcim basin. Before the First World War the Brynica–Przemsza line here marked the eastern boundary of German Poland (Prussian Silesia), while the boundary between adjoining Austrian and Russian Poland followed the Biała Przemsza. Sosnowiec, Czeladź, Będzin and Dąbrowa Górnicza thus lay in the Russian part of

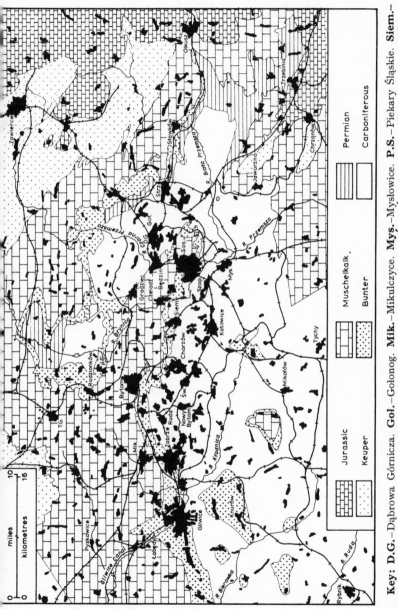

Key: **D.G.**–Dąbrowa Górnicza. **Gol.**–Golonog. **Mik.**–Mikulczyce. **Mys.**–Mysłowice. **P.S.**–Piekary Śląskie. **Siem.**–Siemanowice. **Sos.**–Sosnowiec. **Strz.**–Strzemieszyce. **Szop.**–Szopienice. **Św.**–Świętochłowice. **T.G.**–Tarnowskie Góry.

Fig. 45. The Upper Silesian industrial district: Pre-Tertiary geology, settlement and communications

the coalfield (the 'Dąbrowa' industrial district), while Jaworzno and Chrzanów lay in the less-developed Austrian part. The greater part of the active coalfield was thus held by Germany, and only this part, strictly speaking, fell within the historical limits of Silesia. The 'Upper Silesian coal-basin' therefore covers a rather wider area than Upper Silesia proper.

The coal-basin has been likened to a set of triangular dishes fitting one inside the other but sagging downwards in the centre. There are, however, certain distortions to this symmetry. Lowest in the basin are the Ostrava beds, forming the 'Margin Group'. Above these are the beds of the 'Basin Group', of which the 'Saddle Beds' are the most important. These derive their name from the fact that they reach the surface in the northern part of the basin where a west–east upfold occurs, extending approximately from Zabrze to Mysłowice. North of this feature is the smaller Bytom basin. Generally speaking, except on the outer margins, the coal-seams are only gently inclined, although locally there is faulting, and many of the seams are of considerable thickness (8·6 m/28 ft at Zabrze), so that a high degree of mechanized extraction is possible. The coal-seams tend to become thinner from west to east, but where intervening beds of other material disappear some exceptionally thick composite seams can occur (e.g. over 12 m/40 ft at Mysłowice). Unlike the Ruhr or Donbass fields the proportion of coking coal raised is not high (about 12–15%) and, moreover, some of the coke (especially from the Saddle Beds) tends to be rather soft and not of metallurgical quality. Domestic, gas and steam coals are the dominant categories. The best source of coking coal is the Margin Group on the western side of the basin, e.g. near Zabrze and especially near Rybnik, to the south-west, where structural conditions make available the largest reserves of coking coal. Over the Czechoslovak border the proportion of coking coal increases.

It is important to note that, with the exception of the Rybnik area, the Coal Measures are exposed only in the north of the basin, with the result that this has become the most intensively-exploited district. In the central part of the basin the coal lies at very great depths and consequently is not mined. The northern and north-eastern margins of the coalfield (including the Bytom basin) are overlain by a relatively thin cover of Permian rocks, Bunter Sandstone or Muschelkalk, a shelly limestone that outcrops over a wide area. These rocks usually correspond to higher ground. To the south and west the Carboniferous rocks are overlain by Tertiary deposits. Finally the solid geology is frequently masked by glacial sands, which thin out, however, in the north-eastern part of the basin. As a result there are extensive birch and pine forests and relatively infertile conditions for agriculture. The sands have a particular significance for the coal-mining industry, since they are used in large quantities for filling-in after seams have been extracted. Surface subsidence is thereby reduced.

The very much smaller Lower Silesian field has more difficult working conditions, with thin seams, many faults and igneous intrusions, but nearly half the output is of excellent coking quality. Wałbrzych and Nowa Ruda are the chief mining centres. Output has been static in recent years.

Coal-mining in the Silesian fields dates from the middle of the 18th century, i.e. after Silesia had been taken by Prussia from Austria. By the beginning of the 19th century the Prussian state and the local landed magnates were operating a number of mines in Upper Silesia. The output served the growing ferrous and non-ferrous metal industries and there was also shipment to other parts of Germany by the newly-built Kłodnica canal, connecting Zabrze, via Gliwice, with Koźle, on the Odra. Even so, it was not until the 1820s that output from Upper Silesia exceeded that from the Lower Silesian field. In the Austrian and Russian areas commercial exploitation did not develop until the middle of the 19th century and their output was small compared with that of the German area. Tariff barriers inhibited the free flow of coal over the frontiers, so that the coal produced in each of the three districts tended to be partly used for local purposes and partly shipped to other markets within the three respective Empires, although some coal did move from German to Russian Poland. Moreover, coal from German Poland met keen competition from British and Ruhr coal in Berlin and northern Germany, and the Ostrava field competed with the mines of Austrian Poland in the Habsburg Empire.

Independent Poland faced problems of coal marketing in the inter-war period. The partition of German Upper Silesia between Poland and Germany in 1922 had given the former the greater part of the coal resources, and the Allied Powers laid down that Germany should accept Polish coal exports without any tariff for a three-year period. After 1925 Germany ceased to be a market for Polish coal; a tariff 'war' had developed and Germany vigorously expanded output in her remaining part of the field. In 1926 the British General Strike gave Poland an opportunity to obtain new markets in northern and western Europe in addition to those that she had retained in central Europe. A railway line was built from Katowice to the new port of Gdynia to handle shipments. The depressed years of the 1930s were accompanied by a fall in demand, however, and output never regained the 1929 level. Nevertheless some new mines were opened in the inter-war period, especially in the Rybnik area.

During the Second World War the whole of the Upper Silesian field came under German rule and, with the aid of forced labour, output reached a peak in 1943. When the whole of Silesia came under Polish rule at the end of war coal output fell very greatly, largely as the result of the exodus of many German miners and technical personnel. Considerable numbers of miners of Polish origin living in the 1939 German area remained, however. Output rose again rapidly in the late 1940s and early 1950s and coal exports played a vital role in the nation's recovery, but a large tonnage was delivered to the Soviet Union for low prices and this was one of the causes of the strong anti-Russian feeling in 1956. As a result of some reduction of exports to the Soviet Union and the general European coal-glut since the late 1950s, exports were only 19·3 million tons in 1964 compared with over 25 million tons in the early 1950s.

Today there are about 80 mines in the Upper Silesian field, together with a few open-cast workings. The main mining area extends from Gliwice to Dąbrowa Górnicza and Mysłowice. There are also outlying areas to the south-east (Jaworzno–Chrzanów–Trzebinia), south (Mikołow–Tychy) and south-west (Rybnik). In recent years the sinking of new mines and the expansion of existing ones has occurred in the Rybnik and Przemsza valley areas, the aim in the former being an increased output of coking coal. Even so Poland has to import supplementary amounts of coking coal, chiefly from the Soviet Union (1·2 million tons in 1964). The accompanying table gives details of coal output for various years since 1860. The main part of the coalfield and its associated industries and towns have, since 1953, been placed under one comprehensive planning authority, in order to secure the rational and harmonious development of the whole complex for the first time in its chequered history.

BROWN COAL is mined, chiefly by open-pit methods, at a number of places in Greater Poland, Lower Silesia and Lubusz-land, output reaching 20·3 million tons in 1964. The two most important areas by far are near Turoszów, in the extreme south-western corner of Poland, and the Konin–Turek district, between Łodz and Poznań. Here the output is consumed by large new thermal power-stations, some of the current from Turoszów being transmitted to East Germany, which has collaborated in the further opening-up of Poland's brown-coal deposits. Some brown coal (5·4 million tons in 1964) is also exported, chiefly to East Germany. In central and northern Poland peat deposits are utilized, chiefly by peasants for their own use, but the rate of extraction is tending to fall.

Poland's deposits of petroleum and natural gas, while useful, are completely inadequate for the country's growing needs and she therefore imports considerable quantities of crude petroleum, refined products

TABLE 9

POLISH COAL OUTPUT

(millions of metric tons)

Year	Former German Upper Silesia		Former Russian Poland		Former Austrian Poland	Total Upper Silesian coal-basin	Former German Lower Silesia	Total for post-1945 Poland
1860	2·5		0·2		0·1	2·7	0·7	3·4
1890	16·9		2·5		0·6	20·0	3·2	23·2
1913	43·4		6·8		2·0	52·3	5·5	57·8
	German	*Polish*	*Polish*	*Polish*		*German & Polish*	*German*	*German & Polish*
1929	22·0		46·2			68·2	6·1	74·3
1938	26·0		38·1			64·1	5·3	69·4
	German		*German occupation*			*German*	*German*	*German*
1943	29·2		57·5			86·7	4·7	91·4
	Polish		*Polish*			*Polish*	*Polish*	*Polish*
1946						44·4	2·9	47·3
1950						74·3	3·7	78·0
1964						114·2	3·2	117·4

Sources: Winston, V. H., 'The Polish bituminous coal-mining industry', *American Slavic and East European Review* 15 (1956), and Statistical Yearbooks of Poland.

and natural gas from the Soviet Union. The greater part of her pre-war resources now lie in the Soviet Ukraine, the old 'Galician' oilfield being partitioned as a result of the westward shifting of the frontier after the Second World War. This oilfield was developed under Austrian rule as early as the 1860s and reached its peak of output before the First World War, although since then the output of natural gas has increased. The main zone of exploitation lies in the Carpathian foothills near the small towns of Jasło, Sanok, Krosno, Lesko and Bochnia, the area near the latter now being the most productive. Refining takes place in the oilfield. Recently new gas deposits have been discovered to the north in the Sandomierz depression, near Mielec and Lubaczów, and a new petroleum field is being developed near Krosno on Odra in western Poland. Output of crude petroleum was 282,000 tons in 1964 and natural gas output was 1,231 million cubic metres. Gas pipe-lines link the Carpathian and Lubaczów fields to Kraków and Upper Silesia and a Soviet pipe-line supplies the new chemical centre of Puławy on the Vistula. In 1964 the 'Friendship' oil pipe-line from the Soviet Union started delivery to a large new refinery and petrochemical complex at Płock, on the Vistula. This has been designed to handle 6 million tons of crude per annum but the capacity will eventually be much higher than this. The pipe-line extends westwards to Schwedt in East Germany.

Most of Poland's electricity is generated by thermal means, in view of her generous coal endowment. Thermal stations are chiefly located on the various coalfields or near the leading cities. Hydro generation accounts for only about 2% of total output. This contribution comes from several small stations in the Baltic Lakeland (e.g. River Brda), the Sudet region (e.g. R. Bóbr), and the Carpathians (R. Dunajec, Soła and San). There is also a station at Dębe, associated with the new canal linking Warsaw directly with the Lower Narew and Bug. Regulation of the Vistula downstream from Warsaw will involve a hydro-power station near Włocławek (now under construction) and probably several others.

METALLURGY (Fig. 43)–IRON AND STEEL

Although largely dependent on foreign ore Poland is a considerable producer of iron and steel, ranking fifth in Europe, excluding the USSR. She is also a significant producer of non-ferrous metals, notably zinc.

The iron industry has a long tradition. In the prosperous 16th century a leading area was the *Staropolski* ('Old Polish') district of the Kamienna valley, situated north-east of Kielce in the Holy Cross Mountains. Another important district (then located in Habsburg territory) was the valley of the Mała Panew and neighbouring valleys, situated in the hills east of Opole in Silesia. Both districts had access to various local ores (bog ores chiefly, although Triassic and Jurassic ores were also available), water-power, and timber for charcoal. Towards the end of the 18th century activity in *Staropolski* was stimulated by the Polish government and this interest was later revived by that of the Congress Kingdom. In Upper Silesia the Mała Panew district gained new importance after the province's annexation by Prussia (1741), since state-owned furnaces were built there.

By the end of the 18th century Upper Silesia was in the van of technical progress in the European iron industry, the use of charcoal gradually giving way to that of coal, with a consequent, though gradual, locational shift to the coalfield. The English iron-master, Wilkinson, advised on the coking of coal, and the Scot, Baildon, was employed by the Prussian state in connection with the first coke-using blast-furnace, established at Gliwice in 1796. This was followed by a second state-owned works, the famous Royal Furnace (Królewska Huta, German *Königshütte*), inaugurated in 1802 near Chorzów. Other blast-furnaces followed, chiefly owned by the local magnates, and Baildon himself also established an ironworks. The railway-building boom of the 1840s and 1850s created a lucrative market for the puddled iron of Upper Silesia. Steel-making developed in the 1870s, but the relatively poor development of engineering industries in eastern Germany and neighbouring areas precluded as rapid a rate of growth as in the Ruhr, which, however, had not overtaken Upper Silesia as the leading metallurgical district of Germany until after 1850. By the end of the century the Muschelkalk and Coal Measure ores that had hitherto been used were becoming exhausted and ore from Slovakia, Sweden and the Ukraine was being brought in. At the same time the limitations of Upper Silesian coking-coal resources had already become apparent.

In the Russian part of the coalfield parallel developments took place. In the 1830s the Bank of (Russian) Poland built the coke-using Huta Bankowa at Dąbrowa Górnicza. Later on in the century other ironworks were established, often with the aid of French or German capital. Outside the coalfield ironworks were built at Częstochowa, using local Jurassic ore, and in *Staropolski* there was a gradual switch to coke in place of charcoal. By the end of the 19th century Russian Poland was relying on external sources of coking coal (from Prussian Upper Silesia and the Ostrava field) and also to some extent on Ukrainian ore. In Austrian Poland no important development of the iron industry took place.

Independent Poland was faced with the problem of excess iron and steel capacity now that a number of plants in former German Upper Silesia were cut off from their traditional markets. This factor, together with the relatively slow growth of Polish fabricating industries, resulted in a situation where steel output in 1938 (1·4 million tons) was lower than in the same area in 1913 (1·7). (The remaining, German part of Upper Silesia produced 0·5 million tons of steel in 1938.) Several plants were closed down in the inter-war period, but in the late 1930s some modernization took place in *Staropolski* and a plant for special steels was built at Stalowa Wola in the Sandomierz depression. These moves were part of the government plan for building up a new 'Central Industrial Region'. Nevertheless total steel production outside Upper Silesia was very small on the outbreak of the Second World War.

After the war Poland acquired from Germany the remaining plants in Upper Silesia and also blast-furnaces at Szczecin. Their effectiveness had been reduced by Soviet dismantling, however. Selective re-equipment and expansion have taken place and in addition several completely new establishments have been built. These have been deliberately located outside Upper Silesia. The largest is the integrated Lenin Works at the new town of Nowa Huta ('New Furnace'), just outside Kraków. Utilizing Ukrainian ore and absorbing 'raw' labour from the overpopulated Carpathian foothills of southern Poland it produces about 2·5 million tons of steel per annum (1964) and will eventually be larger. A second new integrated plant is at Częstochowa, near a pre-existing ironworks. This uses much local Jurassic ore and produces 0·5–1 million tons of steel per annum. Thirdly there is a plant for special steels (present capacity 0·3 million tons) at Młociny, on the north-western outskirts of Warsaw.

In the Upper Silesian conurbation there are about a dozen major establishments, of which only six are integrated plants with blast-furnaces, the largest being the Huta Kościuszko (formerly Królewska Huta). There is also an integrated plant at Zawiercie, to the north-east. There is considerable dependence in Upper Silesia on bought-in pig and scrap, therefore. Total annual steel output is over 3 million tons. In addition steel is produced at Ostrowiec (in *Staropolski*) (0·2 million tons), Stalowa Wola (0·3 million tons) and Ozimek (Mała Panew). At Szczecin there are blast-furnaces only.

The Jurassic ores (about 30% iron content) are now virtually the only ones exploited, but despite an increased output (2·7 million tons crude ore mined in 1964) they are quite inadequate for Poland's growing needs. The mining areas are the Częstochowa–Kraków scarplands and the hills of *Staropolski*, chiefly the former. In recent years a deep mine has come into production at Łęczyca, north-west of Łódź. The greater part of ore supplies thus has to be imported (9·1 million tons in 1964), chiefly from the Soviet Union, followed by Sweden (an important market for Polish coal), Brazil and Guinea. Manganese ore also has to be imported (0·4 million tons in 1964), chiefly from the Soviet Union, but nickel can be obtained from Ząbkowice, in the Sudets. In 1964 Poland's total output of pig-iron was 5·6 million tons and of steel 8·6.

Non-Ferrous Metals

Poland is the largest producer of zinc in Europe outside the Soviet Union and her lead output is also substantial. The ores of both metals occur in dolomitic beds within the Triassic Muschelkalk that overlies the northern and eastern margins of the Upper Silesian coal-basin, and they are thus conveniently close to fuel resources for smelting. The ores are mined in the Tarnowskie Góry–Bytom and Olkusz–Chrzanów districts. Calamine (zinc carbonate) was mined as early as the 16th century for brass-making purposes, but zinc smelting as such was not introduced until the early 19th century, when the Prussian state and the local magnates set up smelters. Towards the end of the 19th century the much larger deposits of zinc blende (sulphide) became available as a result of further progress in smelting methods and these are still exploited. During the 19th century Upper Silesia was the world's leading producer of zinc, but in the present century output has fallen both relatively and absolutely. There is, indeed, a considerable import of zinc concentrates to utilize smelting capacity, and refined metal and zinc sheets are exported. Galena (lead sulphide) has also been mined for several centuries, especially in the Tarnowskie Góry area, and there was a great revival at the end of the 18th century when steam-engines enabled water to be pumped from old mines. Lead has never been as important as zinc in modern times, however. Output of ores, by metal content, in 1964 was lead–42,000 tons–and zinc–187,000. Small quantities of silver are obtained from the lead ores and some cadmium from the zinc.

Copper ores are mined in Lower Silesia (37,000 tons by metal content in 1964) near Bolesławiec and Legnica. Processing takes place at Legnica. Much larger deposits (in the underlying Permian rocks) further north, between Lubin and Głogów, are now being opened up and should obviate the need for supplementary imports and eventually provide an export surplus.

Aluminium is produced from imported (chiefly Hungarian) alumina (93,000 tons in 1964) at Skawina, near Kraków, and output (48,000 tons in 1964) will be increased when a new plant at Konin is completed.

OTHER INDUSTRIES

Food industries are widely distributed throughout Poland, both in cities and rural areas, and include such activities as grain-milling, sugar beet refining, milk-processing and meat-packing. Tropical foodstuffs are handled and treated in the three large ports.

The textile industries, on the other hand, display considerable localization. Nearly two-thirds of Poland's output of cotton textiles and over half of that of woollens are produced in Łódź and district. German artisans were encouraged to settle here during the period of the Congress Kingdom, and in the second half of the 19th century growing mass markets in the Russian Empire supported a rapid expansion of steam-driven textile factories. Other textile centres are Białystok, with neighbouring Fasty (cottons and woollens), Bielsko-Biała (high-quality woollens) and Częstochowa (cottons). Other centres are the former German towns in the Sudet zone, where water resources were originally an important factor. Bielawa is the leading member of this group. Artificial fibres are made at a number of places, including Chodaków (west of Warsaw), Łódź, Gorzów, Jelenia Góra, Szczecin, Tomaszów Mazowiecki, Tarnów, Toruń and Wrocław. The clothing industry is located in the Łódź district, Warsaw, and in the leading cities, especially Wrocław. The footwear industry is well represented at Radom but otherwise is rather widely distributed, although most centres are in the south. Three important small towns are Chełmek (near Oświęcim), Krapkowice (south of Opole) and Nowy Targ (in the Carpathians south of Kraków).

The engineering industries cover a wide range of activities. In certain instances they grew up to serve local needs, e.g. wood-working machinery at Bydgoszcz, agricultural machinery at Poznań and textile machinery at Łódź. The three leading ports all have shipbuilding and repairing yards, Gdańsk possessing the most extensive facilities. An important producer of marine diesel engines is the inland city of Poznań, where the old-established 'Cegielski' concern also produces machine-tools and railway wagons. Ships' engines are also produced in Świętochłowice in Upper Silesia. Wrocław is important for railway locomotives and wagons, and other centres of railway engineering are Chrzanów, Ostrowiec and Zielona Góra. Upper Silesia is noted for its heavy engineering products. Electrical machinery is also produced here, as well as in Warsaw, Łódź and Wrocław. Elbląg makes turbo-generators.

The vehicle industry is still of rather modest dimensions when compared with Poland's relatively large population; this is a reflection of the low priority hitherto given to the production of passenger cars (only 21,000 produced in 1964). The main plant for the latter is at Żerań, north of Praga, in right-bank Warsaw. West of the capital tractors are made in the industrial satellite of Ursus. The chief producers of lorries are Starachowice and Lublin. Some small towns in the south are also of note: Jelcz (south-east of Wrocław) for buses and heavy lorries, Nysa (south-west of Opole) for vans and minibuses and Sanok (in the Carpathians) for buses. Motor-cycles, scooters and pedal cycles are variously made in Bydgoszcz, Kielce, Świdnik (near Lublin), Szczecin and Wrocław.

The chemical industry is well developed and chiefly depends on a number of domestic resources. Coke-ovens and non-ferrous metal-smelters provide chemical by-products in the Upper Silesian coalfield and there are coal-chemical plants at Kędzierzyn (fertilizers) and nearby Blachownia and Zdzieszowice, to the north-west of the coalfield, and Oświęcim (plastics, synthetic rubber and petrol) to the south-east. Rubber industries are found in Bydgoszcz, Kraków and Poznań. Olsztyn will become a large centre of tyre production. Dyestuffs and other chemicals needed in the textile trades are produced at Zgierz, near Łódź. Salt has been mined for centuries south of Kraków and activity still continues at Wieliczka and Bochnia. Salt and limestone provide a basis for chemical industries in the Kraków area. South of Bydgoszcz there is salt-mining and brine-extraction in the Wapno–Inowrocław area and near the latter town there is the production of soda ash. Another salt-mining district is south of Włocławek at Kłodawa. At Tarnów natural gas is used in the making of fertilizers and synthetic fibres and Puławy (north-west of Lublin, on the Vistula), also using natural gas, is now becoming an even greater producer of fertilizers. Szczecin makes phosphatic fertilizers with imported materials. In the Sandomierz depression one of the world's largest deposits of sulphur has recently been opened up near Tarnobrzeg (295,000 tons by sulphur content in 1964) and a surplus is available for export, a large part of which goes to Czechoslovakia. Petrochemical products are derived from the complex at Płock processing Soviet oil. In the building industry cement-making is concentrated in or near the limestone districts of the south, chiefly the Lublin Plateau, the Kielce–Radom area, Opole (Cretaceous marls) and Upper Silesia–Kraków.

Distribution of Population and Chief Cities

In 1931 60% of the total population and 64% of the active population were dependent on agriculture. By 1964 these figures had fallen to 38 and 43% respectively, chiefly as a result of the intense industrialization drive after the Second World War. The percentage of the active population engaged in industry (including construction and mining) more than doubled, from 12 in 1931 to 26 in 1964, while the percentage of persons living in towns rose from 27 to 48.

Generally speaking the distribution of population reflects natural conditions for agriculture on the one hand and the pattern of urban centres on the other. In view of the wide distribution of fertile soils in the south-east it is not surprising that fairly high rural densities should have developed in an area bounded approximately by a line Lublin–Radom–Kielce–Kraków. However, holdings are small and usually fragmented, and rural overpopulation was rife here in the inter-war period. Similar conditions prevailed in the adjacent areas to the east, now included in the Soviet Ukraine. The migration of settlers to the Regained Territories between 1945 and 1950 and the movement of others to new industrial employment in their own locality or elsewhere in Poland have reduced this problem, however.

Rural densities tend to be lower in the remainder of the country, with certain exceptions, such as parts of the newly-settled loess lands of the Silesian Plain or intensive market-gardening districts near the cities. The north-east and north-west, where the cultivable area is locally reduced by morainic hills, lakes, marshes or forests, have particularly low densities. Cities such as Szczecin, Białystok and Olsztyn are major urban concentrations commanding wide and thinly-populated hinterlands. The bulk of Poland's population thus lies south of a line Zielona Góra–Poznań–Warsaw–Lublin. A salient extends northwards to embrace the lower Vistula area, including Bydgoszcz and Toruń (40 km/25 miles apart) and the Gdańsk–Gdynia conurbation (*Trójmiasto*).

Most cities and towns, with the chief exception of mining and textile centres, are service centres of varying order of importance, ranging from small administrative and market-towns to major regional cities, such as Kraków, Poznań or Wrocław. Within the last twenty years, however, many have also become manufacturing towns as well. A special problem has arisen in connection with those small towns where industrial development has, for various reasons, not been practicable. These have often stagnated or even declined, as a result of losing many of their service functions. Many of their small shopkeepers, middlemen and craftsmen were Jewish and thus perished during the Second World War. The reorganization of trade into larger units under state auspices was also partly responsible.

There are two leading urban groupings. The first is the Warsaw–Łódź group, consisting of the two largest cities, each with a number of satellites. Some of the latter stretch in a line south-westwards from Warsaw for almost half the distance to Łódź (120 km/75 miles away from the capital). The second grouping is the Upper Silesia–Kraków area, involving the largest conurbation and the third largest city. Katowice, the largest city of the former, is not much more than 70 km/45 miles from Kraków. This second group may be regarded as the central component of a southern axis extending westwards to Opole and Wrocław and eastwards to Tarnów and Rzeszów. Along the lines of communication linking the Warsaw–Łódź area to Katowice and Kraków are several intervening towns such as Częstochowa, Radom and Kielce. The distribution of towns with over 20,000 inhabitants is shown in Fig. 46.

Rapid industrial development, the great housing shortage and cheap workers' travel facilities have resulted in a large volume of commuting from rural areas to factories and offices. Often a peasant holding is looked after by the womenfolk and elderly men. In 1960 more than 1 million persons were classified as simultaneously working in both the agricultural and non-agricultural sectors. But despite the great changes that have taken place it is still broadly true that the old Russian and Austrian territories have a higher proportion of the population committed to agriculture than the former German territories (i.e. both 1914 German Poland and the Regained Territories, settled after 1945), with the exception, however, of Polish East Prussia (Olsztyn voivodship). A north–south line from Elbląg through Łódź to Kraków very approximately divides Poland into a 'more agricultural' east (including, admittedly, the major anomaly of Warsaw) and a 'less agricultural' west. Moreover, within the former the importance of agriculture tends to increase eastwards; the three voivodships of Białystok, Lublin and Rzeszów each have about 60% of their populations dependent on agriculture.

Finally it must be noted that there is a striking difference in rates of

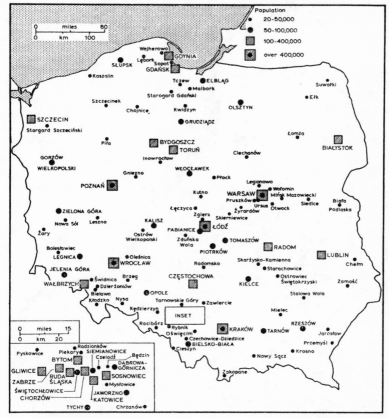

Fig. 46. Distribution of chief cities and towns in Poland

natural increase between the Regained Territories and the rest of the country. This results from the high birth-rates and low death-rates associated with the youthful settler populations of the former. For a number of years the natural increase rate was half as large again as that for the nation as a whole, which itself was at a very high level by European standards (18–20 per 1,000) until the late 1950s. Since then the national rate has fallen (11 in 1964), owing to a fall in the birth-rate, and so have rates in the Regained Territories, while still remaining higher than the national rate, however.

WARSAW (*Warszawa*) (Fig. 47) (1,241,000 in 1964) developed as a major urban centre much later than the two earlier capitals, Poznań and Kraków. While there is evidence of small settlements in the neighbourhood in early medieval times, the first mention of the town of Warsaw

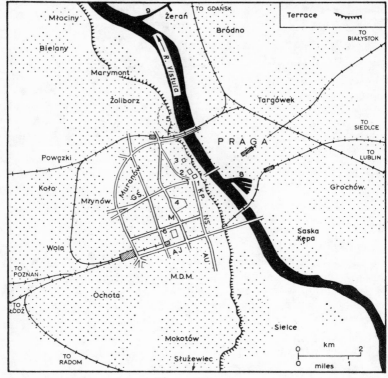

Fig. 47. Warsaw

Key: 1. Site of former Royal Palace. **2.** Old Town Square (Rynek Starego Miasta). **3.** New Town Square (Rynek Nowomiejski). **4.** Saxon Gardens (Ogród Saski). **5.** Site of former Russian citadel. **6.** Palace of Culture and Science (Pałac Kultury i Nauki). **7.** Łazienki Park. **8.** Old river port. **9.** New river port and Żerań–Zegrze canal.

AJ–Aleje Jerozolimskie. **AU**–Aleje Ujazdowskie. **GS**–General K. Świerczewski. **KP**–Krakowskie Przedmieście. **M**–Marszałkowska. **NS**–Nowy Świat.

does not occur until the 14th century. It was then a market-town and river-port, with a castle of the Mazovian princes. The town was situated on the left (west) bank of the Vistula at the top of a high terrace falling away some 30 m/100 ft to the river below. The right bank of the river was lower, with sandbanks and marshes. In the 15th century a twin settlement, the New Town (*Nowe Miasto*), developed immediately to the north of the Old Town (*Stare Miasto*). In the 16th century Warsaw grew to importance; Mazovia was now fully incorporated into Poland, and the union of Poland with Lithuania resulted in the meeting of the joint diet at Warsaw and in the Polish kings being elected at nearby Wola, since Warsaw was more geographically central than Kraków for the two countries. A permanent bridge was now built across the river to the village of Praga on the opposite bank. At the end of the 16th century Sigismund (Zygmunt) III moved with his court from Kraków and thus Warsaw became the new capital. The old Mazovian castle, situated immediately south of the Old Town, was rebuilt for the Polish kings in the early 17th century, and the nobility built a number of mansions.

In the 1650s Warsaw's development suffered a setback owing to the Swedish invasion, but the 18th century was a period of rapid growth. The two Saxon kings of Poland (August II and III) encouraged a programme of building and town-planning with the aid of Dresden architects, and the Saxon Gardens, to the south-west of the Old Town, also date from this period. Their successor and last king, Poniatowski, was also a patron of the arts. By the 1790s Warsaw was a city of about 100,000. Southwards from the Old Town the thoroughfare called *Krakowskie Przedmieście* ('Kraków suburb') and its extension *Nowy Świat* ('New World') contained palaces of the nobility, merchants' houses and fine churches, while still further south were the royal Łazienki and Wilanów Palaces and their parks. The commercial life of the city remained largely concentrated in the Old and New Towns. The buildings of the late 18th century were faithfully recorded by Canaletto, and at the end of the Second World War his paintings were to be of inestimable value in the rebuilding of the city.

Between 1815 and 1830 Warsaw was the capital of the autonomous 'Congress Kingdom'. Much new building took place in this period and small industrial establishments developed near the river and on the periphery. After 1830 Warsaw ceased to be a capital, but it nevertheless grew rapidly as a centre of commerce and light industry (including engineering and textiles), especially after the building of railways from 1845 onwards. These reinforced Warsaw's geographical nodality. Urban growth was hampered to the north of the city by a Russian citadel, but great expansion took place westwards. Here were the large Jewish quarter, Muranów, with its small-scale commerce and handicrafts, and the industrial district of Wola, close to the railway lines. Southwards there was better-class residential development, the *Aleje Ujazdowskie* becoming a 'Champs-Élysées'. In the central part of the city a new north–south axis, *Marszałkowska*, developed, and the district between this and the earlier north–south axis became the commercial heart of modern Warsaw. Across the river Praga grew rapidly as an industrial and working-class suburb, with the railway termini for the east being located here. By 1914 the population of the city exceeded 800,000, but overcrowding and lack of proper planning confronted Warsaw with a legacy of problems when once more it became the capital of an independent country in 1918. In the inter-war period the population rose to 1·3 millions and there was considerable expansion of the built-up area; for instance at Żoliborz to the north (a development made possible by the demolition of the old Russian citadel), at Mokotów to the south, and at Saska Kępa, south of Praga.

Warsaw was severely damaged by German air attacks prior to its capture in September 1939, but an even greater scale of destruction was yet to come. In 1943 there was a rising in the walled-in Jewish ghetto that the Germans had created in Muranów and from which Jews were sent to death camps. The rising was put down and the area completely levelled. The following year the Polish underground Home Army in Warsaw began a rising against the German forces that lasted from August to October. This rising was crushed with enormous loss of life, the surviving population was evicted and the left-bank city was systematic-ally blown up. Soviet armed forces, who had reached Praga during the rising, eventually liberated the derelict city in January 1945. Left-bank Warsaw had a residual population of only 22,000 compared with over 1 million in 1939. Never before had a major city of this size experienced such a scale of loss of life and physical destruction. Several hundred thousand inhabitants (including most of the 350,000 Jews) perished between 1939 and 1944 and over three-quarters of the city was in ruins, although Praga was not so heavily damaged.

An important feature of the rebuilding of Warsaw has been the faithful restoration of the historic areas of the Old and New Towns and also of many of the Baroque and Classical palaces and churches. At the same time the destruction of the city provided an opportunity for replanning the main arteries. Marszałkowska has been widened and extended north-wards to intersect with a new west–east thoroughfare (*General K. Świerczewski*) that reaches a rebuilt ('*Silesia–Dąbrowa*') bridge over the Vistula by means of a tunnel under the Old Town. This route matches the pre-existing west–east thoroughfare to the south of Marszałkowska (*Aleje Jerozolimskie*), giving access to the *Poniatowski* bridge. Recently a more northerly west–east route has been completed, leading to the rebuilt *Gdańsk* bridge. The destruction resulting from the 1943 and 1944 risings meant the disappearance of some of the older high-density residential areas of the central part of the city, and rebuilding has thus been at a lower density. On the levelled rubble of the Muranów ghetto a large new housing district sprang up soon after the war and another rebuilt area is 'M.D.M.' at the southern end of Marszałkowska. In addi-tion to the rebuilding of the central areas further peripheral development of the city has also taken place.

Warsaw continues to be an important centre of light industry and engineering. New industrial districts have developed to the north, at Młociny, on the left bank (plant for special steel), Żerań, on the right bank (motor-cars), and to the south at Służewiec (light industry). Old industrial quarters still exist in Wola and Praga. Despite an enlargement of the administrative area to take in suburban districts, the population of Warsaw will probably not reach the 1939 level until the late 1960s. There is a large volume of commuting to the city, especially from small towns and villages along the main railway routes. Spasmodic urban development extends south-westwards for over 40 km/25 miles, as far as Żyrardów (textiles), passing through Ursus (tractors) and Pruszków (engineering). Similar ribbons of development extend northwards and southwards of Praga to Legionowo and Otwock. The old river-port for barge traffic in Praga has now been superseded by facilities at Żerań, where the new canal from Zegrze, on the Bug, reaches the Vistula.

BIAŁYSTOK (134,000) was chiefly known for its Baroque palace of the Branicki family before the 19th century. After 1806 the town lay just inside Russia, and the availability of its large market encouraged the growth of small-scale textile activities (chiefly woollens) in Białystok and nearby villages. A further stimulus was given after the collapse of the Polish rising of 1830–1, when entrepreneurs and workers from the Łódź area moved here owing to the effect of Russia's economic reprisals against the 'Congress Kingdom' and its export trade to Russia. Eventually steam-power superseded hand methods or water-power in the larger establishments and Białystok, with its main railway communications, became the most important member of the group. On the eve of the First World War nearly half of its population was Jewish and many of the entrepreneurs were German in origin. Between the wars there was some rationalization of the industry, especially as new markets had to be found outside Russia. In the Second World War much of the town, especially the areas built of wood, was destroyed and the Jewish inhabitants exterminated. The composition of the population has thus changed, and a more prepossessing Białystok has taken shape as a result of rebuilding. The textile sector is now relatively less important than previously, and the chief emphasis is on cottons today. Engineering industries have also been developed.

BYDGOSZCZ (250,000), founded in the middle ages, is the chief town of Kujawy. Situated on the Brda, a few miles above its confluence with the Vistula, it is an important centre of inland navigation because of its position at the eastern end of the Bydgoszcz canal, which links the Brda to the Noteć. The town was destroyed by the Swedes in 1656 and became part of Prussia at the time of the partitions. In the second half of the

19th century it developed as a well-laid-out city with expanding commerce and industry, although by 1918 it had become considerably Germanized (*Bromberg*). It is also the most important centre in Poland for
the timber-handling and timber machinery industries. Since the Second
World War it has grown rapidly and has a diversified industrial structure,
including bicycles, chemicals (rubber and photographic), cables, electronic
engineering and boat-building.

CZĘSTOCHOWA (173,000) lies on the left (west) bank of the upper
Warta in the Jurassic limestone country of Lesser Poland. The town is
dominated by the hill known as Jasna Góra ('Shining Mountain') on
which is situated the famous monastery church revered all over Poland
as a place of pilgrimage, because of a famous painting of the Virgin (to
which miracles are attributed) and also because of the triumphant
resistance against a Swedish siege in 1655. Jasna Góra thus symbolizes
both Catholicism and national independence. Częstochowa has cotton
textile industries (developed in the 1860s) and there has also been a large
expansion since the Second World War of the iron and steel industry,
located just outside the built-up area of the town. Other industries
include engineering, glass, paper and foodstuffs.

KRAKÓW (509,000) is situated on the north (left) bank of the upper
Vistula and commands a broad west–east passage-way in southern
Poland between the Uplands of Lesser Poland to the north and the
Beskids and Carpathians to the south. Ancient routes from Kraków thus
led north-westwards to the Odra basin, south-westwards to the Moravian
Gate, north-eastwards to central Poland by means of the Vistula valley,
and eastwards to the Ukraine. The city also commanded vital passes
through the Carpathians to the south. The Wawel Hill, a small eminence
undercut by the meandering Vistula, became an early Polish stronghold,
eventually to be crowned by the famous castle and cathedral that still
survive after centuries of change. Kraków succeeded Poznań as capital
in the early 14th century and from then on until Warsaw became capital
at the end of the 16th century it enjoyed a period of expansion and
prosperity. Even after the transfer Kraków continued to be the place
where kings were crowned and buried. The flowering of Kraków is particularly associated with Casimir the Great, who, in 1364, laid the foundations of what later became the great Jagiellonian University. Later
Kraków was a focus of Renaissance enlightenment, and it was also an
important centre of Jewish culture. In 1794 the Market Place was the
starting point for Kósciuszko's insurrection against the partitioning
powers. In 1815 Kraków and the surrounding district became an independent neutral city-state, but this was annexed to Austria in 1846.
Kraków had again become a leading centre of Polish culture by the end

of the 19th century, as a result of the more liberal policy of Austria compared with Prussia and Russia. The city also grew in size, the old walls being dismantled and replaced by an encircling boulevard. Industrial development was relatively weak, however.

During the Second World War Kraków was the capital of the non-annexed part of German-occupied Poland. Fortunately, although the Jewish population was killed, the city itself suffered little physical damage and so the Market Place, with St Mary's church and the Cloth Hall, as well as the cathedral and castle on the Wawel, have survived as important symbols of medieval and Renaissance Poland. The most important post-war change has been the rapid growth, since 1950, of the planned industrial community of Nowa Huta, located next to the enormous new 'Lenin' iron and steel works. By 1964 the population had already reached 125,000. Although lying about 10 km/6 miles to the east, Nowa Huta is included within the extended limits of the city. Other industries include foodstuffs, chemical engineering, rubber, cables and pharmaceutical products. Chemical industries, based largely on the nearby salt and limestone deposits, are also important. Kraków is the second cultural centre in Poland after Warsaw.

ŁÓDŹ (737,000) was a mere village in the early 19th century, but by 1914 it was an industrial city of half a million inhabitants. The government of the Congress Kingdom persuaded German textile workers (wool and flax) to settle here in the 1820s. For several decades production was either by hand methods or water-power, using small local streams. With the development of railways the growing mass markets of the Russian Empire, especially for cotton textiles, provided a powerful incentive to further growth. Steam-driven factories, many of them owned by German immigrants and using cheap labour from the countryside, became important, even though the nearest source of coal was 160 km/100 miles away in the Dąbrowa field. A large Jewish population was also attracted. Łódź developed in a largely unplanned manner, with few amenities, and thus presented independent Poland with problems of sanitation and housing. Excess capacity in the textile industries, as a result of the loss of the Russian market, was also a problem between the wars. The Jewish minority was exterminated in the Second World War and unassimilated members of the German-speaking minority expelled by liberated Poland at its conclusion. Łódź is still one of Europe's great textile cities, some 135,000 persons (60% women) being employed in textiles (chiefly cotton, but also wool, knitwear and clothing). There are also several satellite towns, including Aleksandrów, Konstantynów, Pabianice and Zgierz (dyestuffs and woollens). Since the Second World War there have been measures to increase engineering employment (hitherto chiefly concerned with textile machinery) in order to provide more varied male employment. Electrical engineering has thus become important. Łódź has also been transformed into an educational and cultural centre as a result of the founding of a new university and the setting-up of film studios and the internationally-famous Film School. The watershed site of Łódź, drained by the headstreams of the Pilica, Warta and Bzura, today presents problems of adequate water supply, especially for the textile-finishing trades. Additional supplies now come by pipe from the Pilica.

LUBLIN (199,000) grew up on a loess-covered hill in the angle of confluence of a small tributary with the Bystrzyca. It commanded a number of old trading routes and achieved additional importance as a result of the signing here of the Act of Union between Poland and Lithuania in 1569 and the holding here, for a period, of the united diet. At this time much of the town was rebuilt in a Renaissance style, but from the middle of the 17th century Lublin declined as a result of the Swedish wars, reviving, however, in modern times. The old city is well preserved and is linked by a bridge with the Royal Castle on an adjoining eminence. The old Jewish quarter lying in between was demolished in the Second World War, however, many of the inhabitants perishing in the nearby Majdanek concentration camp. In 1944 Lublin was the seat of the Russian-supported provisional government of liberated Poland. Modern industries include food-processing and the manufacture of lorries and agricultural machinery. Lublin has both a state university and a Catholic university – the only one in Poland.

POZNAŃ (432,000), early capital of Poland and 10th-century cradle of Polish Christianity, is situated on the Warta. The first settlement was on the 'island' of Tum, lying in the angle of confluence of the Cybina with the Warta, and this site is still occupied by the cathedral. Later, after the Tatar invasion of 1241 and a great flood, the town was rebuilt on the other side of the Warta, on the left (west) bank. Thereafter it flourished as an important trading city, especially in the 15th and 16th centuries, when its magnificent Renaissance Town Hall was built, but it experienced some decline in the 17th as a result of the Swedish invasion. In 1793 it was annexed by Prussia and had undergone considerable Germanization (*Posen*) before it became part of newly-independent Poland in 1918. Between the two World Wars its pre-existing engineering industries expanded in scope and size, and Poznań also became the home of the annual Polish International Trade Fair. The city was damaged as a result of its siege by the Red Army early in 1945. Its well-developed engineering activities today include ships' engines, roller-bearings, agricultural machinery and electrical and railway engineering. Food-processing, rubber and clothing are also important.

RADOM (141,000) was an important medieval town at the junction of several trade routes. It has grown in modern times as a result of industrial development, involving engineering, munitions and footwear.

SZCZECIN (303,000) is situated on the Odra some 60 km/40 miles from the Baltic Sea. An early Slavonic settlement grew up on the high, left (west) bank of the river close to the lowest effective crossing point. Medieval Szczecin was a flourishing port of the Dukedom of Pomerania and it became a member of the Hanseatic League in 1360. By the Peace of Westphalia (1648) it passed to the Swedes and was ceded by them to Brandenburg in 1720, by which time it had already become strongly Germanized (*Stettin*). In the second half of the 19th century considerable growth took place in association with an improvement of inland waterway connections and the growth of railways, especially to Berlin and Silesia. A Free Port was established in the 1890s in an attempt to offset competition from Hamburg. There was also a growth of shipbuilding, engineering, the processing of sugar beet and grain from its agricultural hinterland, and the smelting of imported iron ore. Between the two World Wars Stettin suffered an economic setback as a result of increased competition from Hamburg and the loss of part of its hinterland to independent Poland. At the end of the Second World War, when the city came under Polish rule again after an interval of 800 years, much of it lay in ruins as a result of Allied air attacks.

Today Szczecin has recovered and has a new Polish population. The city looks down eastwards on to the Odra and across to several large islands (the chief being Łasztownia), where docks and shipyards are located. There are other shipyards and port facilities both upstream and downstream from the city on the left bank. Beyond the islands, further to the east, is Lake Dąbie, into which the Odra flows and whence it drains into the great Szczecin Lagoon, separated from the sea by the islands of Wolin and Uznam (the latter partly in East Germany). The main channel draining the lagoon runs between these two islands, and on Uznam is the outport of Świnoujście, established in the 19th century and now important for the handling of bulk cargoes and as a fishing base. Here and at other places seaside resorts are being developed. Świnoujście is served by a car-ferry from the Swedish port of Ystad. Szczecin has the following industries: iron-ore smelting, artificial fibres, fertilizers, paper, motor-cycles and marine engineering and shipbuilding. Its port now has the largest turnover in the whole of the Baltic area.

TORUŃ (112,000), situated on the right bank of the Vistula, became a stronghold of the Teutonic Knights in the 13th century (*Thorn*). In 1454 it reverted to Poland, while enjoying various privileges, and as a river-port for the shipment of grain, it became a member of the Hanseatic

League. It came under Prussian rule at the time of the Partitions. The inner town, with its varied architectural remains, is still partly surrounded by old fortifications and there are gates opening on to the river. Modern suburbs lie beyond the walls, and since 1945 Toruń has had a university (transplanted from Wilno). Industries include electrical equipment, fertilizers and synthetic fibres.

The TRÓJMIASTO ('Tri-city') is the name given to the three municipalities of Gdańsk (313,000), Gdynia (161,000) and Sopot (45,000). The whole forms a loosely-knit conurbation extending for some 30 km/ 20 miles from the northern boundary of Gdynia to the southern boundary of Gdańsk. The conurbation is further prolonged by Rumia to the north and Pruszcz to the south. Gdańsk grew up on the western margin of the Vistula delta on the left bank of the Motława, just above its confluence with the Martwa Wisła ('dead Vistula'), the main western distributary. This reaches the Bay of Gdańsk some four miles to the north. Immediately to the west the site of Gdańsk is overlooked by the edge of a morainic plateau, at the foot of which the canalized Radunia was used for mills in medieval times, so that the early city was almost an island lying between the Radunia and the Motława. Gdańsk was already the leading port of Poland in the early middle ages, but in 1308 it was taken by the Teutonic Knights and when restored to Poland, with self-governing privileges as a Hanseatic town, in 1466, it had become largely German in character (*Danzig*). In the 16th, 17th and early 18th centuries it enjoyed great prosperity as a result of its control of Poland's sea trade. Exports of grain were important. In 1793 it was taken by Prussia at the time of the Second Partition and remained in German hands until the end of the First World War. Under German rule it grew steadily but not dramatically. An outport, Nowy Port, was built at the mouth of the Martwa Vistula and later modern docks and shipyards were built on either side of the river just below the old town. In 1919 the League of Nations authorized the setting-up of a self-governing Free City of Danzig, including the immediate hinterland and most of the delta, but situated within the Polish customs area. While using and, indeed, further developing the facilities of Danzig, Poland nevertheless built a completely new port about 20 km/12½ miles to the north-west at Gdynia, lying in the 'Polish corridor'.

In the early 1920s Gdynia was only a small fishing village, but by 1939 it had become a city with a population of over 120,000, associated with a new port having the largest turnover of any on the Baltic. At Gdynia a broad marshy valley (a *pradolina*) ran out to sea between two slight promontories of morainic material (*Kępa Oksywska* to the north and *Kamienna Góra* to the south). Here the excavation for basins was easy and, moreover, the site was protected by the Hel peninsula. At the end of the Second World War the ports of Gdańsk and Gdynia had been put out of action by the retreating Germans and the old city of Gdańsk almost completely destroyed by the advancing Russians. Its German population had either fled or perished, and as a result the present population of Gdańsk, apart from a small surviving Polish minority, consists essentially of newcomers. The pre-war population has now been exceeded and the old city, with its rich architectural heritage in many styles, has been faithfully restored.

Both ports are now serving the expanding trade of Poland on a co-ordinated basis. Both handle incoming iron ore and outgoing coal, and both have shipyards, but Gdańsk, which has a specialization in trawlers, is the more important. Gdynia is the more important for fishing and also for the processing and warehousing of imported foodstuffs, and it is also the terminal for passenger liners. The turnover of Gdynia is greater than that of Gdańsk, but the latter may well become dominant in the future since it has greater room for harbour expansion in the Vistula delta. The conurbation is chiefly linear in character and lies at the foot of, or on the slopes of, a morainic plateau. A main road and an electric railway link the settlements together. The built-up area extends southwards from Gdańsk to Pruszcz and north-westwards through the large residential suburb of Wrzeszcz to Oliwa, both of which are part of Gdańsk. The line of settlement then continues through the seaside resort of Sopot and so to Gdynia and Rumia.

THE UPPER SILESIAN CONURBATION, the group of towns forming the core of the *Upper Silesian Industrial District* (*Górnośląski Okręg Przemysłowy* or *G.O.P.*), stretches for about 45 km/30 miles from west to east, with a maximum north–south span of about 15 km/10 miles. The conurbation has a population of about 1·6 millions (1962), but about 2 millions live in the entire planning district. The conurbation lies on the low plateau that forms the watershed between the Odra and Vistula drainage systems, the main headstreams being the Kłodnica (to the Odra) and the Brynica and Czarna ('Black') Przemsza (to the Vistula). These rivers and their small tributaries (the Bytomka at Zabrze or the Rawa at Katowice) are, however, little more than highly-polluted ditches. The Gliwice canal, replacing the smaller Kłodnica canal (early 19th century) in 1939, links Łabędy, just north of Gliwice, with Koźle on the Odra. Administratively the conurbation consists of seven large municipalities—Gliwice (147,000), Zabrze (200,000), Bytom (192,000), Ruda Śląska (139,000), Chorzów (153,000), Katowice (284,000), Sosno-wiec (138,000)—with a number of smaller ones lying in between them or on their margins, including Siemanowice, Świętochłowice, Dąbrowa

Górnicza, Mysłowice, Będzin and Czeladź. The larger municipalities often contain smaller towns within their limits as a result of 20th-century amalgamations. Thus Katowice includes Szopienice, Ruda includes Nowy Bytom, Bytom includes Bobrek, and Chorzów includes Hajduki and Królewska Huta (although the latter name is now suppressed).

The towns of the conurbation differ considerably in their origins and morphology, and also in the quality of housing and urban facilities. The towns lying in Russia before 1918 (e.g. Będzin, Dąbrowa Górnicza and Sosnowiec) are worse in this respect than those in the main part of the conurbation formerly lying in Germany. Gliwice and Bytom were medieval towns situated where the trade route between southern Poland and Silesia met that from Moravia. The centres of both retain a medieval street-pattern and both are fairly compact and well-laid-out towns, Gliwice being not unattractive compared with the other cities of Upper Silesia. Będzin and Czeladź, the former with an old castle overlooking the Czarna Przemsza, were also medieval foundations. On the other hand, Chorzów, Katowice, Ruda, Sosnowiec and Zabrze are essentially 19th-century creations and contain typical examples of amorphous, unplanned development where poor-quality housing is interspersed with mines and heavy industry. Chorzów enjoys the doubtful distinction of having the highest degree of air pollution in Poland. The intervening land between the built-up areas variously consists of patches of woodland (birch and pine), allotment gardens, derelict land, pit-heaps, and a few parks (including a large replanted area between Chorzów and Katowice). There are also sand-workings, from where sand is sent by mineral lines for filling in the coal mines as extraction proceeds. The whole area of this typical 19th-century 'Black Country' is served by an intricate maze of railways, tramways and power-lines.

There are serious problems of rehousing, land restoration, and ensuring an adequate water supply (in view of the watershed location and the pollution of underground water). New residential development just outside the conurbation (e.g. at Gołonog, Tychy, Pyskowice, Radzionków and Łabędy) is relieving the former problem, and a large reservoir at Goczałkowice on the upper Vistula has mitigated the water problem. A further question is the provision of adequate light industry in order to diversify the employment structure, especially for women. The solution of all these problems is facilitated by the fact that the whole of the Upper Silesian Industrial District is now being planned for the first time as one entity.

No one city completely dominates the whole conurbation, although Katowice is the leading administrative and cultural centre and its role is being deliberately enhanced. Gliwice is second in importance as regards scope of urban functions. Beyond the main built-up area are outlying industrial or coal-mining towns such as Chrzanów and Jaworzno to the south-east (both in the former Austrian territories), while to the north are Tarnowskie Góry and Piekary, medieval centres for lead, zinc and silver mining, and Zawiercie (steel). To the south and south-west, in a rural area, there are the more recent coal-mining settlements, especially around Rybnik. Kędzierzyn, to the west of *G.O.P.*, is an important centre of the heavy chemical industry, and so is Oświęcim to the south-east (better known as Auschwitz, where several million persons were exterminated during the Second World War in German concentration camps situated near its important railway junction).

WAŁBRZYCH (123,000), an amorphous coal-mining municipality, lies amongst the wooded foothills of the Sudets, at a height of about 450 m/1,500 ft above sea-level. Before the 19th century it was only a small village. After the Second World War many Polish miners and their families who had emigrated to the French coalfields between the wars returned to Poland to re-man the Wałbrzych mines after the departure of most of the German miners. There are coke-ovens and ceramic and engineering industries.

WROCŁAW (466,000) is situated in the heart of the fertile Silesian Plain, for which it has always acted as a regional focus. Here the River Odra divides into several channels and the earliest urban settlements, with their churches, were on two islands. The main part of the medieval town developed opposite, on the left (south) bank of the southernmost channel. After the Tatar invasion of 1241 the town was rebuilt with the aid of German settlers and it became an important ecclesiastical and market-centre, with craft industries and river traffic. With the rest of Silesia Wrocław passed to Bohemia in 1335 and, with Bohemia, it came under Habsburg rule in 1526. In 1741 it became part of Prussia and despite strong Germanization some Polish speakers could still be found in the 19th century. The town (German *Breslau*) grew rapidly at this time and developed a number of industries, the most important being that of railway rolling-stock. Foodstuffs, textiles and clothing were also represented.

At the close of the Second World War Wrocław, one of Germany's finest cities, was besieged and devastated by the Red Army, and rebuilding is not yet complete, although notable medieval buildings, such as the Cathedral and the Town Hall, have been restored. Many of the new Polish settlers were drawn from Lwów, whose university and other cultural institutions were likewise transferred to Wrocław. Wrocław's pre-existing industries, especially railway engineering, have been revived. Electrical and electronic equipment (including computers), artificial fibres and non-ferrous metallurgy are also represented. Wrocław is also a large railway node and has a river-port.

Transport and Trade

Poland's railway system was built chiefly during the period when she was partitioned. As a result, therefore, the lines that were laid down formed part of the networks of either Germany, Austria-Hungary or Russia. The density differed considerably in the Polish territories of the three Empires, the highest being found in German Poland (where the general level of economic development was highest) and the lowest in Russian Poland. Relatively few lines crossed the frontiers of the partitioning powers, owing to strategic considerations. German strategic policy was to build railway lines *to* the frontiers, however, while Russian policy was to avoid them. The Russian lines (with the exception of the main line from Upper Silesia to Warsaw) were broad gauge, in contrast to the standard gauge of Germany. Independent Poland therefore had the task of integrating the peripheral portions of three distinct networks into a coherent whole. Broad-gauge lines were converted and some new lines were built, including those between Poznań and Warsaw and between Upper Silesia and the new port of Gdynia. New stretches of line were also needed to connect Kraków and Lwów with Warsaw.

Further changes occurred after 1945, when Poland acquired additional parts of German territory, with a well-developed network, lying northwards and westwards of the inter-war boundaries, while in the east she lost territory with a sparse network to the Soviet Union. The length of railway lines taken from Germany was about twice that of the lines that were ceded – and on a smaller total area. Further adjustments have thus been necessary since 1945. Despite modifications in recent decades anyone presented with a railway map of contemporary Poland can easily sketch in the 1914 boundary of the old German Empire by noting where there is a sudden decline in the density of lines.

Although Warsaw was the main focus of lines in pre-1914 Russian Poland direct connections to the leading cities of Austrian and German Poland were not completed until the inter-war period, as we have seen. After 1945 Warsaw's nodality was affected by the westward shift of the frontier with the Soviet Union, while at the same time the annexation of the Regained Territories presented new problems of railway links with the capital. Thus the route from Wrocław to Warsaw is still rather a circuitous one. Warsaw's chief connections are as follows: (1) to Białystok (and then to Leningrad via Grodno and Vilnius), (2) to Siedlce (and thence to Moscow via Brest and Minsk), (3) to Lublin (for south-eastern Poland and also Kiev), (4) to Kraków, via Radom and Kielce, (5) to Łódź and, via Częstochowa, to Upper Silesia, (6) to Poznań (for Frankfurt-on-Oder and Berlin), and (7) to Gdańsk, either direct or via Toruń and Bydgoszcz. Important lines not radiating from Warsaw include the main southern axis, Wrocław–Katowice–Kraków, and its extensions westwards to Germany and eastwards to the Ukraine, the route along the Baltic coastal plain from Szczecin to Gdańsk and the Sczecin–Poznań–Wrocław line. Southwards from Katowice a very important route leads to Ostrava and thence, by the Moravian Gate, to Vienna, with branches from the Moravian corridor for Prague and Budapest. Most of the leading provincial cities are important traffic nodes, but Łódź is rather weak in this respect, although it is now the most centrally-placed city of Poland. Since the Second World War there has developed a considerable traffic across Poland, both commercial and military, between the Soviet Union and East Germany, and a new line running south of Warsaw enables the capital to be by-passed. In recent years electrification of some of the main lines has been carried out, viz. Warsaw–Łódź, Warsaw–Katowice, Warsaw–Poznań, Katowice–Wrocław, Katowice–Kraków–Soviet border and Katowice–Czech border. The 'coal-line' from Katowice to Gdynia, via Bydgoszcz, is also being electrified, as well as the line from Łódź to Wałbrzych, via Wrocław. There are also some electrified local lines radiating from Warsaw, and an electric line links Gdańsk to Gdynia. By 1964 over 1,800 km/1,100 miles had been electrified and further lines are still being converted.

The railways carry 60% of Poland's internal freight (in ton–km), although road traffic is growing. Over one-third of all railway freight is accounted for by coal and coke. Passenger traffic is also high on the railways, especially as private motoring is still at a low level (only 156,000 private cars in 1963), although there are over 1 million motor-bicycles and scooters. The road network still leaves much to be desired. Internal air traffic is also growing, especially between the capital and the leading cities, and there is an international airport at Okęcie, south of Warsaw. Kraków and Poznań also have some international flights.

Inland waterways have a long history. For many centuries the Vistula and Odra have been used by small craft, and Gdańsk was once noted for its exports of grain brought down the river from the loess lands of the south, including the western Ukraine, formerly part of Poland. Low water in the summer and freezing for part of the winter have always hampered navigation on both rivers, however. Canals have been built at various times since the 18th century. In the 1770s the Noteć was linked by the Bydgoszcz canal to the Brda, a tributary of the Vistula, and the Pina, a tributary of the Pripyat', was connected to the Muchawiec, a tributary of the Bug. This canal, once known as the 'Royal Canal', is now in the Soviet Union and called the Dnepr–Bug canal. It has recently been enlarged. Water links created in the 19th century include the Kłodnica canal (from Koźle, on the Odra, to Zabrze in the Upper Silesian coal-basin), the Augustów canal (connecting the Biebrza with the Czarna Hańcza, a tributary of the Neman), the Upper Noteć canal (from the Bydgoszcz canal to Lake Gopło), and the Elbląg canal.

Developments in the present century include the replacement of the small and moribund Kłodnica canal by the much larger Gliwice canal (1939) and a canal from Lake Gopło to the Warta (1949). In the 1960s a drainage canal was built on the western margins of the Pripyat' Marshes from the Krzna to the Wieprz. More important is the new canal between the Bug–Narew confluence (Dębe dam and Zegrze lake) and Żerań. This is part of a long-term programme involving the modernization of water links with the Soviet Union, via the lower Bug and the old Royal Canal, and the regulation of the whole length of the Vistula itself for improved navigation and water supply. The Włocławek dam is part of this project. Ukrainian iron ore and coking coal may one day thus be able to reach Nowa Huta by water. Various navigational improvements, including also the building of new reservoirs in addition to the existing ones at Otmuchów and Turawa, are proceeding on the Odra, which has links to the rivers Havel and Spree in East Germany. There are also plans for a connection between the Kłodnica canal and the Upper Vistula and for a new 'Central Canal' between the latter and the middle Vistula (near Włocławek). This would link opposite sides of a 'water-ring' formed of the Odra, Vistula and Noteć, which would cater for craft of 500–1,000 tons and also redistribute water supplies. A further project is the long-deferred canal between the Odra and the Morava, giving a connection from the Baltic to the Danube and thus to the Black Sea.

The present volume of traffic on Poland's waterways is unimpressive when compared with that on the Elbe, let alone the Rhine, and it accounts for less than 1% of all internal freight traffic. The chief com-modities carried are fuels, agricultural produce, building materials and some imported ores trans-shipped at Szczecin for Upper Silesia, Czecho-slovakia and East Germany. In the northern lakes region the floating of timber is locally important.

Practically all of Poland's sea-borne trade is carried out through the three major ports of Gdańsk, Gdynia and Szczecin (including Świnoujście). The minor ports, which are very small by comparison, include Kołobrzeg, Darłowo and Ustka. Władysławowo, Hel and Łeba are small fishing ports. The tonnage of merchandise handled by the three large ports in 1964 was about 27 million tons, the largest individual items being exports of coal and coke (7·9) and timber (0·8) and imports of ores (3·5) and grain (3·7). Szczecin had the largest turnover (11·0), followed by Gdynia (8·9) and Gdańsk (6·7). All three handle the major commodities noted above, but Szczecin has by far the largest transit traffic to and from other countries, particularly Czechoslovakia, East Germany and Hungary. Poland's merchant fleet (853,000 gross registered tons in 1964) has grown rapidly since the Second World War, but is, however, no larger than those of some smaller nations, such as Finland or Jugoslavia. Several state-owned shipping lines operate to distant parts of the world and their increasing activity reflects the widening scope of Poland's foreign trade. Gdynia is the chief passenger port. Despite the importance of sea traffic the greater part of Poland's foreign trade is conducted by land-routes (rail, road and pipe-line).

Before the Second World War Poland's trade with the Soviet Union was negligible; today it accounts for about one-third of total foreign trade. The Soviet Union supplies iron ore, petroleum, cotton and supplementary supplies of coking coal. The proportion of trade with the Socialist countries as a whole amounts to over 60%. Czechoslovakia and East Germany are the next largest partners after the Soviet Union. Amongst West European countries the leading place is held by Great Britain, together with West Germany (despite an absence of diplomatic relations). The USA is a leading supplier of grain.

The structure of foreign trade has also undergone a change. Before 1939 Poland's chief exports were coal and foodstuffs, together with some timber, cotton textiles and metals. These have all remained important— indeed, in the immediate post-war period coal shipments for a time accounted for over half the export trade. Today, however, machinery (including ships, rolling-stock, machine-tools and complete factory installations) accounts for about one-third of all exports (1964). On the other hand, machinery also accounts for about one-third of all imports.

TABLE 10

FOREIGN TRADE OF POLAND, 1964
(Percentages for chief categories)

Category	Exports	Imports	Category
Machinery	33·4	30·6	Machinery
Coal and coke	15·2	8·5	Fuels (esp. petroleum)
Metals (iron, steel, zinc)	8·1	16·2	Metals and ores
Chemicals	3·7	6·7	Chemicals (including rubber)
Foodstuffs	18·7	15·3	Foodstuffs (grain and tropical)
Consumers' manufactures (esp. textiles)	12·4	5·4	Consumers' manufactures
		8·7	Textile fibres
Wood and products	2·7	2·0	Wood and products

Source: Mały Rocznik Statystyczny, 1965

Table 10 shows the surplus in coal and the deficit in petroleum, and also the extent to which Poland has become an importer of raw materials and exporter of finished or semi-finished products. Foodstuffs (e.g. bacon, butter, eggs, ham, vodka) remain a valuable export, however. With a rapidly-growing population, an increasing bill for food imports, especially grain and tropical produce, and a not particularly buoyant market for her coal outside Eastern Europe, it is only to be expected that the new emphasis on exports of engineering goods and other manufactures, as well as chemical products, will increase still further in the future. Markets for these are being sought in the developing countries of the Near East and the tropics, usually on the basis of bilateral agreements involving the import of raw materials or foodstuffs. Tourist receipts are not large for a country of Poland's size, although attempts are being made to increase these. Sopot on the Baltic and Zakopane in the Tatras are the best-known resort towns, but by international standards they are rather small.

Chapter 9

RUMANIA · ROMÂNIA

Introduction

Rumania may be likened to a sphere with a diameter of about 525 km/325 miles. Its shape is slightly flattened in the north, however, and there are two projecting salients—a small one to the west beyond Arad and Timişoara and a larger one to the south-east consisting of the Danube delta and the Dobrogea Platform. The country is adjoined on the north and east by the Soviet Union, on the south by Bulgaria, on the south-west by Jugoslavia and on the north-west by Hungary. On the south-east, bordering the Black Sea, there is a coastline over 200 km/125 miles long, which includes the Danube delta and the spits, lagoons and cliffs of the Dobrogea. Rumania consists of a low central plateau encircled by the Carpathians and three outer plains flanking the latter—the Tisa Plain to the west (i.e. the eastern margins of the Pannonian Plain), the Moldavian Platform to the east, and the Danubian or Wallachian Plain to the south and south-east. Further to the south-east is the Dobrogea Platform. Northwards the Carpathians extend across the frontier into the Soviet Ukraine, while to the south-west they continue into north-eastern Jugoslavia across the Danube, which has here cut a winding gorge through them.

To the east and the south Rumania's frontiers adhere to river and coast, if we exclude the land frontier with Bulgaria that crosses the southern part of the rather thinly-populated Dobrogea Platform. The eastern frontier with the Soviet Union successively follows the Prut, the lower Danube immediately above its delta, and then the northern, Chilia, distributary. To the south the Danube acts as the border with both Bulgaria and Jugoslavia. To the west, however, the remaining part of the border with Jugoslavia and the entire length of the border with Hungary run through the eastern margins of the Pannonian Plain and thus cross a number of rivers flowing westwards to the Tisa and Danube, such as the Criş, Mureş and Timiş. To the north the border runs through the forested Carpathians and partly follows the Suceava and the upper Tisa.

The present frontiers date from the end of the Second World War. Rumania's frontiers have undergone a number of changes since 1859, when the two Turkish vassal-states of Moldavia and Wallachia united to

283

form Rumania. In 1878, after Turkey's defeat by Russia and Rumania,
Rumania gained the Danube delta and the greater part of the Dobrogea
from Turkey. In 1913 she gained the southern part of the Dobrogea from
Bulgaria after the Second Balkan War.

At the end of the First World War Rumania, as an ally of the Western
Powers, obtained large territories from the Habsburg Empire of Austria–
Hungary. Transylvania, Crişana, Maramures, and part of the Banat were
annexed from Hungary, and most of the Bucovina from Austria (Fig. 48).

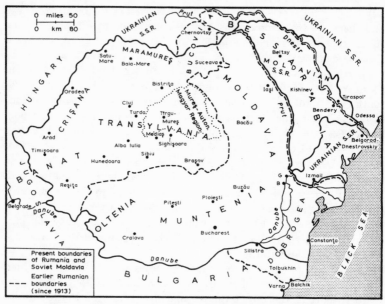

Fig. 48. Changes in the boundaries of Rumania since 1913

This latter territory, a part of old Moldavia, had been taken by Austria
from Turkey in 1774. To the east territory was gained from Russia, when
Bessarabia, the part of old Moldavia lying between the Prut and the
Dnestr that had been taken by Russia from Turkey in 1812, broke away
during the Revolutionary period and, after an initial declaration of
independence, subsequently sought union with Rumania. As a result of
all these gains Rumania more than doubled in area and population.

In 1940, when deprived of Western support owing to the Second World
War, Rumania was forced to yield large areas to her neighbours. First
of all the Soviet Union compelled her to surrender Bessarabia and the
northern part of the Bucovina (the latter admittedly with a considerable
Ukrainian population). Shortly afterwards Germany and Italy forced

Rumania to retrocede to Hungary large parts of Crişana and Transylvania as well as all of Maramureş. These territories formed a large wedge extending into the heart of the country as far as the Carpathian curve. Thirdly, Bulgaria, also with the support of Germany and Italy, regained the southern Dobrogea by the Treaty of Craiova. The losses to Hungary proved to be of short duration, however, since the areas concerned were restored to Rumania by the Soviet Union at the end of the war. The Soviet Union and Bulgaria both retained their gains, however.

The origin of the Rumanian people is a problem that still fascinates historian and philologist alike. The consensus of opinion seems to be that they may well represent the descendants of the Roman and Romanized population of the lower Danubian plains, the Banat and Transylvania who, after the withdrawal of Roman power, were able to resist extinction or absorption by later invaders as a result of their retreat into the relative safety of the Carpathian zone. It is also likely, however, that some of the population retreated southwards across the Danube with the Roman legions. When more settled conditions eventually prevailed, the Carpathian 'Rumanians' were able to take up permanent settlement in the surrounding lowlands, where small pockets of their fellow-countrymen may, indeed, have survived. Until recently the official Hungarian view was that the original Romanized population never retained such a mountain homeland and that the present Rumanians are descended from groups of Romanized immigrants who moved in at a much later date from south of the Danube. According to this view their penetration into Transylvania must have post-dated the establishment of Magyar control there, which took place as early as the 11th century. Such an argument was formerly used to support Hungary's title to Transylvania despite its large Rumanian population.

It is true that even today there are small residual groups of people in the Balkans speaking Romance dialects akin to Rumanian. Frequently they follow pastoral pursuits in upland areas. They are usually known to other peoples as 'Vlachs',* a name also applied to the Rumanians, but not used by them to describe themselves. Thus the Latinized name 'Wallachia', used to designate the Danubian lowlands of Rumania, is a geographical name used only by foreigners. To the Rumanians Wallachia is 'Ţara Românească' (i.e. the 'Rumanian land'), consisting of Oltenia ('Little Wallachia'), west of the Olt, and Muntenia ('Great Wallachia'), lying between the Olt and the lower Siret. The very name 'Muntenia' is

---

* The word *Vlach*, *Vlah*, or variants, is a Slavonic form of a generic term applied by the Germanic peoples to Roman provincials and other 'strangers'. The *Walloons* of Belgium derive their name in this way, and, although a Celtic-speaking area, *Wales* also has the same origin. It may be noted that Italy itself is still known to the Poles as *Włochy*.

held by the Rumanians to indicate their mountain (i.e. Carpathian) antecedents. The Wallachian (Danubian) Plain is usually known as the Rumanian Plain.

Whatever the precise details of their early history the Rumanians undoubtedly represent the largest group of descendants of the Romanized Lower Danubian and Balkan peoples. While the idea of some continuous occupance of the Carpathian area in the Dark Ages now seems generally accepted, there may well have been later supplementation of the Rumanian stock from areas south of the Danube. It is nevertheless rather surprising that south of the Danube Slavonic infiltration led in time to the almost complete absorption of the surviving Romanized population, while north of the Danube, where, ironically, the Roman occupation had been much shorter (little more than 150 years), the Latin tongue eventually prevailed after successfully resisting or absorbing later influences, including the Slavonic. Many Slavonic words are, however, found in Rumanian, especially for agricultural terms, and others have been deliberately discarded in the last hundred years. Many place-names are also Slavonic. Words of Hungarian, Greek, Turkish and Albanian origin can also be detected. (Albanian is probably descended from the pre-Roman speech of the Balkans.)

The present population of Rumania is 18·9 millions (1964). About 15% of the population (2·5 millions out of 17·5 in 1956) belong to the various minorities, however, compared with over 20% in 1930 (present area). This relative decline is chiefly the result of a considerable volume of voluntary emigration or forced repatriation during and after the Second World War. The Hungarians, numbering 1·59 millions (1·42 in 1930), are by far the largest minority. They are located (a) in the Tisa Plain just outside the post-1918 borders of Hungary (about 500,000) and (b) in Transylvania and adjoining Maramureş (about 1 million). Within Transylvania there is a distinction between the 'Szeklers' and the Hungarians proper. The former are the descendants of the earliest Magyar or allied settlers (11th century) and they occupy an area in eastern Transylvania both within and to the west of the Eastern Carpathians. Today most of the Szeklers (about 500,000) are to be found within the Mureş–Autonomous Magyar Region, set up in 1952, with its capital at Tîrgu Mureş (Hungarian *Marosvásárhely*). Here they constitute over three-quarters of the population. In addition to the Szeklers there are another half-million persons of Hungarian speech in the rest of Transylvania and in Maramureş. Cluj is an important centre of Hungarian culture.

The German-speaking minority totals 385,000 (633,000 in 1930) and is the largest such group remaining in any country of Central and Eastern Europe after the emigration or eviction of German minorities as a result of the Second World War. The forefathers of the present minority settled in Rumania at various times in the past. Most of the Germans of Transylvania are the descendants of settlers invited by the Hungarian kings in the 12th and 13th centuries. Like the Szeklers they helped in consolidating Hungarian rule on the inner flanks of the Carpathians. They became known, rather erroneously, as the 'Saxons'. They were responsible for establishing vigorous urban centres, which, with their Gothic churches and picturesque old streets, still retain a distinctive Germanic atmosphere. The German name for Transylvania, *Siebenbürgen*, tells of the seven municipalities that developed here. In the Banat there are the so-called 'Swabians', whose ancestors took part in the great agricultural resettlement schemes sponsored by the Habsburgs in the 18th century after the retreat of the Turks. These two groups of Germans are approximately equal in size.

Before the First World War the urban population of Transylvania, Crişana and the Banat was chiefly non-Rumanian in character. Satu-Mare, Oradea, Arad and Timişoara had a large Hungarian population, the latter having also a considerable German element, and in Transylvania Hungarians and Germans predominated in most of the towns. Between the wars and especially after the Second World War, as a result of partial German and Hungarian repatriation and increased Rumanian urbanization, the Rumanian proportion has tended to increase markedly.

There are also much smaller minorities. The Jewish minority (146,000), once considerably greater (452,000 in 1930), has been reduced by partial wartime extermination and by waves of emigration to Israel at various times since 1945. The Jews have always been predominantly urban in character and approximately one-third of the present total live in Bucharest and a further third in the towns of Moldavia. Of some 60,000 Ukrainians the majority live in the northern Carpathians on the borders of the Soviet Ukraine, while most of the 47,000 Jugoslavs, 35,000 Czechs and Slovaks and 12,000 Bulgarians are found in the ethnically-mixed Banat. In the Danube delta and the Dobrogea there are smaller minorities of Russians, Tatars and Turks. There is also a scattered Gypsy population of over 100,000. While the rights of the minorities are officially guaranteed, only in the Szekler country is there any degree of administrative autonomy.

Beyond the Prut there lies the Moldavian Soviet Socialist Republic, a constituent member of the Soviet Union, and corresponding to the greater part of Bessarabia, with the addition of a small tract beyond the Dnestr. The Moldavians beyond the Prut are essentially Rumanian in language and culture (except that the Cyrillic alphabet is used), and such differentiation as has occurred has been primarily due to Russian influence. Bessarabia experienced considerable Russification while part of the Tsarist Empire between 1812 and 1918 and, in addition, Russian, Ukrainian, Bulgarian and German settlers were encouraged. There was also a large Jewish minority. Between the two World Wars Bessarabia was an integral part of Rumania. Since the Second World War Russian cultural influences have been reinstated as a result of reabsorption into the Soviet Union. The southern part of Bessarabia, with its admittedly very mixed population, is now part of the Ukraine. At the 1959 census of the Soviet Union Soviet Moldavia contained a population of 2·9 millions, of whom 1·9 were 'Moldavians'. In addition over 300,000 'Moldavians' and 'Rumanians' were living in the Ukraine, presumably in the remainder of Bessarabia and in northern Bucovina. Apart from the Rumanians of the Soviet Union there are very small minorities in adjoining parts of Bulgaria and Hungary and a larger minority (61,000 in 1961) in Jugoslavia (in adjacent parts of Serbia).

Historical Background

At the beginning of the Christian era the present territory of Rumania was chiefly populated by the Getae or Dacians, a people at a relatively high level of development. Their capital was at Sarmisegetuza, southwest of Hunedoara. Greek colonies had existed on the Black Sea coast of the Dobrogea for several centuries (e.g. Histria, north of Constanţa) and, together with the other areas south of the lower Danube, they formed part of the Roman province of Moesia. The Dacians made incursions across the Danube and at the beginning of the 2nd century A.D. the Emperor Trajan finally succeeded in subduing them after building his famous bridge across the Danube near Turnu Severin. Traces remain of this and also of the road built through the Danube gorge along its southern bank. Numerous settlers came to the areas later to be known as the Banat, Transylvania and Oltenia, and the surviving Dacian population itself became Romanized. Gold, iron and salt were mined and a number of important towns developed, often on the basis of existing Dacian settlements, such as Alba Iulia, Cluj, Craiova, Turda and Turnu Severin.

Roman forces began to withdraw to the right bank of the Danube in A.D. 271 and Dacia thereafter experienced several centuries of barbarian invasions, including those of the Goths, Huns, Gepidae, Avars, Slavs and Bulgars. Part of the Romano–Dacian population was apparently able to survive in the Carpathians, however. Conversion to the Orthodox form of Christianity probably came about during the period (9th–10th centuries) of the Slav–Bulgar state that for a time extended on both sides of the Danube. As a result the Old Slavonic liturgy was in use in Rumania until the 18th century.

At the end of the 9th century the Magyars passed westwards through the Carpathians and established their new homeland in the Pannonian Basin. Later, in the 11th century, they extended their control eastwards into Transylvania, and from then on until 1918 the history of the province was therefore closely associated with that of Hungary. East and south of the Carpathians the Pechenegs and Cumans successively held sway, and then in 1241 the destructive Tatar invasion took place. As a result the two feudal Rumanian principalities of Wallachia and Moldavia did not crystallize until the late 13th and 14th centuries, their consolidation supposedly being associated with an outward spread of the Rumanians from the Carpathians. Scarcely had the Principalities established themselves before they were threatened, in the late 14th century, by the expanding power of Turkey to the south. After a period of resistance Wallachia accepted Turkish suzerainty, although control passed temporarily to Hungary in the second half of the 15th century. Moldavia, with intermittent Polish protection, was able to hold out much longer. Stephen the Great (1457–1504) heavily defeated the Turks in 1475, earning the description of 'Athlete of Christ' from the Pope, but after his death Moldavia, like Wallachia, became a Turkish vassal state. For a very short time (1599–1600) Michael the Brave of Wallachia was able to challenge the Turkish overlordship and also gain control not only of Moldavia, but also of Transylvania. This was the only occasion, prior to 1918, when all the Rumanian lands were united.

Turkish overlordship involved the exaction of heavy tribute, collected through the reigning prince and the nobles ('boyars'). In the early 18th century native princes were succeeded by Greek 'Phanariots' from Constantinople, who bid for the lucrative privilege of ruling one of the two principalities, if only for several years. This system led to a worsening of the lot of the Rumanian peasantry and to some degree of cultural Hellenization.

By the beginning of the 18th century both Austria and Russia were pushing back the limits of the Turkish Empire and both showed an active interest in the Principalities. Austria occupied Oltenia between 1718 and 1739, and in 1774 she obtained the Bucovina district of Moldavia (including Suceava, the old capital of the Principality). Russia intervened in Moldavia several times during the 18th century and in 1774, by the Treaty of Kuchuk Kainardzhi (south-east of Silistra), Turkey effectively recognized her as protector of the religious rights of the Balkan Christians. In 1812, after a Russo–Turkish war, Russia annexed Bessarabia, then largely Rumanian in character.

In 1821 there was unrest in both Moldavia and Wallachia. In the former, Ypsilanti, a Phanariot, led an unsuccessful Greek rebellion against Turkey, while in Wallachia Vladimirescu led a more popular Rumanian movement against the boyars, only to be executed by Ypsilanti's followers. The outcome was nevertheless favourable for Rumania in that the Sultan decided that native rulers would once more govern the Principalities. In 1828-9 another war took place between Russia and Turkey, and by the Treaty of Adrianople (Turkish *Edirne*) the latter agreed to abolish the Turkish monopoly in foreign trade in the Principalities and to permit a temporary Russian occupation. A Russian-inspired constitution was now introduced and various reforms took place under the auspices of General Kiselev. In the revolutionary year of 1848, however, Russian troops supported the Sultan in suppressing a rebel movement in Wallachia.

As a result of Russia's defeat in the Crimean War of 1854-6, Moldavia regained the southern part of Bessarabia and the Danube was put under the control of an international commission. Austria and Britain were reluctant to permit the union that the Principalities desired, but in 1859 both Moldavia and Wallachia elected Prince Cuza as joint ruler and eventually, in 1861, the Great Powers and Turkey formally agreed to full union. Rumania, with a population of 4 millions and its capital of Bucharest, now appeared on the map of Europe for the first time.

Cuza proved to be a reforming autocrat. Serfdom was abolished in 1864 and a measure of land-reform put into effect, involving the expropriation of Church lands. Forced to abdicate in 1866, he was succeeded by Prince Charles of Hohenzollern–Sigmaringen, as Carol I, and a new constitution was introduced, modelled on that of Belgium. During the Russo–Turkish War of 1877-8 Rumanian and Russian troops together defeated the Turks at Pleven in Bulgaria. The ensuing Treaty of Berlin recognized Rumania's 1877 declaration of independence, granted her the Danube delta and most of the Dobrogea, but authorized Russia's re-annexation of southern Bessarabia. In 1881 a Kingdom was declared.

Rapid economic development took place in the latter decades of the 19th century and the early part of the 20th. A railway network was developed, ports were improved to deal with a greatly increased foreign trade resting on exports of grain, timber and, increasingly, of oil. Bucharest experienced mushroom growth, largely of an unplanned character. Much of this economic development was rendered possible by foreign capital, especially German, and by high protective tariffs. On the other hand, the pre-existing cultural contacts with France remained strong: 19th-century revolutionary and constitutional agitation had drawn inspiration from the French example, and the linguistic connection was also important. The problem of land-hunger became acute, peasants on the great estates being particularly dissatisfied, and a serious rising in 1907 was harshly suppressed.

Rumania's attack on Bulgaria in the Second Balkan War enabled her to acquire the southern Dobrogea in 1913. On the outbreak of the First World War Rumania remained neutral, despite the king's strong pro-German feelings, but, having been promised territory at Hungary's expense, she joined the war against the Austro–Hungarian and German Empires in 1916. After initial Rumanian successes in Transylvania, the penetration of German and Bulgarian troops forced a retreat to Moldavia, and despite successful battles in the summer of 1917 Rumania had to seek peace later in the year, especially as revolutionary Russia on her eastern flank had done the same. After a partial withdrawal of the Germans Rumania was able to take up arms again very shortly before the end of the war and thereby quickly gain control of the Hungarian territories that she had been promised by the Western Allies. In 1919 Hungarian forces under Béla Kun's Communist régime attacked the Rumanian forces occupying eastern Hungary and were thrown back, the Rumanians occupying Budapest for a while.

It is now necessary to review the history of Transylvania up to 1918. It had become part of the Hungarian kingdom in the 11th century, but the Rumanian peasantry had always been at a disadvantage compared with the three 'privileged nations'–the Szeklers, the Saxons and the Hungarian nobles. After the Turkish victory at Mohács in 1526 the Hungarian kingdom began to disintegrate, and after 1541 Transylvania became an autonomous Turkish vassal state under its own princes, with their capital at Alba Iulia. Religious toleration allowed a vigorous growth of Protestantism, to which many Hungarians and Germans were converted, but the Rumanian population generally clung to the Orthodox faith. Transylvania clashed with the Habsburgs when the Turks withdrew from Hungary proper at the end of the 17th century. An accommodation was reached by which Transylvania retained certain rights, although the Emperor became ruling Prince ('Diploma Leopoldinum' of 1691). Another result (1698) was the conversion of part of the Rumanians to the 'Uniate' or 'Greek Catholic' Church, which retained the Orthodox form of worship while acknowledging Papal supremacy. In 1718 the Banat was retrieved by the Habsburgs and its lowland areas were resettled by peasants of varied ethnic character. In 1784 there was a Transylvanian revolt led by Horia against the Hungarian nobles, while in 1848 there were revolutionary demonstrations, as elsewhere in the Habsburg Empire, but the Rumanians were alienated by the aggressive nationalism of rebel Hungary and supported the Emperor's cause. This attitude brought no substantial concessions, however, and later, by the 'Ausgleich' of 1867, Transylvania became an integral part of Hungary again after over 300 years of separation. Thereafter there was a strong process of Magyarization, but despite the inferior position of the Rumanians it must not be overlooked that the general economic level of Transylvania was above that of Moldavia and Wallachia.

After the First World War Rumania was faced with several problems in addition to the general problem of recovery. The amalgamation of Bessarabia, Bucovina and the former Hungarian territories with the 'Old Kingdom' (*Regat*) presented transitional difficulties, and the vociferous opposition of the Hungarian minority, together with Hungary's international agitation for a revision of the new frontiers, did not ease the situation. Rumania insured herself by forming the 'Little Entente' with Czechoslovakia and Jugoslavia. There was also the refusal of the Soviet Union to recognize officially the loss of Bessarabia and significantly Rumania made an alliance with Poland. Internally left-wing elements were suppressed, the Communist Party being outlawed in 1924. In 1933 strike demonstrations at the Bucharest railway workshops were put down with bloodshed. Amongst those imprisoned was Gheorghiu-Dej, later to be the Communist leader of Rumania after the Second World War.

During the First World War King Ferdinand had promised the nation a major land-reform and such a measure was duly enacted in 1921. The State took over the large estates and distributed the land to the peasants on an instalment-payment system. Despite some imperfections the scheme was one of the most far-reaching of its kind at the time. After 1929 Rumania experienced an economic crisis as a result of the World Depression. The reduced level of agricultural prices and the inadequate provision of rural credit led to an impoverishment of the peasantry, while at the same time land-hunger still remained a problem, especially as the rural population was growing rapidly. Political life now took on a more violent character, and a sinister feature was the rise of the Iron Guard fascist movement. In 1938 Carol II instituted a personal dictatorship, ostensibly in an attempt to achieve stability. Nevertheless the inter-war period was one of fairly substantial progress in the industrial field, including the oil industry. It was true, however, that most key sectors were dominated by foreign capital, with the State also playing an important role.

After the outbreak of the Second World War it became apparent that Rumania's allies, Britain and France, were no longer in a position to support her. In 1940, therefore, she had to agree to Russia's annexation of Bessarabia and northern Bucovina and, at the behest of Germany and

Italy, to territorial losses to Hungary and Bulgaria. Carol II abdicated and the fascist régime of General Antonescu ensued, although the Iron Guard movement was later suppressed by him. In 1941 Rumania participated in Germany's attack on the Soviet Union, thereby temporarily regaining Bessarabia, but she experienced German economic control and suffered many casualties on the Russian front.

As the Red Army advanced westwards and crossed the Prut in 1944 young King Mihai (Michael), with the assistance of anti-German political groups, including the Communists, ousted the government, declared war on Germany and installed a broad coalition in power. Rumanian forces thereafter fought against Germany in central Europe. Despite a promise by the Soviet Union that the existing social structure would not be affected by the imminent military occupation the Soviet Union in fact actively favoured those political elements anxious to carry out revolutionary changes and in 1945 helped into power the Communist-dominated Groza government. A new land-reform measure was put into effect, whereby large farms and the remaining estates were expropriated. The elections held the following year were not regarded as genuine by the Western Allies. The opposition leaders were imprisoned, and finally, in December 1947, the king was prevailed on to abdicate and a People's Republic was declared. This was followed by the formation of the Rumanian Workers' Party and the inauguration of new constitutions (1948 and 1952). Nationalization measures were put into force and the upper and middle classes were dispossessed. Collectivization of the land was embarked on, but at a relatively slow pace. As late as 1957 half the farmland was still in private hands, but by 1962 the figure had been reduced to only 6%. The Orthodox and Protestant Churches came under close government supervision and the Catholic Church suffered severe disabilities. The Uniate Church was disbanded and reabsorbed by the Orthodox Church.

For about ten years after the Second World War there was close Soviet control of the Rumanian economy, aided by the setting-up of joint Soviet–Rumanian enterprises to run the leading sectors of the economy. Indeed, Soviet political and economic control from 1945 to the mid-1950s was probably more far-reaching in Rumania than in any other country of Europe, with the exception of Eastern Germany. By the early 1960s, however, Rumania had decisively emerged as mistress in her own house and was pursuing external policies that clearly did not always meet with complete Soviet approval. Officially at least Rumania has renounced her claim to Bessarabia, but the continued partition of old Moldavia is not easily forgotten and her now rather lukewarm friendship with the Soviet Union may be contrasted with the much stronger ties that exist between the Soviet Union and Bulgaria. Bulgaria, however, has never had territorial disputes with the Soviet Union and, moreover, has close cultural and linguistic affinities.

In 1965 the Rumanian People's Republic became the Socialist Republic of Rumania.

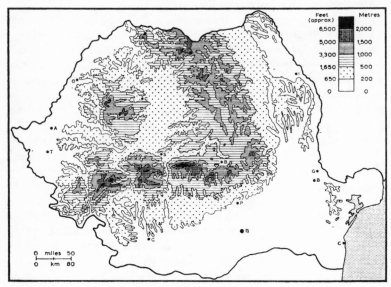

Fig. 49. Relief of Rumania

The Land (Figs. 49, 50, 51)

The upland heart of Rumania is part of the Tertiary fold-mountain system of the Carpathians, extending north-westwards into the Soviet Ukraine and south-westwards into Serbia. The Rumanian Carpathian zone consists essentially of a vast central depression, the Transylvanian Plateau Basin, and surrounding mountain ranges, which incorporate some Hercynian elements, disposed in an almost triangular manner around it. The mountain ranges consist of the Eastern, Southern and Western Carpathians. The former extend south-eastwards, for some 350 km/200 miles, from the Oaş, Gutîi, Maramureş and Obcine ranges, on the Ukrainian border, to the Vrancea and Penteleu ranges, where the Carpathians swing westwards again in a great arc. Conventionally the Eastern Carpathians then continue as far as the Prahova valley and thus also include the Ciucaş and Bai ranges.

In general the Eastern Carpathians consist of a central zone of old crystalline rocks of a largely schistose character (part of Maramureş and

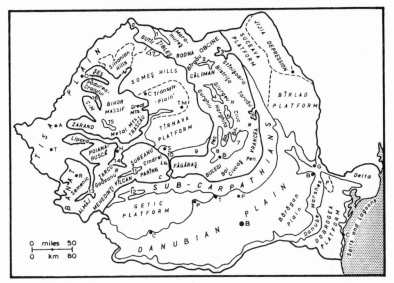

Fig. 50. Generalized physiographic regions of Rumania

Key: Depressions: **1.** Maramureş. **2.** Dorna. **3.** Cîmpulung Mold.. **4.** Giurgeu. **5.** Ciuc. **6.** Dărmăneşti. **7.** Tîrgu Săcuiesc. **8.** Braşov. **9.** Făgăraş. **10.** Sibiu. **11.** Petroşeni. **12.** Tîrgu-Jiu. **13.** Timiş. **14.** Haţeg. **15.** Brad. **16.** Beiuş. **17.** Lăpuş.

Ranges: **Ba** Baraolt. **Bo** Bodoc. **C** Căpăţîna. **C–M** Codru-Moma. **H** Hăghimaş. **Lo** Lotru. **M** Meseş. **N** Nemira. **O** Oaş. **P** Pricopan. **Pen** Penteleu. **Per** Perşani. **R** Retezat.

the Obcine, Bistriţa, Giurgeu, Hăghimaş ranges), flanked on the west by Tertiary volcanic ranges (Oaş, Gutîi, Ţibleş, Căliman, Gurghiu, Harghita), and on the east and south by Cretaceous and Lower Tertiary rocks largely having the character of flysch (Obcine, Stînişoara, Tarcău, Nemira, Ciuc, Bodoc, Baraolt, Vrancea, Penteleu, Ciucaş and Bai). Large tectonic depressions lie within the Eastern Carpathians, thus aiding both settlement and communications. The more extensive are those of Maramureş, Dorna, Giurgeu, Ciuc, and Braşov–Tîrgu Săcuiesc, the latter being by far the largest (90 km/55 miles long). On the exterior margin of the Eastern Carpathians there are the depressions of Cîmpulung–Moldovanesc and Dărmăneşti.

The Southern Carpathians, also known as the 'Transylvanian Alps', extend westwards for about 250 km/150 miles, from the Prahova valley to the Iron Gates gorge of the Danube, and include the Bucegi, Iezer, Făgăraş, Căpăţîna, Lotru, Parîng, Cindrel, Şureanu, Retezat, Vîlcan, Godeanu, Tarcu and Mehedinţi ranges. Geologically the Southern Carpathians consist mainly of schists, with granites becoming more frequent

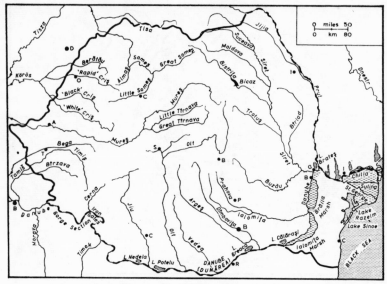

Fig. 51. Drainage of Rumania

to the west. Peaks and plateaux of Cretaceous limestone occur respectively in the Bucegi and the Mehedinți, however. Intramontane depressions are few compared with the Eastern Carpathians, the largest being that of Petroșeni, with its coal-basin.

The Western Carpathians, over 300 km/200 miles long, form a much more broken and less coherent group. In the south are the mountains of the Banat, extending up to the Danube gorge. Two leading ranges are the Almăj and Semenic, separated from the Southern Carpathians by the Timiș depression. The Banat Mountains are chiefly crystalline in character, but there are Mesozoic limestones in the interior and Reșița has a Carboniferous coal-basin. Northwards, beyond the Timiș, is the Poiana–Ruscă Massif (crystalline), with its Tertiary salient of the Lipova Hills. Between the Poiana–Ruscă and the Șureanu Mountains is the Hațeg depression. Northwards again, beyond the Mureș, are the 'Western Mountains' (*Munții Apuseni*), consisting of the Bihor Massif, with a number of ranges radiating from it. The Bihor Massif, of Hercynian origin, is a complicated area geologically, mainly consisting of schists, granites and volcanic rocks. The Trascău, Codru–Moma and Pădurea–Craiului ranges have sedimentary Mesozoic rocks, chiefly limestones. Within and on the margins of the Western Mountains are a number of depressions, the largest being those of Brad and Beiuș. North-east of the Bihor Massif there occurs the only major break in the Carpathian girdle.

Here, beyond the Meseş Mountains and Silvanian Hills, there is an embayment drained by the Someş. To the south, before the Someş Hills are reached, there are several small ranges that enclose a depression drained by the upper Lăpuş, a tributary of the Someş. Ancient crystalline rocks locally emerge from beneath the Tertiary cover of all these hill and mountain ranges.

Within the outer framework of the Carpathian ranges described above is the Transylvanian Plateau Basin, an area of subsidence covered with Tertiary clays and sandstones dissected to form gently-rolling country, with an elevation of 300–600 m/1,000–2,000 ft. There is a difference, however, between the 'Transylvanian Plain', stretching approximately from Cluj to Tîrgu Mureş, and the rather higher Someş Hills to the north and the Tîrnava Platform to the south, which increases in height to the south-east. Between the Tîrnava Platform and the steep northern slopes of the Southern Carpathians lie the elongated Făgăraş depression, followed by the River Olt, and the smaller Sibiu depression, while to the west of the Platform is the broad corridor of the Mureş, which continues through the Western Carpathians and so out of the Basin into the Tisa Plain.

Of the three main Carpathian ranges the Southern is the loftiest, with wide areas rising to over 1,500 m/5,000 ft. The highest summits, exceeding 2,500 m/8,200 ft, include Moldoveanu (2,543 m/8,344 ft), Negoi (2,535 m/8,317 ft) in the Făgăraş, Gt. Parîng (2,518 m/8,261 ft), Peleaga (2,509 m/8,232 ft) in the Retezat, and Om (2,507 m/8,225 ft) in the Bucegi. Only relatively small areas exceed 1,500 m/5,000 ft in height in the Eastern Carpathians and the Western Carpathians, these being found, respectively, in the Bihor Massif (Curcubăta, 1,848 m/6,065 ft) and the Căliman, Maramureş and Rodna ranges (Pietros, 2,305 m/7,563 ft). The Carpathians show subdued relief-forms usually, with extensive development of erosion surfaces. Active glaciers are no longer present, but in the higher mountains fretted peaks and corrie lakes indicate glaciation in the past, especially in the Făgăraş, Parîng, Retezat and Bucegi ranges in the south and the Rodna range in the north.

Despite their considerable height and width (50–120 km/30–75 miles) the Carpathian ranges do not always constitute a serious barrier to communications, owing to the presence of both large intramontane depressions and broad corridors or gorges followed by the rivers draining outwards from the Transylvanian Plateau Basin. The fragmented character of the Western Carpathians has already been indicated and an important feature is the series of wide valleys opening out on to the Tisa Plain. In the Banat and the Southern Carpathians there are a number of natural routeways giving access from the interior to the Wallachian Plain. These include (a) the 'Porta Orientalis', linking the Timiş depression with the lower Cerna valley and its gorge, the latter terminating at Orşova in the Danube gorge; (b) the Merişor and Lainici passes linking the Petroşeni basin respectively with the Haţeg depression to the north and the Carpathian foothills to the south, the Lainici pass being followed by the River Jiu; (c) the 'Red Tower'–Cozia gorge, followed by the Olt and commanded by Sibiu; (d) the Bran and Predeal passes, connecting Braşov with the Plain by two routes using low watersheds. There are also passes in the Eastern Carpathians, which either link up the various depressions or give access to them from Transylvania or Moldavia. Thus there are through routes using (a) the Dorna and Cîmpulung depressions, (b) the Bistriţa valley and the Giurgeu depression, (c) the Trotuş valley and the Tîrgu Săcuiesc depression, and (d) the Trotuş valley and the Ciuc depression.

The Mureş, Olt and Someş valleys are of importance in integrating Transylvania with the exterior. The Mureş rises in the Giurgeu depression, cuts a gorge between the Căliman and Gurghiu ranges, crosses the Transylvanian Plain, and then follows a broad corridor between the Poiana–Ruscă and Bihor Massifs, eventually to emerge in the Tisa Plain. The Olt rises close to the Mureş in the Ciuc depression, flows successively into the Braşov and Făgăraş depressions and then cuts a gorge through the Carpathians before entering the Danubian Plain. The Someş, with head-streams rising in both the Bihor Massif and the Rodna, passes through the Someş Hills and thence to the Tisa Plain. Nevertheless, in spite of the possibilities of inter-communication (permitting the development of a single Rumanian language and culture), it should not be forgotten that for nearly a thousand years, until 1918, the Eastern and Southern Carpathians formed an effective, and generally stable, frontier-zone between the Hungarian realm and the foothills and plains to the east and south, where the two Principalities of Moldavia and Wallachia eventually took shape.

On the outer margins of the Eastern and Southern Carpathians there is a well-marked transitional area of foothills–the 'Sub-Carpathians'– before the Danubian and Moldavian Plains are reached, although in the far north this zone is virtually absent. These hills, of gently-folded Miocene and Pliocene sandstones and clays, have numerous longitudinal depressions, especially at their junction with the mountains. Other depressions lie further forward, such as that of Tîrgu-Jiu. The foothill zone is much dissected by rivers and streams flowing to the Danube and Siret and their emergence into the plains is often marked by extensive alluvial fans. In the west the descent to the Wallachian Plain is much more gentle, owing to the existence of the broad Getic Platform of

Pliocene deposits, with an elevation rising from 200 m/650 ft to 350 m/ 1,150 ft.

There is an important contrast between the lowlands of Moldavia and Wallachia. The former, mainly lying east of the rivers Moldova and Siret, constitute a platform of almost undisturbed horizontally-bedded rocks, forming an extension of the 'Russian' or 'Black Sea' Platform, and covered with Tertiary material. The large Jijia Depression in the north-east is at a lower level (100 m/325 ft to 200 m/650 ft), however, than the adjoining Suceava and Bîrlad Platforms (rising to 450 m/1,500 ft). The main rivers and their tributaries drain in a predominantly north-west to south-east direction and the surface of the land has a corrugated appearance, with shallow trench-like valleys and broad flat-topped interfluves. Wide areas of loess occur in the Jijia Depression and the southern part of the Bîrlad Platform.

The Danubian Plain, gradually falling in height south-eastwards from under 200 m/650 ft to only 25 m/80 ft above sea-level in the Bărăgan Plain, represents a broad and deep Tertiary depression lying between the Southern Carpathians and the rising ground of the North Bulgarian and Dobrogea Platforms beyond the Danube. Its thick Tertiary deposits filling the depression are completely concealed by a Quaternary cover consisting mainly of loess, but also including sand-dunes (especially in parts of the south-west and the Bărăgan Plain) and marshy alluvium along the Danube and its tributaries. A wide zone of marshland with numerous lakes extends along the Danube and reaches its broadest span where the river turns northwards. Here are the Ialomiţa and Brăila Marshes.

Near Galaţi the Danube turns eastwards again round the northern end of the Dobrogea and so enters its large delta, crossed by three main distributaries, the Chilia, Sulina and St George arms. The delta is still undergoing active sedimentation, and constant dredging is necessary to allow navigation of the delta and its approaches. Southwards there is a notable development of spits and lagoons along the coast of the Dobrogea.

The Dobrogea Platform, extending southwards into Bulgaria, consists of two main portions. The lower, southern part, mainly below 150 m/ 500 ft, consists of undisturbed Cretaceous and Tertiary limestones over-lain by loess. The north, however, incorporates an old Hercynian range, where Silurian and other Palaeozoic rocks, together with granites, emerge from beneath a later cover of Mesozoic limestones and Quaternary loess. In the north-west the striking Pricopan range rises up abruptly from the Danube marshes to 400 m/1,300 ft.

Finally, beyond the Western Carpathians, lies the Tisa Plain, with its alluvial deposits and loess, corresponding to the eastern fringes of the

Pannonian Basin. Here wide embayments penetrate the mountains, thus producing an interdigitation of range and plain.

Climate and Soils

A leading feature of the climate of Rumania is the role played by the Eastern and Southern Carpathians in acting as a barrier to the admittedly rather weak Oceanic influences emanating from the west. As a result the climate of Moldavia and Wallachia is more typically Continental than that of the Tisa Plain and the Transylvanian Basin, which have a smaller annual temperature range and also slightly moister conditions than Moldavia and the eastern part of Wallachia, together with an earlier spring and a later onset of winter.

All parts of Rumania have average temperatures below freezing-point in January, with the exception of a small strip along the Dobrogea coast, where the temperature is at or only just below this. Temperatures are below − 2·5°C/27·5°F in Moldavia, eastern Wallachia and, owing to altitude, in the Transylvanian Basin. In the Tisa Plain and western Wallachia the averages are above this. In July the warmest areas (over 22°C/71·5°F) are the Wallachian Plain, the Banat lowlands and the southern Dobrogea. The Tisa Plain and Moldavian Platform have temperatures of 20°–22°C/68·0°–71·5°F, while conditions are slightly cooler in Transylvania. Average annual rainfall is lowest in the southern

TABLE 11

CLIMATIC STATISTICS · RUMANIA

Station	Average temperature January		Average temperature July		Average annual precipitation	
	°C	°F	°C	°F	mm	in
Bucharest	−2·8	27·0	22·9	73·2	580	22·8
Arad	−1·1	30·0	21·4	70·5	577	22·7
Brăila	−2·3	27·9	23·1	73·6	440	17·3
Cluj	−4·4	24·1	18·9	66·0	613	24·1
Constanţa	−0·3	31·5	22·2	72·0	370	14·6
Gheorghieni	−6·8	19·8	16·0	60·8	603	23·7
Iaşi	−3·6	25·5	21·3	70·3	518	20·4
Petroşeni	−4·5	23·9	16·7	62·1	694	27·3

Dobrogea and the Danube delta (less than 450 mm/16 in), the proximity of the Black Sea having no effect on precipitation. In Wallachia rainfall increases in a westerly direction and in Moldavia in a northerly direction, from below 450 mm/17·5 in in the Bărăgan Plain and the lower Siret plain to over 600 mm/23·5 in in the Getic Platform and parts of northern

Moldavia. Both the Tisa Plain and the Transylvanian Basin have rain-falls of over 550 mm/21·5 in, with totals rising to 700 mm/27·5 in in parts of the latter. Everywhere in Rumania the late spring and early summer period has the most precipitation, the month of June showing the highest total.

The Carpathian ranges, owing to their height and width, constitute a separate climatic zone. Temperatures are lower than on the adjoining plains and precipitation is everywhere over 750 mm/30 in, exceeding 1,400 mm/55 in in the highest parts or in those areas exposed to the west. The Sub-Carpathian hills have a climate transitional between that of the mountains and the plains. In the Banat and northern Moldavia conditions can be modified by the operation of 'Sub-Mediterranean' and 'Sub-Baltic' influences respectively. In the former cyclonic influences tend to increase autumn rainfall, while in the latter cool, moist conditions sometimes penetrate from the North European Plain. In the Transyl-vanian Basin local winds, such as those of a *föhn* type, can have a marked effect on temperature, and in the intramontane depressions winter fogs and temperature inversions can also occur.

Some of these climatic variations are illustrated by the accompanying figures. Thus Bucharest, in the Wallachian Plain, has a greater tempera-ture range than Arad, in the Tisa Plain. Brăila, in eastern Wallachia, has less rainfall than Bucharest, and Constanţa (with one of the highest January temperatures in the whole country) has less than either. The figures for Cluj, Gheorghieni (in the Giurgeu depression) and Petroşeni show the effect of altitude and situation on temperature and rainfall within the Carpathian zone.

Soils in Rumania fall into three broad groups. In the upper parts of the Carpathian Mountains podzol soils are typical, with skeletal soils at the higher altitudes. Brown-forest soils occur in the lower parts of the Carpathians and in the Transylvanian Basin, the Pannonian fringes of the Western Carpathians and the Sub-Carpathian hills of Moldavia and Wallachia, together with the Getic and Suceava Platforms. They also extend into adjacent parts of the Bîrlad Platform and the Danubian Plain. In the latter there is also a crescentic zone of russet-brown soils passing through Bucharest and Craiova. These appear to be transitional to leached chernozems. The third group of soils consists of *chernozems* ('black-earths') of varying types. They occur in the Transylvanian Plain, the Tisa Plain, the Jijia Depression, the Bîrlad Platform, the southern and eastern parts of the Danubian Plain and the Dobrogea. In the drier Bărăgan Plain and the Dobrogea chocolate- and chestnut-coloured types have developed. Alluvial soils of a marshy character occur in the Danube delta and wide areas along the Danube and lower Siret. Alluvial tracts also extend up the main river valleys of Moldavia, Wallachia and the Tisa Plain.

Land-Use (Fig. 52) and Farming

A striking feature of land-use in Rumania is the sharp contrast between the thickly-forested Carpathians and the highly-cultivated

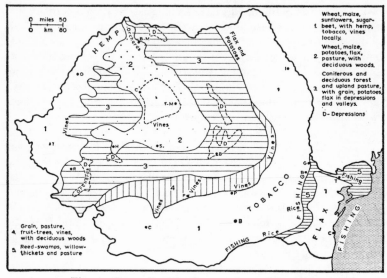

Fig. 52. Generalized land-use regions of Rumania

plains of Moldavia, Wallachia and the Tisa Plain. Forming an important transitional zone, however, between these two extremes are the Sub-Carpathian hills and the Pannonian margins of the Western Carpathians.

With the exception of wooded areas in the northern Dobrogea and in parts of the Moldavian Platform, the forests are essentially coincident with the Carpathians. Above about 1,750 m/5,750 ft there is an upper zone above the tree-line, characterized by 'Alpine' grasses and sparse shrub vegetation. Below this zone there are extensive coniferous forests, chiefly of spruce, but with silver fir and also beech appearing at lower altitudes. Beech forest is dominant below about 1,000 m/3,250 ft, but on the eastern side of the Eastern Carpathians this zone is virtually non-existent owing to slightly cooler conditions. Mountain grasslands, often due to clearing by man in the past, occur within the forest zone and provide valuable summer pasture. Deciduous woodlands, dominated by beech at higher levels and oak at the lower, still cover wide areas of the Sub-Carpathian zone, the outer fringes of the Western Carpathians, the Someş Hills, the Tîrnava Platform and the northern part of the Getic Platform.

The natural vegetation of the plains is wooded steppe, developing into steppe proper in the Bărăgan Plain and the lower parts of the Dobrogea (with the exception of its northern oak-forest), but the original cover has been removed as a result of cultivation. In the Suceava Platform and the northern part of the Bîrlad Platform tree-cover was probably more extensive and quite considerable areas of deciduous woodland still remain. Along the valleys of the Danube and its tributaries, as well as in the delta, the vegetation consists largely of willow and poplar thickets, with expanses of reeds in areas of shallow water. Some of the Danube floodlands are now being embanked and drained for cultivation (e.g. near Călăraşi). The Danube delta, with its teeming bird-life, is an important nature reserve.

The timber resources of Rumania are one of the country's most important assets and are the largest in Europe outside the Soviet Union and Scandinavia. Forests cover more than a quarter of the country's area and timber and timber products are important in the export trade. The Eastern Carpathians have the greatest area of coniferous stands, while in the Southern and Western Carpathians and their foothills hardwoods (especially beech and oak) are relatively more important. Exports of timber from the Carpathians to neighbouring areas of timber shortage have been important for centuries. Some rafting down the Siret and its tributaries to Galaţi still takes place, but is less important than it used to be owing to the availability of rail and road transport. Rafting on the Bistriţa has almost ceased owing to hydro-power developments. The timber-processing industry is located at a large number of centres in the Carpathian Mountains and foothills and in the Transylvanian Basin. Dej, Piteşti, Suceava and Tîrgu-Jiu are four of the leading centres. In recent years the mechanical harvesting of reeds in the Danube delta has provided a new source of cellulose, and a plant at Chiscani, near Brăila, processes these into paper and artificial fibres. Brăila also processes local poplar and willow.

Favourable natural conditions, combined with only a moderate population density by West European standards, make Rumania a land that is self-supporting in temperate foodstuffs and also one that has a substantial export surplus. Exports of grain have declined since the First World War, however, and emphasis has gradually shifted to food products.

The lowland areas, with their fertile soils and hot, sunny summers, are well suited to grain production, notably wheat and maize. Periodic drought can nevertheless be a hazard. Two-thirds of the country's farm-land is under the plough and 70% of this is under grain. Sunflowers and forage crops are also widely grown in lowland areas, and sugar beet is cultivated where there is adequate moisture and access to refineries. The cultivation of hemp and tobacco occurs sporadically; the chief district for the former is the Tisa Plain and that for the latter an area to the north-east of Bucharest. Some rice is grown in parts of the Bărăgan Plain close to the Danube, and flax for oil is cultivated in the Dobrogea. Vines are widely grown. North of Suceava, at the foot of the Carpathians, there is an area of flax and potato cultivation.

The Sub-Carpathian zone of Wallachia and southern Moldavia is an area of more intensive and more mixed farming. Patches of grain are intermingled with pasture and woodland, and fruit-trees (apples, pears, cherries and especially plums, the latter for *ţuica* or plum brandy) and vines are very important. While this zone produces the bulk of Rumania's wine output, for both domestic and export markets, some of the quality export wines also come from the Dobrogea and northern Moldavia.

The Transylvanian Plain is broadly similar to other lowland areas as regards its crops, but the higher, outer parts of the Transylvanian Basin (including the Someş Hills and Tîrnava Platform) have more pasture and woodland, and potatoes and flax become commoner crops. South-west of Tîrgu–Mureş is the important Tîrnava vine district. In the Carpathian ranges there are large areas of forest and upland pasture, but in the depressions and valleys grain, potatoes and flax are cultivated and sugar beet is grown in the Braşov depression. Certain hill-slope areas of western Rumania are important for their fruit orchards, especially near Baia-Mare and on the fringes of the Banat Mountains. Vines are important near Arad.

Livestock numbers are dominated by sheep, followed by pigs and cattle. Many of the latter are still used for draught purposes, but their number has fallen greatly (as has that of horses) owing to mechanization under the collective farm system. Sheep, pigs and cattle are widely distributed, although in the Dobrogea there is an emphasis on sheep and in the Tisa Plain on pigs. The greatest density of livestock is found in the Sub-Carpathian zone. Formerly there was a large summer movement of sheep flocks from the plains to the Carpathian pastures, but the effect of collectivization has been to reduce this. Fishing takes place in the Black Sea and the Danube. Sturgeon, for caviar, is highly prized.

Industry and Mining

Although Rumania has a wide range of raw materials industrial development tended to proceed at only a relatively slow pace before the Second World War. From the 1950s onwards, however, the country has achieved one of the highest rates of industrial expansion in the world, with chemical industries playing a major role, based on resources of petroleum, natural gas and salt. The engineering industries have also been greatly expanded. With the important exception of oil-refining, the chief fields of activity were formerly the processing of agricultural commodities and timber. In the old Hungarian territories Rumania inherited iron and steel and non-ferrous metal plants after 1918, however, and in the 1930s and early 1940s both the State and foreign concerns were promoting the development of metallurgical and engineering industries, including armaments.

Energy Supplies (Fig. 53)

Rumania has ample resources of petroleum and natural gas and is the second largest producer of both in Europe after the Soviet Union. On the other hand she has only modest supplies of black coal, and imports are necessary, especially of coking coal and coke. There are widely-distributed deposits of brown coal and lignite, however, and a considerable hydro-power potential is available. Total coal output was 11·1 m tons in 1964.

The limited resources of black coal occur mainly in two areas in the south-west of the country. Three very small fields lie in the Banat Mountains between Reşiţa and the Danube gorge (Anina, Doman-Secu and Baia Nouă). Total annual production is only about 0·3 m tons, but some of the coal is of anthracite and coking quality. Further east is the much larger upper Jiu valley field, in the Petroşeni depression, where the coal is of a rather low-grade bituminous type. Nevertheless some of it can be used for coking. Total output is about 5–6 m tons. To the south is the tiny anthracite field of Schela. Brown coal (total production about 1 m tons) is mined in two areas in the Almaş basin (north-west of Cluj) and at Comăneşti (in the Dărmăneşti depression in the Trotuş valley), while lignite (total output about 4 m tons) is chiefly exploited north-east of Oradea; in the Jiu valley, south of Tîrgu-Jiu; north of Braşov; and in a broad zone extending from Piteşti to Ploieşti. The Tîrgu-Jiu area is now rapidly increasing in importance, and there are also new workings in the Motru valley to the west.

The commercial exploitation of petroleum dates from the 1860s, when its chief use was for lighting. Output remained very small until the end of the century, however, when an Act of 1895 permitted the entry of foreign capital. As a result output grew rapidly to about 2 million tons by the time of the First World War. Inter-war output reached a peak of 8·7 million tons in 1936, when the Ploieşti fields, located mainly in the Prahova and Ialomiţa valleys, but also including the Buzău district to the east, were responsible for over 99% of output. During the Second World War much damage was done by Allied air attacks. After the war the foreign companies (chiefly British and American) were taken over. Since then the main field has been extended westwards towards Piteşti,

Fig. 53. Mineral exploitation in Rumania

a new field has been developed south of Tîrgu-Jiu, and there has been a great expansion in the formerly very small Moineşti field in Moldavia, west of Bacău. These three new areas of exploitation now account for well over two-thirds of total output, which reached a record 12·4 million tons in 1964 (although the rate of growth had slowed down since the mid-1950s). The output of the Ploieşti area has thus declined absolutely.

There are several refineries in Ploieşti and neighbourhood (at Brazi, Teleajen and Cîmpina) and there are pipe-lines for petroleum products from here to Giurgiu, Constanţa and Galaţi. From Galaţi there is an extension to Odessa in the Soviet Union. The Moineşti field has refineries at Borzeşti and Dărmăneşti, but the crude from the Tîrgu-Jiu and Piteşti areas is piped to the Ploieşti refineries or carried by tankers. About half the total oil output is exported, usually entirely in the form of refined products, and much of the remainder is used in petrochemical industries.

Considerable quantities of casing-head gas are also obtained from the oilfields (4,100 million cubic metres in 1964), but nearly three times this quantity is obtained from the natural gas field of the Transylvanian Basin (11,500 million cubic metres), where exploitation on a small scale began just before the First World War. Chemical processing of the gas first began in the late 1930s. Gas pipe-lines now radiate from Transylvania and the oilfields to most of the large cities and also to a number of individual chemical, metallurgical and glass-making plants and electric power-stations. Industry absorbs 90% of the output. Some gas is also supplied to Hungary.

Electricity generation is chiefly by thermal means (95%) and depends predominantly on natural gas and the poorer grades of coal. Stations are located near to these resources, although greater locational flexibility is possible where gas is used. The largest hydro-power station, completed in the early 1960s, is that of Bicaz in the Eastern Carpathians, where a dam has been built across a gorge of the Bistriţa. A series of twelve smaller dams is in process of completion downstream. There are several rather small stations, both old and new, in the Southern Carpathians–on the upper Ialomiţa, the Sadu (south of Sibiu) and the Bîrzava (south-east of Reşiţa). A large project is nearing completion on the upper Argeş and one is planned for the Lotru (a tributary of the Olt). The joint construction by Rumania and Jugoslavia of a dam across the Danube at the Iron Gates will eventually lead to a great increase in hydro-power generation, since each country will have a station of about 1,000,000 kW capacity on its own side of the river. A joint Rumanian–Bulgarian dam on the Danube is planned for the Islaz–Somovit area, upstream of Turnu–Măgurele.

METALLURGY (Fig. 53)

The mining of metal ores (precious, ferrous and non-ferrous) in the Banat and Transylvania goes back to Roman times at least. Before 1918 these areas were part of Hungary and their union with the Old Kingdom after 1918 was of great significance in view of the absence of metallurgical activities in the latter.

The relatively small iron and steel industry is overwhelmingly located in the south-western part of the country, and the present sites all date back to the 18th or 19th centuries, when charcoal- and later coke-using furnaces were erected. The only two integrated iron and steel works, modernized and expanded in the 1930s and 1940s, are those of Reşiţa and Hunedoara. Both have been extended subsequently. Reşiţa uses local Banat ore and coal, and Hunedoara uses local Poiana-Ruscă ore and Jiu valley coal. At the same time both partially depend on imported iron ore and coking coal, chiefly from the Soviet Union, in view of the inadequacy of home supplies. Iron ore output was 1·9 m tons in 1964, and 2·3 were imported. Manganese supplies (from the Reşiţa area and the Iacobeni district in the Eastern Carpathians) are ample, however, and offer a margin for export, Rumania being one of the largest producers in Europe. Close to Hunedoara there is a smaller blast-furnace centre at Călan, while between Hunedoara and Reşiţa are Oţelu Roşu ('Red Steel'), formerly called Ferdinand, which has steel furnaces, and Nădrag, which rolls iron products. In Transylvania there is a small blast-furnace centre, dependent on local ores, at Vlăhiţa, north of Braşov, while at Cîmpia Turzii, near Cluj, special steels are made. Bucharest makes steel tubes and Brăila and Galaţi have rolling mills. In Moldavia a new tube plant is located at Roman. The present pattern of iron and steel output will be greatly changed when the large new integrated works at Galaţi comes into production, using imported ore and coal. The output of steel from Galaţi may approach 3 m tons by 1970. Total national output of pig-iron reached 1·9 m tons in 1964 and steel 3·0 m tons.

Although details of output are not published, Rumania is known to be a significant producer of precious and non-ferrous metals. Gold and silver ores are mined in the 'Metalliferous' Mountains, forming the southern part of the Bihor Massif, in the neighbourhood of Zlatna. Mercury is also obtained in this area. The most important area for the mining of non-ferrous metal ores is the Baia-Mare district of the Gutii and Tibleş Mountains. Here complex ores yield copper, lead, zinc, gold and silver. Copper, lead and zinc are also mined in the Maramureş Mountains. Much of the processing takes place at Baia-Mare and nearby Ferneziu but zinc is treated at Copşa-Mică, in Transylvania. Copper is also mined at Bălan and Leşul Ursului (Eastern Carpathians), in the Poiana-Ruscă, and at Moldova Nouă (Banat). Lead and zinc are also obtained in the Poiana-Ruscă. The aluminium industry will have greatly expanded by the late 1960s. Bauxite is exploited near Dobreşti, south-east of Oradea, and is converted to alumina at Oradea, but the production of aluminium takes place at Slatina, east of Craiova, in order to be nearer supplies of electric power, both thermal and hydro. Uranium is mined in the Banat Mountains and the Bihor Massif and will eventually be used for atomic power stations.

OTHER INDUSTRIES

Despite the continuing growth of the food-processing and timber-working industries their share of the industrial sector tends to fall, owing to the more rapid growth of other industries, especially engineering and chemicals. Engineering is represented by a widening range of products. Bucharest is the largest individual centre and produces numerous items. Specialities of other towns are as follows: BRAȘOV–lorries, tractors, ball-bearings; ARAD–railway rolling-stock, machine-tools; CRAIOVA–electrical engineering (including locomotives); the PLOIEȘTI district–oil-field and refinery equipment; REȘIȚA–heavy electrical engineering, locomotive diesel engines; CLUJ–refrigerating plant; SIBIU–weighing-machines; SATU MARE–mining equipment; BRĂILA–road-building machinery. Brăila, Galați, Constanța, Oltenița and Turnu Severin have shipyards of varying size. Amongst the smaller towns with a relatively large commitment to engineering are Bîrlad (ball-bearing), Colibași (near Pitești) (lorry-parts for Brașov), and Tîrgoviște (oilfield equipment).

The chemical industries rest on a variety of basic materials, including petroleum, natural gas, salt and sulphuric acid from the non-ferrous metal plants. The salt deposits, of Tertiary age, occur on the margins of the Transylvanian Basin and in the Sub-Carpathian hills, i.e. broadly in the same locations as the petroleum and natural gas. Output was 1·8 million tons in 1964. Chemical centres utilizing natural gas in Transylvania include Făgăraș and Victoria (in the Olt valley between Brașov and Sibiu), Tîrnăveni (north of Mediaș) and Copșa-Mică (carbon black). Petrochemicals are important in the Ploiești district (especially Brazi), while in the neighbourhood of Borzești and Gheorghe Gheorghiu-Dej (formerly Onești), in the Trotuș valley of Moldavia, large plants have recently been built, using gas, petroleum and salt. Synthetic rubber is one of the products. Further north, near Piatra Neamț, natural gas is used for synthetic fibres at Săvinești. At Piatra Neamț and nearby Roznov and at Craiova, Rîșnov and Tîrgu Mureș nitrogenous fertilizers are made with the aid of natural gas. Copper pyrites from Moldova Nouă will be the basis of a fertilizer industry at Turnu-Măgurele, west of Giurgiu on the Danube. Năvodari, north of Constanța, produces super-phosphates. Salt deposits are used for sodium products at Turda, Ocna Mureș (near Turda) and Govora (near Rîmnicu-Vîlcea). Bucharest has rubber-processing industries, including tyre manufacture, and tyres are also made at Ploiești. Iași has a plastics-moulding industry.

The textile, clothing and footwear industries are widely distributed. Bucharest is the most important centre, but Arad, Brașov, Cluj, Iași, Sibiu and Timișoara are also important. In the building-materials industry there are large concentrations of cement-making at Turda, Bicaz,

Fieni (near Cîmpina), Tîrgu-Jiu and Medgidia, close to limestone supplies. Transylvania has notable glass and ceramic industries, using
natural gas, located at Mediaş, Sighişoara, Tîrnaveni and Turda.

Despite the rapid growth of industry since the early 1950s it must be
remembered that Rumania is still one of the least industrialized countries
of Europe. In 1963 60% of the occupied population were still engaged
in agriculture, but even so the industrial labour force had increased by
over 80% since 1950. Apart from the general need to maintain a high
rate of industrial growth there is also the special problem of Oltenia
and Moldavia, where the rural population is relatively large and where
industrial development was almost non-existent until recently.

Distribution of Population and Chief Cities

One of the most important features of the population pattern is the
way in which the chief areas of low density correspond to the Carpathian
ranges, with their generally unfavourable conditions for agriculture.
Nevertheless it would be incorrect to regard such areas as a population
'vacuum'. The intramontane depressions can be cultivated, and lumbering and mining communities are also important (the upper Jiu valley
being the outstanding example of the latter). There are also metallurgical
centres (the largest being Hunedoara and Reşiţa) and small mountain
resorts and spa-towns (especially in the Eastern and Southern Carpathians). The surrounding plains are more populous, although it should
be noted that the areas of best soils do not necessarily carry the highest
rural densities. Thus these are rather low in the southernmost parts of
the Danubian Plain, and also in the Bărăgan Plain and the Dobrogea.
These areas were not brought under widespread cultivation until the
19th century, when large estates producing grain for the export trade
were developed. Their scarce surface-water supplies and rather low rainfall meant that they had not been attractive to a subsistence peasantry.
The highest rural densities of Moldavia and Wallachia are found, in fact,
in the Sub-Carpathian belt and the adjoining part of the plains. Here a
broad populous zone stretches in a great arc from Suceava through
Bacău, Ploieşti and Piteşti, to Turnu Severin. This zone is fairly well
watered and presented an environment where cultivation, pastoral
activities and fruit-growing could be combined. Lying away from the
routes taken across the plains by invading peoples and enjoying some
degree of natural protection this zone was the cradle of the two Principalities. In modern times this populous zone has been further reinforced as
a result of the development of the oilfields, especially that of Ploieşti.
A further contrast with the plains is that villages tend to be smaller and
closer together.

Lying within the Carpathian ramparts is the well-populated Transylvanian Basin with its old-established urban centres and modern industries. This zone has links south-westwards along the Mureş to Deva and Hunedoara, south-eastwards to Braşov, lying in its depression, and north-westwards over the low Someş Hills to Baia-Mare and the Tisa Plain. The latter is also well populated, and, owing to the way in which broad embayments penetrate the Western Carpathians, the mountainous areas do not present such a sharp contrast in density as do the Southern Carpathians in Wallachia. The Danube delta, owing to its natural conditions, is very thinly peopled.

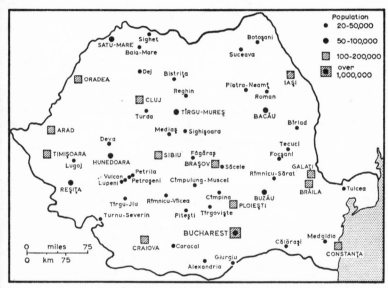

Fig. 54. Distribution of chief cities and towns in Rumania

Urbanization of the population has been gathering momentum in recent years. In 1948 less than a quarter of the population was living in towns, but by 1964 the proportion was one-third. Many small towns have undergone industrialization and some new urban communities have also developed, usually in connection with either mining or chemicals. For instance, a chain of small centres has developed in the Trotuş valley of Moldavia, where brown coal is mined for power-stations and local petroleum and salt are utilized, together with Transylvanian natural gas, for the chemical industry. Bucharest, with one-fifth of the urban population, remains by far the largest city. The location of towns with more than 20,000 inhabitants is shown in Fig. 54.

BUCHAREST (*Bucureşti*) (Fig. 55) (1,240,000 in 1964, or 1,372,000 with suburbs) is first mentioned, as the 'Dîmboviţa citadel', in the 14th century, and in the 17th century it became the capital of the Principality of Wallachia, supplanting Tîrgovişte, which itself had succeeded Curtea de Argeş (north of Piteşti) in the 16th. Like other towns of the Wallachian Plain or the Carpathian foothills, its early functions

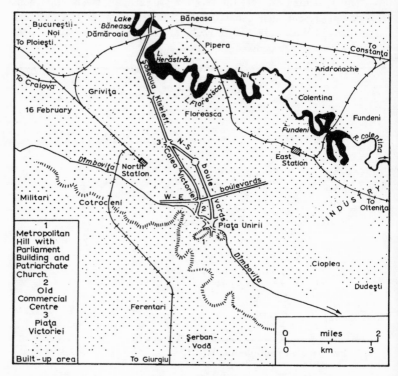

Fig. 55. Bucharest

were primarily those of a trading centre strategically located between the Carpathians and the Danube.

The early settlement, lying astride the small, meandering River Dîmboviţa, developed on and around several hillocks corresponding to dissected terrace-remnants. The *Curtea Veche* (Old Palace), located on the north bank of the stream, has long since disappeared, but three small eminences on the south bank still survive, together with their 16th–17th-century churches. The middle one is crowned by the Patriarchate Church and the adjacent, but more modern, Parliament Building.

At its foot part of the centre of the old city is now represented by the large open space known as Union Square (*Piaţa Unirii*), under which flows the culverted Dîmboviţa.

When Bucharest became the capital of Rumania after the union of the Principalities in 1859 it was a sprawling semi-rural city of about 100,000 inhabitants that had doubled in population in the previous three decades. Shops, workshops and inns, interspersed with the great houses and gardens of the wealthy boyars, lined the thoroughfares radiating from the banks of the Dîmboviţa, and already the lower end of the *Calea Victoriei* (Victory Street) and the area adjoining it to the east had become the commercial heart of the city. The northward extension of the *Calea Victoriei*, the Kiseleff Highway (*Şoseaua Kiseleff*), had been laid out in the 1830s under the stimulus of the Russian governor whose name it still bears.

In the half-century between 1859 and the First World War there was further rapid growth, the population rising to about 350,000. The first railway connection (to Giurgiu on the Danube) was completed in 1869, with a terminus in the south of the city. Subsequently other lines converged on the North station (1870), which became the main passenger station (the East station being chiefly important for freight). There was also substantial factory development, chiefly concerned with foodstuffs, textiles and other consumer goods. Ornate public buildings provided a new element in the heterogeneous townscape of central Bucharest, the west–east boulevards took shape, and the course of the Dîmboviţa was straightened and regulated. New residential areas, often of poor quality, proliferated in a largely unplanned manner.

Between the two World Wars the population more than doubled, and it was now that Bucharest became nicknamed 'Little Paris' (complete with an Arc de Triomphe). In the centre of the city the broad north–south boulevards were completed, superseding the narrow, but fashionable, Calea Victoriei as the main north–south artery. The two thoroughfares converge at the Piaţa Victoriei. The building of shops, flats and hotels in a very modern style produced what is still the most impressive thoroughfare in south-eastern Europe. Further north high-class villas were built. Such developments contrasted with the unpaved side streets and insanitary conditions existing in large parts of the city, with which town-planning schemes of the time were unable to cope. Since the Second World War, during which Bucharest received (1944) damage from Allied air attacks, much has been done to remedy these shortcomings and new residential areas have also been laid out.

There was also a further expansion of industry between the wars, in particular the growth of the large 'Malaxa' metallurgical and engineering complex on the east side of the city, partly controlled by foreign interests. Since the war industry has shown further expansion, related both to the enlarging of existing plants and to the building of new ones. Today Bucharest accounts for about one-fifth of Rumania's industrial output. To the east of the city is the enlarged 'Malaxa' works (now '23 August') and the adjoining 'Republica' steel-tube plant, while another industrial zone exists to the west, including railway workshops and a chemical engineering plant in Griviţa and factories for agricultural machinery, food-products and ready-made clothing in Cotroceni and Militari. The area near the East station also has industrial premises. There is a large tyre factory at Popeşti-Leordeni to the south-east, and another rubber works is located to the south at Jilava. Other products of Bucharest are motor-buses, trolley-buses, rail tankers, machine-tools, oilfield equipment, radio and electrical equipment and varied foodstuffs and textiles.

As a city of the plains Bucharest experiences biting winter winds and oppressive dusty conditions in the summer months, when the now-vanished wealthy classes used to retreat to resorts in the Carpathians. Summer amenities are provided locally by the parks and lidos on the banks of the lakes that are situated along the course of the Colentina (a tributary of Dîmboviţa) on the northern and north-eastern fringes of the city.

ARAD (115,000) is situated on the right bank of the Mureş, with an old Habsburg fortress lying within a meander on the opposite bank, where also newer quarters have developed. There are food-processing and textile industries and large railway workshops producing carriages and wagons. The production of machine-tools has recently developed. Part of the population is Hungarian.

BRĂILA (122,000) is only 20 km/12 miles upstream from Galaţi, but is separated from it by marshy ground along the River Siret. Like Galaţi the town developed rapidly in the 19th century, and it was laid out according to a pattern of concentric streets intersected by radiating thoroughfares. In addition to the building and repair of river-craft and varied engineering activities there is a new factory nearby that processes the reeds of the Danube delta into cellulose for board and artificial fibres.

BRAŞOV (Hungarian *Brassó*, German *Kronstadt*) (137,000) is situated about 625 m/2,000 ft above sea-level and lies at the foot of the Carpathians, on the southern margin of the extensive Braşov or Bîrsa depression. Controlling the important Predeal pass leading southwards to the Wallachian Plain, Braşov developed as a medieval 'Saxon' town. The centre, dominated by an old fortress, still maintains a Germanic appearance, with a massive Gothic church overlooking a large market-square with radiating narrow streets. Germans and Hungarians still form a considerable part of the population. In the 1920s an aircraft industry was set up and more recently Braşov has become a major centre for the manufacture of ball-bearings, lorries and tractors. There are a number of industrial satellites, including Rîşnov and Săcele, and the whole administrative territory of Braşov has a population of 225,000.

CLUJ (Hungarian *Kolozsvár*, German *Klausenburg*) (167,000) was once the site of the Roman-Dacian city of *Napoca*, but the present settlement was established in the 12th century by 'Saxon' settlers. The city, with its fine Gothic churches and remains of old walls, lies on the Little Someş in a broad depression that opens out eastwards into the Transylvanian Plain. It has always been an important centre of Hungarian and Rumanian culture and there is a joint university using both languages. In addition to food-processing activities there is a footwear industry, and new factories make electrodes, sparking-plugs, textile machinery and refrigerators.

CONSTANŢA (121,000), the leading seaport of Rumania, occupies the site of the ancient Greek (later Roman) city of *Tomis*, which was devastated by the Avars in about A.D. 600. The present city dates essentially from the 19th century and was greatly stimulated by the building of the railway to Cernavodă, on the Danube, in 1860. The harbour, overlooked by the town, occupies the northern side of a slight embayment cut into the low Dobrogea platform. The rapid growth of turnover (about 7 m tons in 1965) is leading to harbour extensions in a southward direction. Oil, grain and timber are the traditional exports of Constanţa, but the growth of Rumanian industry is now leading to exports of cement, chemicals and machinery. To the north and south of Constanţa there is a chain of growing seaside resorts, including Mamaia, Eforie and Mangalia, while Techirghiol has a mud lake with therapeutic properties.

CRAIOVA (122,000), the chief town of Oltenia, is situated where the Getic Platform merges into the Wallachian Plain. It is an ancient trading centre with Roman antecedents (*Pelendava*), where routes from the Plain met those from the Carpathian passes. In addition to food-processing and textile factories, there is a new electrical engineering industry (locomotives and transformers). A large chemical complex using natural gas is being developed north of the city, together with a large thermal power-station served by lignite from the Jiu and Motru valleys.

GALAŢI (113,000) is one of the two leading river-ports and will shortly become Rumania's chief iron and steel centre when the large new plant is completed. The town stands above the river, with the port and main industrial zone located on lower ground further downstream near Lake Brateş. Galaţi has engineering works, shipyards and a steel-rolling mill and it is also an important railway node. The town was badly damaged in the Second World War.

IAŞI (124,000) occupies rising ground on the north side of the valley of the Bahlui, a tributary of the Jijia. It is an old trading centre and succeeded Suceava as the Moldavian capital in 1565, since when it has been one of the leading centres of Rumanian culture, although in modern times it has been very much overshadowed in size and influence by Bucharest. There are numerous churches and monasteries, chiefly dating from the 16th and 17th centuries. Iaşi is an important railway centre and also has modern textile, timber-working, plastics and pharmaceutical factories. It still retains a considerable Jewish population, but this is less numerous than formerly.

ORADEA (Hungarian *Nagyvárád*) (111,000) is situated on the 'Rapid' Criş, where the western foothills of the Bihor Massif descend to the Tisa Plain. It was an important urban centre of medieval Hungary, but was devastated by the Turks in the 16th century and did not fully recover until the 18th, after their withdrawal. In addition to food-processing and textile activities there are footwear and engineering, including machine-tool, factories. Much of the population is Hungarian.

PETROŞENI (32,000) is the leading town of the upper Jiu valley coalfield. Its administrative territory also includes a number of other mining towns, including Lupeni, Petrila and Vulcan (total population 137,000).

PLOIEŞTI (134,000) lies nearly 60 km/35 miles north of Bucharest near the northern margin of the Danubian Plain. It grew rapidly after the development of the Prahova valley oilfield in the latter part of the 19th century, but suffered considerable damage in the Second World War. In addition to oil-refineries, there is an oilfield equipment industry that also serves foreign markets.

SIBIU (Hungarian *Nagyszeben*, German *Hermannstadt*) (103,000) was founded by 'Saxon' settlers in the 12th century on an old Romano-Dacian site and, like Braşov, it still retains a considerable German population. The picturesque old town is situated on a slight eminence within the Sibiu depression, lying between the Carpathians and the low, rolling Tîrnava Platform. To the south is the Red Tower Pass leading to the Danubian Plain. Sibiu has textile and engineering industries.

TIMIŞOARA (Hungarian *Temesvár*) (152,000) lies on the canalized Bega (navigable for small craft), the old town being built around a fortress on the north bank. Between 1552 and 1716 it was under Turkish occupation. It is the chief urban centre of the rich Banat lowlands and has Hungarian, Serb and 'Swabian' German minorities. There are engineering, footwear and food-processing industries.

Transport and Trade

The railway network of Rumania is not dense by West European standards and only a few lines are as yet double-track (e.g. Bucharest–Braşov) or electrified. Although extensions to the system continue to be made, its main outline was laid down before 1918 and thus still reflects to some extent the fact that the network in Moldavia and Wallachia was developed separately from that of Transylvania and adjoining territories then forming part of Hungary. The 1918 frontier coincided, moreover, with the Eastern and Southern Carpathians, so that physical geography reinforced the effect of political separation. Even today there are only six trans-Carpathian lines between the Ukrainian border in the north and the Danube gorge in the south-west. They use, respectively, the following routes: Cîmpulung and Dorna depressions, Trotuş valley–Ciuc depression (Ghimeş–Palanca pass), Predeal, 'Red Tower', Lainici, and Cerna–Timiş valleys ('Porta Orientalis').

The fact that Transylvania has failed to develop a central major railway node would appear to be due to the effect of the Carpathians as a physical, and formerly political, obstacle, and to the fact that Bucharest, centrally placed for Moldavia–Wallachia, was retained as capital after the territorial enlargement following the First World War. Only Braşov, which controls traffic passing between Bucharest and Transylvania, can be said to be an important junction. Most of the major traffic nodes are thus located in the plains, Bucharest and Timişoara being particularly important.

The railway pattern consists of what may be described as an outer 'horse-shoe' of lowland lines running parallel to the Eastern, Southern and Western Carpathians, with routes branching off to the Soviet Ukraine, Soviet Moldavia, Constanţa, the Danube bank (opposite Bulgaria), Jugoslavia and Hungary. There are also lines leading through the Carpathians into Transylvania, where the network is further strengthened by a number of cross-links. Even so the Transylvanian network lacks coherence, having been built by a large number of private companies. There is no direct line between Braşov and Cluj, the two largest cities.

Bucharest is the centre of a radial network that reaches out to (a) Ploieşti, Braşov and Transylvania, (b) the Moldavian Platform and Galaţi and Brăila, (c) Constanţa, via the Feteşti–Cernavodă bridge (1895) over the Danube and the Ialomiţa Marsh, (d) Giurgiu and thence, by the Friendship Bridge (1954), over the Danube to Ruse in Bulgaria, (e) Craiova via Caracal (which has a line through the Red Tower gorge to Sibiu), (f) Piteşti, with branches to Tîrgovişte and Cîmpulung-Muscel.

In Moldavia there are two north–south lines passing through Suceava, Roman, Bacău and Focşani (for Bucharest) and through Iaşi, Bîrlad and Tecuci (for Bucharest, Constanţa and Galaţi). Craiova commands routes through the Cerna and Timiş valleys to Timişoara (via Turnu Severin) and through the Lainici pass to Petroşeni (a Carpathian link only completed in the 1940s). In the Tisa Plain there is a line northwards from Timişoara to Arad, Oradea and Satu-Mare. Road transport, although growing, is as yet relatively little developed and much improvement of the highway network remains to be done. Băneasa airport, north of Bucharest, has connections with the leading provincial cities and also with many countries of Europe.

Waterway communications in Rumania relate almost entirely to the Danube. Timişoara, in the Banat, has barge traffic on the canalized Bega, however, and the lower courses of the Danube's tributaries are also navigable for small craft, especially the Prut and the Siret. While the Danube is an important traffic artery its very width makes it a formidable physical obstacle to land communications with Bulgaria. The only bridge linking the two countries (the combined road and rail 'Friendship' Bridge between Giurgiu and Ruse) was completed as recently as 1954. Rail-head ports on the Rumanian bank of the Danube are connected by ferry or boat with Bulgarian ports, but only at Calafat is there a Bulgarian rail-head directly opposite (at Vidin).

Navigation of the Danube, which flows through Rumanian territory for over 1,000 km/620 miles, is hampered by certain natural obstacles, although these have been partially overcome since the late 19th century. The two chief areas of difficulty are the gorge section and the delta. Frozen conditions for several weeks in the winter and low water conditions in the late summer can also impede navigation. The gorge section occurs where the Danube has incised a meandering course through the Carpathians (Banat Mountains), here over 100 km/60 miles wide, as they swing southwards into Serbia. Gorge features do not occur continuously, however, and there are several broad open stretches. The hazard to navigation consists of the shallow waters and rocks of the five cataracts, with their swift currents. The lowest, between Orşova and Turnu Severin and known as the Iron Gate or Gates, sometimes gives its name, rather erroneously, to the whole length of the gorge section. In the 1890s, under Austro–Hungarian auspices, great improvements were made, as a result of the blasting of channels through the reefs, combined with protection by a mole at the Iron Gates (Sip canal of 1898), where, however, locomotive traction on the Jugoslav bank is necessary to haul vessels upstream. Vessels of 1,000 tons can navigate the gorge section under normal conditions. Some trans-shipment of goods to the railway system takes place at Orşova. Conditions in the gorge section will be radically changed as a result of the joint project for hydro-power and navigation now being undertaken by Rumania and Jugoslavia and scheduled for completion by the early 1970s. A large dam (54 m/177 ft high) at Gura Văii (opposite Sip in Jugoslavia), with a power-station and lock-gates at either end, will impound a lake stretching back up the gorge section for over 100 km/60 miles. The time needed for passage will be greatly reduced and simultaneous two-way traffic, as well as night navigation, will be possible. Craft of 4,000–5,000 tons will be able to use the improved facilities.

In the delta the chief difficulty is silting, resulting in the need for constant dredging. Here, too, improvements were made at the end of the 19th century; the Sulina arm was straightened and deepened (1902) to become the navigable channel through the delta. Projects for a canal through the Dobrogea which would avoid the delta and thus reduce the distance from the sea by 250 km/150 miles, were put forward over a hundred years ago, and the British company that built the railway line from Cernavodă to Constanţa in 1860 obtained a concession for this purpose also. In the early 1950s a wasteful attempt was made by Rumania to fulfil such a dream. The canal was to run from Cernavodă to a point north of Constanţa, utilizing small valleys cut into the low platform of the southern Dobrogea. Eventually, in 1953, the project was quietly abandoned.

Traffic on the Danube increased considerably in the years before the First World War, and between the wars continued to rise, although spasmodically. Much damage to installations and river-craft occurred in the Second World War and the restoration of pre-1939 facilities took much time. Moreover, for several years after 1948, the defection of Jugoslavia from the Soviet bloc led to some interruption of traffic. Commodity-flows on the Danube have always tended to be predominantly downstream and before the Second World War typically involved oil, timber and grain. Today upward movements are tending to increase as a result of the import of raw materials, especially fuels and metal ores, to sustain the growing industrial potential of Rumania and also Bulgaria, Jugoslavia, Hungary and Slovakia. Nevertheless the volume of traffic on the Danube remains small by comparison with that on the Rhine. Traffic may be expected to increase impressively with the completion of the Iron Gates project. The Rhine–Main–Danube canal should also be completed in the 1970s and possibly the Odra–Danube canal.

Owing to its economic and strategic importance to both riparian and non-riparian states the Danube has been subjected to some degree of international control in modern times. At the end of the Crimean War a

European Danube Commission was created by the Treaty of Paris (1856), consisting of Rumania, Great Britain, France and Italy. It exercised authority over the 'maritime' part of the river and delta, from Brăila to the sea, and carried out improvements for navigation. In 1921 an International Danube Commission was set up to promote freedom of navigation and also technical improvements on the 'fluvial' section of the river, i.e. upstream from Brăila to Ulm in Germany. The Commissions lapsed in the Second World War, and in 1948 a new Commission sponsored by the Soviet Union was set up (against the protests of the Western Powers), consisting only of the riparian states in the Soviet bloc, including the Soviet Union itself. The Soviet Union jointly controls the delta with Rumania, and Jugoslavia and Rumania administer the gorge section.

The chief port and only significant seaport of Rumania is Constanţa. It handles over two-thirds of all water-borne foreign trade. Next in importance are the two large river-ports of Galaţi and Brăila, which are accessible to sea-going vessels of 6,000 tons. Brăila is 170 km/100 miles from the sea. The close proximity to each other of the two ports is due to the fact that before the political and economic union of the Principalities Galaţi served Moldavia and Brăila Wallachia. Traditionally the former specialized in handling timber, floated down the Siret, and the latter in grain, but this distinction is no longer so marked. The river-port of Giurgiu is connected by a short rail haul (1869) to Bucharest and also has a pipe-line link with the Ploieşti oilfields. Its large oil exports have at times made it the second port of the country. The smaller river-ports include Orşova, Turnu Severin, Calafat, Corabia, Turnu Măgurele, Zimnicea, Olteniţa, Călăraşi, Cernavodă, Hîrşova and Măcin. In the delta Tulcea is a fishing port and Sulina is a small port of call for vessels entering the river. About 40% of Rumania's foreign trade is conducted by sea and nearly all the remainder moves by rail.

Before the Second World War Rumania's exports chiefly consisted of petroleum products, timber and foodstuffs, especially grain. These still remain important, but increasing emphasis is now placed on higher-value food products, such as refined sugar, sunflower oil, wines and preserved fruit, meat and vegetables, and a wide variety of wood products is also exported, including furniture, packing-cases, veneers, woodblocks, plywood, pulp, paper and fibreboard. Manufactured items, including engineering products (e.g. electrical goods, oilfield equipment, railway rolling-stock, tractors, lorries, ships and river-craft), cement, chemicals, tyres, footwear and textiles, are now also achieving importance. Some raw materials are exported, such as natural gas (to Hungary) and manganese ore, as well as non-ferrous metals. Imports include machinery, vehicles, coking coal and iron ore. Tropical foodstuffs and raw materials are increasingly purchased from underdeveloped countries in exchange for Rumanian manufactures and capital equipment. Rumania is active in the export of oil-drilling and refinery equipment, for instance. Over two-thirds of the foreign trade turnover is with the other Socialist countries, especially the Soviet Union, with whom Rumania had negligible contacts in the inter-war period. Much industrial plant is now supplied to Rumania by Western countries, however. Tourism is being encouraged as a source of foreign exchange, the Black Sea and Carpathian resorts being the chief attractions. Foreign trade is growing rapidly and the Rumanian economy had one of the highest rates of expansion in the world in the early 1960s. With large labour reserves, a wide variety of raw materials and a surplus of food output Rumania can look forward to a prosperous future as a balanced industrial-agricultural state.

Appendix 1

THE LANGUAGES OF EAST-CENTRAL EUROPE

Article One of the Universal Declaration of Human Rights (1948) of the United Nations Organization is reproduced below in English and in fourteen national and minority languages of East-Central Europe, so that some of the linguistic similarities and differences alluded to in the text may be readily observed.

Of special interest are: the closeness to each other of the various Slavonic languages, the similarity of Rumanian to Italian, and the obvious lack of resemblance of Hungarian (and Turkish) to any of the Indo-European languages. Amongst the latter the words for 'brother' ('frat-', 'brat-', etc.) show a close affinity.

In some instances external influences are discernible: thus Romance elements (e.g. the words for 'dignity' and 'conscience') are found in Albanian–as also in English. The Rumanian verb 'trebuie' (denoting obligation) is Slavonic in origin, and if a more colloquial passage could have been chosen the frequency of Slavonic words would have been higher. Amongst the Slavonic languages Bulgarian and Macedonian are distinctive for their use of a post-positional definite article (e.g. endings in '-to' and '-ta').

A. Indo-European Languages

(a) GERMANIC

English:

All human beings are born free and equal in dignity and rights. They are endowed with reason and conscience and should act towards one another in a spirit of brotherhood.

German:

Alle Menschen sind frei und gleich an Würde und Rechten geboren. Sie sind mit Vernunft und Gewissen begabt und sollen einander im Geiste der Brüderlichkeit begegnen.

(b) ROMANCE (LATIN)

Italian:

Tutti gli esseri umani nascono liberi ed eguali in dignità e diritti. Essi sono dotati di ragione e di coscienza e devono agire gli uni verso gli altri in spirito di fratellanza.

Rumanian:

Toti oamenii se nasc liberi şi egali în demnitate şi în drepturi. Ei sînt înzestraţi cu raţiune şi conştiintă si trebuie să se comporte unii faţă de ceilalţi în spirit frăţesc.

322

(c) South Slavonic

Bulgarian: *
Vsichki choveshki sŭshtestva se razhdat svobodin i ravni po dostoynstvo i prava. Te sa nadareni s razum i sŭznanie i tryabva da deystvuvat v otnosheniyata si edni kŭm drugi v dukh na bratstvo.

Macedonian: †
Site čovečki suštestva se raďaat slobodni i ednakvi vo dostoinstvoto i pravata. Tie se obdareni so razum i svest i treba edni sprema drugi da postapuvaat vo duhot na bratstvoto.

Serbo-Croat:
Sva ljudska bića raďaju se slobodna i jednaka u dostojanstvu i pravima. Ona su obdarena razumom i svešću i treba jedni prema drugima da postupaju u duhu bratstva.

Slovene:
Vsi ljudje se rodijo prosti in imajo enako dostojanstvo in enake pravice. Obdarjeni so s pametjo in zavestjo in bi morali ravnati drug z drugim kakor bratje.

(d) West and East Slavonic

Czech:
Všichni lidé rodí se svobodní a sobě rovní co do důstojnosti a práv. Jsou nadáni rozumem a svědomím a mají spolu jednati v duchu bratrství.

Slovak:
Všetci l'udia sa rodia slobodní a sebe rovní, čo sa týka ich dôstojnosti a práv. Sú obdarení rozumom a majú navzájom jednat' v bratskom duchu.

Polish:
Wszyscy ludzie rodzą się wolni i równi pod względem swej godności i swych praw. Są oni obdarzeni rozumem i sumieniem i powinni postępować wobec innych w duchu braterstwa.

Ukrainian East Slavonic: ‡
Vsi lyudy narodzhuyut'sya vil'nymy i rivnymy u svoyiy hidnosti ta pravakh. Vony nadileni rozumom i sovistyu i povynni diyaty u vidnoshenni odyn do odnoho v dusi braterstva.

(e) Other

Albanian:
Të gjitha krijesat njerzore lindin të lira dhe të barabarta në dinjitetin dhe të drejtat. Ato disponojnë arsyen dhe koshjencën dhe njeni ndaj tjetrit duhet të verpojë në frymën e vllaznimit.

* Transliterated from the Cyrillic according to the system adopted by the Permanent Committee on Geographical Names for British Official Use.
† Transliterated from the Cyrillic according to the Serbo–Croat Roman system.
‡ Transliterated from the Cyrillic according to the system proposed by the Permanent Committee on Geographical Names for British Official Use.

B. Other Languages

Hungarian (Magyar):

Minden emberi lény szabadon születik és egyenlő méltósága és joga van. Az emberek, ésszel és lelkiismerettel birván, egymással szemben testvéri szellemben kell hogy viseltessenek.

Turkish:

Bütün insanlar hür, haysiyet ve haklar bakımından eşit doğarlar. Akıl ve vicdana sahiptirler ve birbirlerine karşı kardeşlik zihniyeti ile hareket etmelidirler.

Appendix 2

GUIDE TO THE PRONUNCIATION OF GEOGRAPHICAL NAMES

The pronunciation of foreign place-names is a problem that is only too readily glossed over by many teachers and students of geography. Ease of familiarization with a country is reduced if a place-name has to be remembered merely as an awkward sequence of letters to which a fumbling and knowingly make-shift pronunciation is given by each individual. Only French place-names appear to be immune from this fate, no doubt for the simple reason that French is the first foreign language taught in most schools. No one would refer to Bordeaux as 'Bor-dukes', yet few geographers take the trouble to discover the correct pronunciation of, say, Katowice, Liberec, Szeged, Rijeka or Timisoara, even though the languages of East-Central Europe are written phonetically to a very large extent. Englishmen are disconcerted if a foreigner refers to Carlisle as 'Tsar-lis-lé', but at the same time they usually feel entitled to award any pronunciation they wish to other nations' place-names. The fact that a Pole pronounces Łódź as 'Woodge' (approximately) is no more quaint than the fact that the Englishman uses the form 'Carlisle' where the Pole would write 'Karlajl'.

It is with these thoughts in mind that a guide to the approximate pro-nunciation of place-names in East-Central Europe is given below, in the hope that readers will not be too self-conscious to try it out. After much considera-tion it was decided that to adopt the International Phonetic Alphabet would be too unwieldy a solution, and so a very simple English transcription has been used that will do service for all the languages involved. While far from perfect the system will give the user a recognizable imitation of the correct pro-nunciation. Details are given below. Stressed syllables are shown in italics. All renderings have been checked with speakers of the languages concerned.

KEY

1. Vowels

a – as in 'bar', but slightly shorter

e – as in 'bet'

i – as in 'machine'

o – as in 'for' or 'fog' – preferably between the two

u – as in 'rule'

ŭ – as in 'bun'

y – as in 'hymn', (*a*) when between two consonants, or (*b*) when at the end of a word and following a consonant. (See 2b and 3 below for the use of y after and before a vowel)

Unstressed vowel sounds often tend to lose their full value

2. Diphthongs

(a) au – as in 'Frau' or 'sauerkraut'

eu – like 'airw' in 'airway', but *without* pronouncing the 'r'

ou – as in 'mould'

ŭu – like 'Urw' in 'Urwin', but *without* pronouncing the 'r' (or like 'aw' in 'away')

(b) ay – as in 'Aye, aye, Sir', 'kayak' or 'Haydn'

ey – as in 'they'

oy – as in 'boy'

uy – like '-ue y-' in 'blue yarn' said quickly

ŭy – like '-ur y-' in 'cur yelp' said quickly, but *without* pronouncing the 'r' (or as in French 'feuille' or 'œil')

3. Consonants

As in English approximately, but note the following:

ch – always as in 'church'

g – always as in 'get'

h – in the Slavonic languages it usually resembles the 'ch' in Scots 'loch' or German 'Bach', rather than the English 'h'

(A 'k' sound must be carefully avoided, however)

r – always 'rolled' (as in Scots pronunciation)

s – always as in 'soon' or 'alas'

y – before a vowel like 'y' in 'yet'

zh – like 's' in 'measure' (or French 'je')

Note that 'dzh' is therefore like the 'dg' in 'edge'

' – 'softens' the preceding consonant. The sound is similar to the beginning of the 'y' sound in such words as 'Goodyear', 'Lockyer', 'halyard', 'canyon' or 'Lutyens'. Compare the softened 'n' in the French 'campagne'

4. Stress

The syllable with the main stress is indicated in italics. In some instances the method of splitting words into syllables is deliberately unconventional in order to aid more accurate pronunciation. Thus, for instance, stressed syllables ending in 'o' have been avoided where possible, so that English diphthongs shall not be unconsciously introduced. (If English-speaking persons could be trusted to pronounce 'fo' as in 'for' or 'fog' and not as in 'foe' this would not be necessary.)

ALBANIAN

The stress follows certain rules relating to the inflection of nouns, but generalization is not possible.

Place-name spellings may differ from one source to another, for the following reasons. Firstly, Italian renderings may be used, e.g. Durazzo for Durrës, or

Valona for Vlorë. Secondly, there are differences resulting from the existence of the two dialects, e.g. substitution of Tosk 'r' by Geg 'n' and vice versa, so that both Gjinokastër and Gjirokastër and Vlonë and Vlorë may be used, although the local, Tosk, population would use the latter form in both instances.

Thirdly, there is the frequent use in Albanian of the 'definite' form of place-names instead of the 'indefinite', e.g. Durrës–indefinite, but Durrësi–definite, or Shkodër–indefinite, but Shkodra–definite. The definite form tends to be used on Albanian-produced maps, although road-signs use the indefinite form. The latter is preferred here, in conformity with the system adopted by the Permanent Committee on Geographical Names for British Official Use.

Note:

VOWELS

ë –ŭ (but silent in Geg)

y   s in French 'tu', but shown below as 'u'

CONSONANTS

c –ts

ç –ch

dh–as in English 'the', and shown below as 'th'

gj –dy (or gy)

j   –y

q –ch (or ky)

th –as in English 'thin'

x –dz

xh –dzh

B		**G**	
Berat	Be-*rat*	Gjirokastër	Dyi-ro-*kas*-tŭr
Bistricë	Bi-*stri*-tsŭ	Gjuhëz	Dyu-*hŭz*
Bulqizë	Bul-*chi*-zŭ	**J**	
Buenë	Bu-*e*-nŭ	Jezercë	Ye-*zer*-tsŭ
C		**K**	
Cërrik	Tsŭr-*rik*	Karaburun	Ka-ra-bu-*run*
Çermenikë	Cher-me-*ni*-kŭ	Kavajë	Kav-*ay*-ŭ
D		Korçë	*Kor*-chŭ
Dajti	*Day*-ti	Krrabë	*Kra*-bŭ
Devoll	De-*vol*	Kuçovë	Ku-*chov*-ŭ
Drin i bardhë	Drin i barth-(ŭ)	Kukës	*Ku*-kŭs
Durrës	*Dur*-rŭs	Kurbnesh	Kurb-*nesh*
E		**L**	
Elbasan	El-ba-*san*	Lushnjë	*Lush*-nyŭ
Erzen	Er-*zen*	**M**	
F		Maliq	Ma-*lich*
Fier	Fi-*er*	Mallakastër	Ma-la-*kas*-tŭr

Memaliaj	Mem-al-i-*ay*
Mirditë	Mir-*di*-tŭ
Myzeqe	Mu-*ze*-che

O

Ohër	*O*-hŭr
Osum	Os-*um*

P

Pishkash	Pish-*kash*
Pogradec	Pog-ra-*dets*
Prenjës	*Pren*-yŭs

Q

Qytet(i) Stalin	Chu-*tet*-(i) *Sta*-lin

R

Rubik	Ru-*bik*

S

Sarandë	Sa-*ran*-dŭ
Sazan	Sa-*zan*
Selenicë	Se-le-*ni*-tsŭ
Seman	Se-*man*
Shëngjin	Shŭn-*dyin*
Shkodër	*Shkod*-ŭr
Shkumbin	Shkum-*bin*
Shqiperia	Shchi-pe-*ri*-a
Shushicë	Shu-*shi*-tsŭ

T

Tepelenë	Te-pe-*le*-nŭ
Tiranë	Ti-*ra*-nŭ

U

Ulzë	*Ul*-zŭ

V

Vjosë	*Vyo*-sŭ
Vlorë	*Vlor*-ŭ

BULGARIAN

Place-names have been transliterated from the Cyrillic alphabet according to the system adopted by the Permanent Committee on Geographical Names for British Official Use (*List of Names: New Series*, 4: *Bulgaria*) (Royal Geographical Society, 1959). The only difference between this system and the one adopted by the author for pronunciation purposes is the P.C.G.N. use of 'kh' instead of 'h' for the Cyrillic letter x. A Roman alphabet with diacritical signs is sometimes used on maps of Bulgaria for foreigners. The P.C.G.N. letter 'ŭ' is represented by 'å' in this system.

A

Ar-da
A-*sen*-ov-grad

B

Ba-*tak*
Be-*las*-i-tsa
Be-lo-grad-*chik*
Bla-*go*-ev-grad
Bob-ov-dol
Bot-ev-grad
Bre-*zha*-ni

C

Chip-rov-tsi

D

Di-*mi*-trov-grad
Dob-ru-dzha

Dol-ni Dŭb-*nik*
Drag-o-*man*
Drag-o-*vish*-ti-tsa

E

E-*le*-na
E-li-*sey*-na
Em-i-ne

G

Gab-ro-vo
Gol-*yam* Pe-re-*lik*
Gor-na Or-*yakh*-o-vi-tsa

I

Ikh-ti-*man*
Is-kŭr
I-*vay*-lov-grad

K

Kal-i-*ak*-ra
Kam-chi-ya
Kar-no-*bat*
Kar-lo-vo
Kaz-an-*lŭk*
Khas-ko-vo
Ko-*la*-rov-grad
Kra-*ish*-te
Kre-*mi*-kov-tsi
Kru-mo-vo
Kŭr-dzha-li

L

Lov-ech
Lu-do-*gor*-i-e

M

Ma-*dan*

Ma-*ri*-tsa
Mar-*ti*-no-vo
Me-*det*
Mes-ta
Mo-*chu*-ri-tsa
Mom-in
Mu-sa-*la*

N

Ne-*seb*-ŭr
Ni-*sha*-va

O

Og-*os*-ta
Og-*razh*-den
Os-og-*ov*-o
Os-ŭm

P

Pa-na-*gyu*-rish-te
Paz-ar-dzhik
Per-nik
Pir-*dop*
Pi-rin
Plach-kov-tsi
Plev-en
Plis-ka
Plov-div
Po-*mor*-i-e
Pres-*lav*
Pro-*va*-di-ya

R

Ra-*kov*-ski
Rad-o-mir
Raz-grad
Re-*ka Dev*-nya
Ri-la
Ro-*dop*-i

Ros-en
Ros-*i*-tsa
Ru-do-*zem*
Ru-en
Ru-*pel*
Ru-se

S

Sa-*kar*
Sam-o-kov
Saz-*li*-yk-a
Sev-*li*-e-vo
Shab-la
Ship-ka
Si-*li*-stra
Sli-ven
Sof-i-a
Sred-na Gor-*a*
Stam-bo-*li*-ys-ki
Stan-ke Di-mi-*trov*
Sta-ra Pla-ni-*na*

Sta-ra Za-*gor*-a
Stran-dzha
Stru-ma
Stru-*mesh*-ni-tsa
Stru-*mi*-tsa
Strya-ma
Stu-*den Klad*-en-ets
Stu-*de*-na
Sŭr-ne-na *Sred*-na
   Gor-*a*
Sŭsh-*tin*-ska *Sred*-na
   Gor-*a*
Svi-len-grad
Svish-*tov*
Svog-e
Syut-*kyar*

T

Tol-*bu*-khin
To-*pol*-ni-tsa
Troy-*an*

Tun-dzha
Tŭrn-o-vo

U

U-strem

V

Var-na
Vel-in-grad
Vi-din
Vikh-ren
Visk-*yar*
Vi-to-sha
Vrats-a
Vŭch-a

Y

Yam-bol

Z

Zlat-ni *Pyas*-ŭt-si

CZECHOSLOVAK

In Czech the stress is on the first syllable, but not always so in Slovak.

Note:

VOWELS

á   –long a

é   –long e

ě   –ye

í ⎫
ý ⎬ –long i

ú, ů –long u

CONSONANTS

c –ts

č –ch

ch –like ch in 'loch', but shown below as h

ď –dy (d')

h –English h

j –y

ň –ny (n')

ř –like rzh or rsh (but the r often scarcely audible)

š –sh

v –often like f when final or before another consonant

ž –zh

B

Banská Bystrica	*Ban*-ska *Bys*-tri-tsa
Banská Štiavnica	*Ban*-ska *Shtyav*-ni-tsa
Bečva	*Bech*-va
Berounka	*Be*-roun-ka
Bílina	*Bi*-li-na
Bohumín	*Bo*-hu-min
Botič	*Bot*-ich
Bratislava	*Brat*-i-sla-va
Brdy	*Bŭr*-dy
Brno	*Bŭr*-no
Břeclav	B(ŭ)r-*zhets*-lav
Bubeneč	*Bu*-be-nech

C

Cheb	Heb
Chomutov	*Hom*-u-tov
Chřiby	H(ŭ)r-*zhi*-by
Chvaletice	*Hval*-e-ti-tse
Čerchov	*Cher*-hov
České Budějovice	*Ches*-ke *Bud*-yey-o-vi-tse
České Kraje	*Ches*-ke *Kray*-e
České Středohoří	*Ches*-ke St(ŭ)rzh-*ed*-o-hor-zhi
Českomoravská vrchovina	*Ches*-ko-mor-av-ska *vŭr*-ho-vi-na
Československo	*Ches*-ko-slo-*ven*-sko
Český Les	*Ches*-ki Les
Čierna	Chi-*er*-na

D

Děčín	*Dye*-chin
Děčínské stěny	*Dye*-chin-ske *styen*-y
Dejvice	*Dey*-vi-tse
Drahany	*Dra*-ha-ny
Dřevnice	D(ŭ)r-*zhev*-ni-tse
Dyje	*Dy*-ye

Ď

Ďumbier	*Dyum*-bi-er

F

Fil'akovo	*Fil*-ya-kov-o
Františkovy Lázně	*Fran*-tish-kov-y *Laz*-nye
Frýdek-Místek	*Fri*-dek-*Mis*-tek

G

Gabčíkovo	*Gab*-chi-kov-o
Gerlach	*Ger*-lah
Gottwaldov	*Got*-vald-ov

H

Haná	*Han*-a
Handlová	*Hand*-lo-va
Havířov	*Hav*-ir-zhov
Havlíčkův Brod	*Hav*-lich-kuv Brod
Hodonín	*Hod*-o-nin
Holešovice	*Hol*-esh-o-vi-tse
Hornád	*Hor*-nad
Hostýn	*Hos*-tin
Hradčany	*Hrad*-cha-ny
Hradec Králové	*Hrad*-ets *Kra*-lo-ve
Hranice	*Hran*-i-tse
Humenné	*Hu*-men-ne

I

Inovec	*I*-no-vets
Ipel'	*I*-pel'
Istebné	*I*-steb-ne

J

Jablonec	*Yab*-lo-nets
Jablunkov	*Yab*-lun-kov
Jáchymov	*Ya*-hym-ov
Javorník	*Jav*-or-nik
Jeseník	*Yes*-en-ik
Jičín	*Yich*-in
Jihlava	*Yi*-hla-va
Jizera	*Yiz*-e-ra

K

Karlín	*Kar*-lin
Karlovo náměstí	*Kar*-lo-vo *na*-myes-ti
Karlovy Vary	*Kar*-lo-vy *Var*-y
Karviná	*Kar*-vi-na
Klínovec	*Kli*-no-vets
Kolín	*Kol*-in
Komárno	Kom-*ar*-no
Kopřivnice	*Kop*-zhiv-ni-tse
Košice	*Kosh*-i-tse
Kralupy	*Kral*-u-py
Králův Dvůr	*Kra*-luv Dvur
Kremnica	*Krem*-ni-tsa
Krkonoše	*Kŭr*-kon-osh-e
Krnov	*Kŭr*-nov
Kroměříž	*Krom*-yerzh-izh
Krompachy	*Krom*-pa-hy
Krupina	*Kru*-pi-na
Krušné hory	*Krush*-ne *hor*-y
Kunčice	*Kun*-chi-tse
Kutná Horá	*Kut*-na *Hor*-a

L

Labe	*La*-be
Laborec	*Lab*-or-ets

Levoča	*Lev*-o-cha	Plechý	*Ple*-hi
Libeň	*Li*-ben'	Plzeň	Pŭl-*zen*'
Liberec	*Li*-be-rets	Podbrezová	*Pod*-brez-o-va
Liptovska Mará	*Lip*-tov-ska *Ma*-ra	Polabí	*Pol*-a-bi
Litoměřice	*Li*-tom-yerzh-i-tse	Poprad	*Pop*-rad
Litvínov	Lit-*vi*-nov	Poruba	*Por*-u-ba
Lužické hory	*Lu*-zhits-ke *hor*-y	Považska Bystrica	Pov-*azh*-ska *Bys*-tri-tsa
Lužnice	*Luzh*-ni-tse	Praha	*Pra*-ha

M

		Prešov	*Presh*-ov
Magura	*Mag*-u-ra	Prievidza	Pri-*ev*-id-za
Malá Strana	Ma-*la Stran*-a	Prostějov	*Prost*-ye-yov
Mariánské Lázně	*Mar*-i-an-ske *Laz*-nye	Přerov	*Psher*-ov
Mělník	*Myel*-nik	Příbram	*Pshi*-bram
Michalovce	*Mi*-ha-*lov*-tse		
Mladá Boleslav	*Mlad*-a *Bol*-es-lav		

R

Mnichovo Hradiště	*Mni*-ho-vo *Hrad*-isht-ye	Radotín	*Rad*-o-tin
		Rakovník	*Rak*-ov-nik
Modrý Kameň	*Mod*-ri *Kam*-en'	Rimava	*Ri*-ma-va
Morava	*Mor*-a-va	Ruzyně	*Ru*-zyn-ye
Moravice	*Mor*-a-vi-tse		

N

S

Na Příkopě	Na *Pshi*-kop-ye	Sázava	*Sa*-za-va
Náchod	*Na*-hod	Sered'	*Se*-red'
Neratovice	*Ne*-ra-to-vi-tse	Slaná	*Slan*-a
Nitra	*Ni*-tra	Sliač	*Sli*-ach
Nováky	No-*va*-ky	Slovenské rudohorie	Slov-*en*-ske *ru*-do-hor-ye
Nové Město	*Nov*-e *Myes*-to	Slovenský kras	Slov-*en*-ski kras
Nové Zámky	*Nov*-e *Zam*-ky	Smíchov	*Smi*-hov
Nusle	*Nus*-le	Sněžka	*Snyezh*-ka

O

		Sokolov	*Sok*-o-lov
		Staré Město	*Star*-e *Myes*-to
Ohře	*Ohr*-zhe	Strakonice	*Strak*-o-ni-tse
Olomouc	*Ol*-o-mouts	Strážov	*Stra*-zhov
Olše	*Ol*-she	Sudety	Su-*dct*-y
Ondava	*On*-da-va	Svitava	*Svi*-ta-va
Opava	*Op*-a-va	Svitavy	*Svi*-ta-vy
Orava	*Or*-a-va	Svratka	*Svrat*-ka
Orlice	*Or*-li-tse		
Orlík	*Or*-lik		

Š

Orlová	*Or*-lo-va	Šaľa	*Shal*-ya
Ostrava, Moravská	*Ost*-ra-va, *Mor*-av-ska	Špilberk	*Shpil*-berk
Ostrava, Slezská	*Ost*-ra-va, *Slez*-ska	Šumava	*Shu*-ma-va
Ostravice	*Ost*-ra-vi-tse	Šumperk	*Shum*-perk
Otava	*Ot*-a-va		
Otrokovice	*Ot*-rok-o-vi-tse		

T

		Tábor	*Ta*-bor
		Teplá	*Tep*-la

P

Pardubice	*Par*-du-bi-tse	Teplice	*Tep*-li-tse
Partizánske	Par-ti-*zan*-ske	Těšín	*Tyesh*-in
Petřín	*Pet*-zhin	Tisovec	*Ti*-so-vets
Piešťany	*Pyesh*-tya-ny	Topľa	*Top*-lya
Písek	*Pi*-sek	Torysa	*Tor*-ys-a
Planá	*Plan*-a	Trenčín	*Tren*-chin

Tríbeč	*Tri*-bech	Vltava	*Vŭl*-ta-va
Trnava	*Tŭr*-na-va	Vršovice	*Vŭr*-sho-vi-tse
Třeboň	T(ŭ)r-*zheb*-on'	Vtačnik	*Vtach*-nik
Třebová	T(ŭ)r-*zheb*-o-va	Vysočány	*Vys*-o-cha-ny
Třinec	T(ŭ)r-*zhi*-nets	Vyšehrad	*Vysh*-e-hrad
Týnec	*Ti*-nets		

U

Ústí   *U*-sti

V

Vaclavské náměstí	*Vats*-lav-ske *na*-myes-ti
Vihorlat	*Vi*-hor-lat
Vinohrady	*Vi*-no-hra-dy
Vítkovice	*Vit*-ko-vi-tse

Z

Znojmo	*Znoy*-mo
Zvolen	*Zvol*-en
Žacléř	*Zhats*-leyrsh
Žatec	*Zhat*-ets
Ždánice	Zhŭd-*a*-ni-tse
Žd'ár	Zhŭd-*yar*
Žiar	Zhi-*ar*
Žilina	*Zhi*-li-na
Žižkov	*Zhizh*-kov

HUNGARIAN

The stress falls on the first syllable.

Note:

VOWELS

a – o rather than a, and therefore shown as o below (except in some unstressed syllables, particularly at the end of a word)

á – a

é – ey

ó – long o

ö – ŭ

ő – shown below as ŭ, but pronounced as in French 'yeux'

ú – long u

ü – as in French 'tu' ⎫
ű – same, but longer ⎭ shown below as u

CONSONANTS

c – ts

cs – ch

gy – dy (d')

j – y

ly – y

ny – n' (when final)

s – sh

sz – s

zs – zh

A

Ajka	*Oy*-ka
Alföld	*Ol*-füld
Almásfüzitő	*Ol*-mash-fu-zi-tŭ
Angyalföld	*On*-dyol-füld

B

Babócsa	*Bob*-o-cha
Bácska	*Bach*-ka
Badacsony	*Bod*-a-chon'
Baja	*Boy*-a
Bakony	*Bok*-on'
Balaton	*Bol*-a-ton
Békéscsaba	*Bey*-keysh-chob-a
Belváros	*Bel*-var-osh
Berettyó	*Be*-ret-tyo
Bodrogköz	*Bod*-rog-kŭz
Borsod	*Bor*-shod
Borsodnádasd	*Bor*-shod-nad-oshd
Börzsöny	*Bŭr*-zhŭn'
Brassó	*Brosh*-sho
Budafapuszta	*Bu*-da-fa-pus-ta
Budaörs	*Bu*-da-ŭrsh
Budapest	*Bu*-da-pesht

C

Cegléd	*Tseg*-leyd
Csepel	*Chep*-el
Cserehát	*Che*-re-hat
Cserhát	*Cher*-hat
Csongrád	*Chon*-grad

D

Debrecen	*Deb*-rets-en
Diósgyőr	*Di*-osh-dyŭr
Dunántúl	*Du*-nan-tul
Dunaújváros	*Du*-na-uy-va-rosh

E

Eger	*Eg*-er
Erdély	*Er*-dey
Esztergom	*Es*-ter-gom

F

Ferihegy	*Fe*-ri-hed'
Fertő	*Fer*-tŭ

G

Gellérthegy	*Gel*-leyrt-hed'
Gerecse	*Ge*-re-che
Gödöllő	*Gŭd*-ül-ŭ
Gyöngyös	*Dyŭn*-dyŭsh
Gyöngyösoroszi	*Dyŭn*-dyŭsh-or-os-i
Győr	*Dyŭr*
Gyula	*Dyu*-la

H

Hajdúboszló	*Hoy*-du-bos-lo
Hajdúböszörmény	*Hoy*-du-bŭs-ŭr-meyn'
Hajdúság	*Hoy*-du-shag
Halimba	*Hol*-im-ba
Hanság	*Hon*-shag
Hatvan	*Hot*-von
Hegyeshalom	*Hed*-yesh-hol-om
Hernád	*Her*-nad
Hódmezővásárhely	*Hod*-me-zŭ-vash-ar-hey
Hortobágy	*Hor*-to-bad'

I

Inota	*I*-no-ta
Ipoly	*I*-poy
Iszkaszentgyörgy	*Is*-ka-sent-dyŭrd'

J

Jászberény	*Yas*-be-reyn'
Jászság	*Yas*-shag

K

Kalocsa	*Kol*-och-a
Kapos	*Kop*-osh
Kaposvár	*Kop*-osh-var
Karcag	*Kor*-tsog
Kassa	*Kosh*-sha
Kazincbarcika	*Koz*-ints-bor-tsi-ka
Kecskemét	*Kech*-kem-eyt
Kékes	*Key*-kesh
Kelenföld	*Kel*-en-füld
Kesthely	*Kest*-hey
Kisalföld	*Kish*-ol-füld
Kiskörút	*Kish*-kŭr-ut
Kiskunfélegyháza	*Kish*-kun-fey-led'-ha-za
Kiskunhalas	*Kish*-kun-hol-osh
Kiskunság	*Kish*-kun-shag
Kispest	*Kish*-pest
Kőbánya	*Kŭ*-ban-ya
Kolozsvár	*Kol*-ozh-var
Komárom	*Kom*-ar-om
Körös	*Kŭr*-üsh
Középhegység	*Kŭz*-eyp-hed'-sheyg
Kőszeg	*Kŭ*-seg

L

Lágymányos	*Lad*'-man-yosh

M

Magyarország	*Mod*-yor-or-sag
Makó	*Mok*-o
Marcal	*Mor*-tsol
Margitsziget	*Mor*-git-sig-et

Maros	*Mor*-osh	Sárköz	*Shar*-kŭz
Marosvásárhely	*Mor*-osh-vash-ar-hey	Sárrét	*Shar*-reyt
Mátraalja	*Mat*-ra-ol-ya	Sió	*Shi*-o
Mecsek	*Mech*-ek	Solt	Sholt
Mezőföld	*Mez*-ŭ-fŭld	Sopron	*Shop*-ron
Mezőtúr	*Mez*-ŭ-tur	Soroksár	*Shor*-ok-shar
Miskolc	*Mish*-kolts	Szabadka	*Sob*-od-ka
Mohács	*Mo*-hach	Szatmár	*Sot*-mar
Mosonmagyaróvár	*Mosh*-on-mod-yor-o-var	Százhalombatta	*Saz*-hol-om-bot-ta
		Szeged	*Seg*-ed
		Székesfehérvár	*Sey*-kesh-fe-heyr-var

N

		Szentes	*Sen*-tesh
Nagyalföld	*Nod'*-ol-fŭld	Szerencs	*Se*-rench
Nagykanizsa	*Nod'*-kon-i-zha	Szigetköz	*Si*-get-kŭz
Nagykörút	*Nod'*-kŭr-ut	Szinva	*Sin*-va
Nagykőrös	*Nod'*-kŭr-ŭsh	Szob	Sob
Nagykunság	*Nod'*-kun-shag	Szolnok	*Sol*-nok
Nagylengyel	*Nod'*-lend-yel	Szombathely	*Som*-bot-hey
Nagymaros	*Nod'*-mor-osh		
Nagyszeben	*Nod'*-seb-en		

T

Nagyvárad	*Nod'*-var-od		
Nógrád	*No*-grad	Tatabánya	*Tot*-a-ban-ya
Nyergesújfalu	*Nyer*-gesh-uy-fol-u	Temesvár	*Tem*-esh-var
Nyírád	*Nyi*-rad	Tisza	*Ti*-sa
Nyíregyháza	*Nyi*-red'-ha-za	Tiszalök	*Ti*-sa-lŭk
Nyírség	*Nyir*-sheyg	Tiszántúl	*Ti*-san-tul
		Tiszapalkonya	*Ti*-sa-pol-kon-ya
		Tiszaszederkény	*Ti*-sa-sed-er-keyn'

O

		Tokay	*Tok*-oy
Óbuda	*O*-bu-da	Törökszentmiklós	*Tŭr*-ük-sent-mi-klosh
Orosháza	*Or*-osh-ha-za		
Oroszlány	*Or*-os-lan'		

Ű

		Újpest	*Uy*-pesht
		Újvidék	*Uy*-vi-deyk

P

		Úrkút	*Ur*-kut
Pécs	Peych		
Pesterzsébet	*Pesht*-er-zhey-bet		
Pilis	*Pi*-lish		

V

Pozsony	*Pozh*-on'		
Puszta	*Pus*-ta	Várkegy	*Var*-hed'
Pusztaföldvár	*Pus*-ta-fŭld-var	Várpalota	*Var*-pol-ot-a
		Velence	*Vel*-en-tse
		Vértes	*Veyr*-tesh

R

		Veszprém	*Ves*-preym
Rábaköz	*Ra*-ba-kŭz	Villány	*Vil*-lan'
Rákosszentmihály	*Ra*-kosh-sent-mi-hay	Visegrád	*Vi*-she-grad
Rétköz	*Reyt*-kŭz		
Rózsadomb	*Ro*-zha-domb		

Z

Rudabánya	*Ru*-da-ban-ya		
		Zagyva	*Zod'*-va
		Zalaegerszeg	*Zol*-a-eg-er-seg

S

		Zemplén	*Zem*-pleyn
Sajó	*Shoy*-o	Zugló	*Zug*-lo
Salgótarján	*Shol*-go-tor-yan		

JUGOSLAV

In Serbo-Croat, but not in Macedonian or Slovene, the stress often falls on the antepenultimate syllable. Unstressed vowels do not lose their value.

Note:

c −ts
ć, č–ch (ć is almost t)
đ −dy (d')
j −y or '

š−sh
ž−zh

In Slovene 'v' sometimes pronounced as 'u'

A

Aleksinac	Al-*ek*-si-nats

B

Bačka	*Bach*-ka
Bajina Bašta	*Bay*-i-na *Bash*-ta
Banja Luka	*Ban*-ya *Lu*-ka
Banovići	*Ban*-o-vi-chi
Baranja	*Ba*-ran-ya
Bečej	*Bech*-ey
Begej	*Beg*-ey
Belasica	Bel-*as*-i-tsa
Beograd	*Be*-og-rad
Besna Kobila	*Bes*-na *Kob*-i-la
Bihać	*Bi*-hach
Biokovo	Bi-*ok*-o-vo
Bitola	*Bi*-tol-a
Bjelasica	Byel-*as*-i-tsa
Bjelašnica	Byel-*ash*-ni-tsa
Bojana	*Boy*-a-na
Borovo	*Bor*-ov-o
Bosanski Brod	*Bos*-an-ski Brod
Bregalnica	Breg-*al*-ni-tsa
Brčko	*Bŭrch*-ko
Bulevar Revolucije	*Bu*-le-var Re-vo-*lu*-tsi-ye

C

Celje	*Tsel*-ye
Cetina	*Tset*-i-na
Cetinje	*Tset*-in-ye
Cincer	*Tsin*-tser
Crna Gora	*Tsŭr*-na *Gor*-a
Crna Reka	*Tsŭr*-na *Re*-ka

Ć

Ćićarija	Chi-*cha*-ri-ya

Č

Čačak	*Chach*-ak
Čevljanovići	Chev-*lya*-no-vi-chi
Čiovo	*Chi*-ov-o
Čubura	*Chu*-bu-ra
Čukarica	Chu-*ka*-ri-tsa
Čvrsnica	*Chvŭr*-sni-tsa

D

Dedinje	*Ded*-in-ye
Deliblato	*Del*-i-bla-to
Donji grad	*Don*-yi grad
Dorćol	*Dor*-chol
Dragoman	*Drag*-o-man
Drniš	*Dŭr*-nish
Dubrovnik	Du-*brov*-nik

Đ

Đakovica	*Dyak*-o-vi-tsa
Đerdap	*Dyer*-dap

F

Fruška Gora	*Frush*-ka *Gor*-a

G

Gacka	*Gats*-ka
Gacko	*Gats*-ko
Glamoč	*Glam*-och
Golija	*Gol*-i-ya
Gorica	Gor-*i*-tsa
Gorjanci	Gor-*yan*-tsi
Gornji grad	*Gorn*-yi-grad

H

Hercegovina	Her-tse-*gov*-i-na
Hrasnica	*Hras*-ni-tsa
Hrvatska	*Hŭr*-vat-ska

I

Idrija	*I*-dri-ya
Ilica	*I*-li-ca
Ilijiaš	*I*-li-yash

J

Jablanica	*Yab*-la-ni-tsa
Jajce	*Yay*-tse
Jesenice	Ye-se-*ni*-tse

K

Kakanj	*Kak*-an'
Kapela	*Kap*-e-la
Karadžica	Ka-*radzh*-i-tsa
Karavanke	Ka-ra-*van*-ke
Karlovac	*Kar*-lo-vats
Karlovci	*Kar*-lov-tsi
Kaštela	*Kash*-te-la
Kičevo	*Ki*-che-vo
Kidričevo	*Kid*-ri-che-vo
Kikinda	Ki-*kin*-da
Kneza Mihajla	*Kne*-za Mi-*hay*-la
Kolubara	*Kol*-u-ba-ra
Komovi	*Kom*-ov-i
Kopaonik	Kop-*a*-on-ik
Korčula	*Kor*-chu-la
Kosovo polje	*Kos*-o-vo *pol*-ye
Kosovska Mitrovica	*Kos*-ov-ska *Mi*-tro-vi-tsa
Košutnjak	*Kosh*-ut-nyak
Kozara	*Koz*-a-ra
Kragujevac	*Krag*-u-ye-vats
Kraljevica	*Kral*-ye-vi-tsa
Kraljevo	*Kral*-ye-vo
Kranj	Kran'
Krk	Kŭrk
Krka	*Kŭr*-ka
Kruševac	*Kru*-she-vats
Kumanovo	Ku-*ma*-no-vo

L

Lastovo	*Las*-to-vo
Lendava	*Len*-da-va
Leskovac	*Les*-ko-vats
Ljubija	*Lyu*-bi-ya
Ljubišnja	Lyu-*bish*-nya
Ljubljana	Lyub-*lya*-na
Ljubljanica	Lyub-*lya*-ni-tsa
Lonja	*Lon*-ya
Lošinj	*Losh*-in'
Lovćen	*Lov*-chen
Loznica	*Loz*-ni-tsa
Lozovac	*Loz*-o-vats
Lukavac	*Lu*-ka-vats

M

Mačva	*Mach*-va
Majdanpek	*May*-dan-pek
Majevica	*May*-e-vi-tsa
Makedonija	Mak-e-*don*-i-ya
Maribor	*Mar*-i-bor
Marjan	*Mar*-jan
Maršala Tita	Mar-*sha*-la *Ti*-ta
Mavrovo	*Mav*-ro-vo
Medvednica	*Med*-ved-ni-tsa
Međimurje	*Med*-yi-mur-ye
Metohija	Me-*to*-hi-ya
Mežica	*Mezh*-i-tsa
Miljacka	*Mil*-yats-ka
Mljet	Mŭl-*yet*
Morača	*Mor*-a-cha
Morava	*Mor*-a-va
Moste	*Mos*-te

N

Neretva	*Ne*-ret-va
Nevesinje	Ne-*ves*-in-ye
Nidže	*Nid*-zhe
Nikšić	*Nik*-shich
Niš	Nish
Nišava	*Nish*-a-va

O

Ogražden	*Og*-razh-den
Omiš	*Om*-ish
Opatija	Op-*at*-i-ya
Osijek	*Os*-i-yek
Osogovo	Os-*og*-o-vo

P

Pančevo	*Pan*-che-vo
Pčinja	Pŭch-*in*-ya
Peć	Pech
Petrovaradin	Pet-ro-*va*-ra-din
Plačkovica	*Plach*-ko-vi-tsa
Plješevica	*Plyesh*-e-vi-tsa
Ploče	*Ploch*-e
Podgorica	*Pod*-gor-i-tsa
Podravina	*Pod*-ra-vi-na
Pohorje	*Po*-hor-ye
Popovo polje	*Pop*-o-vo *pol*-ye
Posavina	*Pos*-a-vi-na
Požarevac	Pozh-*ar*-ev-ats
Prahovo	*Pra*-ho-vo
Prekmurje	*Prek*-mur-ye
Prenj	Pren'
Priboj	*Pri*-boy
Primorje	*Pri*-mor-ye
Priština	*Prish*-ti-na
Prokletije	Prok-*let*-i-ye
Psunj	Psun'
Ptuj	Pŭt-*uy*

R

Rakovica	*Rak*-o-vi-tsa
Raša	*Rash*-a
Raška	*Rash*-ka
Ravni Kotari	*Rav*-ni *Kot*-a-ri
Ražine	*Razh*-i-ne
Rijeka	Ri-*ye*-ka
Rječina	*Ryech*-i-na
Rodopi	Rod-*op*-i
Rtanj	*Ŭr*-tan'

S

Sarajevo	*Sa*-ra-ye-vo
Savinja	Sav-*in*-ya
Senjak	*Sen*-yak
Senje	*Sen*-ye
Senovo	*Sen*-o-vo
Sevojno	*Sev*-oy-no
Sinj	Sin'
Sinjajevina	Sin-ya-*ye*-vi-na
Sitnica	*Sit*-ni-tsa
Skopje	*Skop*-ye
Slavonski Brod	*Slav*-on-ski Brod
Slovenska Bistrica	Slo-*ven*-ska *Bi*-stri-tsa
Smederevo	*Smed*-e-re-vo
Soča	*Soch*-a
Spreča	*Spre*-cha
Srbija	*Sŭr*-bi-ya
Sremska Mitrovica	*Srem*-ska *Mi*-tro-vi-tsa
Strumica	*Stru*-mi-tsa
Stružec	*Stru*-zhets
Subotica	Su-*bot*-i-tsa
Surčin	*Sur*-chin
Sušak	*Su*-shak
Svetozarevo	Svet-o-*za*-re-vo

Š

Šabac	*Shab*-ats
Šar Planina	Shar *Plan*-i-na
Šibenik	*Shib*-en-ik
Šumadija	Shu-*ma*-di-ya

T

Tamiš	*Tam*-ish
Terazije	Te-*raz*-i-ye
Tetovo	*Tet*-o-vo
Titograd	*Ti*-to-grad

Titov Veles	*Ti*-tov *Vel*-es
Titovo Užice	*Ti*-to-vo *U*-zhi-tse
Topčider	*Top*-chi-der
Toplica	*Top*-li-tsa
Trbovlje	Tŭr-*bou*-lye
Trebišnjica	Treb-*ish*-nyi-tsa
Trepča	*Trep*-cha
Treskavica	*Tres*-ka-vi-tsa
Trg Republike	Tŭrg Re-*pub*-li-ke
Triglav	*Tri*-glau
Trogir	*Trog*-ir
Turopolje	*Tu*-ro-pol-ye

V

Valjevo	*Val*-ye-vo
Varaždin	*Va*-razh-din
Vareš	*Va*-resh
Velebit	*Vel*-e-bit
Velenje	Vel-*en*-ye
Vinkovci	*Vin*-kov-tsi
Vipava	Vi-*pa*-va
Vlasina	*Vlas*-i-na
Vlašić	*Vlash*-ich
Vogošća	*Vog*-osh-cha
Vojvodina	*Voy*-vod-i-na
Voždovac	*Vozh*-do-vats
Vrbas	*Vŭr*-bas
Vrpolje	*Vŭr*-pol-ye
Vršac	*Vŭr*-shats
Vukovar	*Vu*-ko-var

Z

Zadar	*Zad*-ar
Zagorje	{*Zag*-*or*-ye (Slovenia) / *Zag*-or-ye (Croatia)
Zagreb	*Zag*-reb
Zajača	*Zay*-a-cha
Zaječar	*Zay*-e-char
Zelengora	*Zel*-en-gor-a
Zemun	*Zem*-un
Zenica	*Ze*-ni-tsa
Zeta	*Ze*-ta
Zletovo	*Zlet*-o-vo
Zrenjanin	*Zren*-ya-nin
Zrmanja	*Zŭr*-man-ya
Zvezdara	*Zvez*-da-ra

Ž

Železnik	*Zhel*-ez-nik

POLISH

The stress falls on the penultimate syllable.

Note:

VOWELS

ą ⎱ nasal vowels, often –om, on
ę ⎰ pronounced as   –em, en
ó   –u

CONSONANTS

c	–ts
ć, cz; c when followed by i	–ch
ch	–h
j	–y
ł	–w

but:

ał ⎫ when followed
    ⎬ by a consonant –au
eł ⎧ or when at end
    ⎭ of word –eu

ń	–n'
rz, ż, ź; z when followed by i	–zh
ś, sz; s when followed by i	–sh
w	–v (often like f when final or before another consonant)

A

Aleksandrów	Al-eks-*and*-ruv
Aleje Jerozolimskie	Al-*ey*-e Je-ro-zo-*limsk*-ye
Aleje Ujazdowskie	Al-*ey*-e U-yaz-*dovsk*-ye
Augustów	Au-*gus*-tuv

B

Babia Góra	*Bab*-ya *Gu*-ra
Barycz	*Ba*-rych
Beskidy	Bes-*ki*-dy
Będzin	*Ben*-dzhin
Biała Podlaska	*Bya*-wa Pod-*las*-ka
Białowieża	Bya-wov-*yezh*-a
Białystok	Bya-*wys*-tok
Biebrza	*Byeb*-zha
Bielany	Bye-*la*-ny

Bielawa	Bye-*la*-va
Bielsko-Biała	*Byel*-sko *Bya*-wa
Bierawka	Bye-*rav*-ka
Blachownia	Bla-*hov*-nya
Bochnia	*Boh*-nya
Bolesławiec	Bol-es-*wav*-yets
Bóbr	Bubr
Brda	Bŭr-*da*
Bródno	*Brud*-no
Brynica	Bryn-*i*-tsa
Brzeg	Bzheg
Bydgoszcz	*Byd*-goshch
Bystrzyca	Byst-*zhyts*-a
Bytom	*Byt*-om
Bzura	*Bzu*-ra

C

Chełm	Heum

Chełmek *Heu*-mek
Chojnice Hoy-*ni*-tse
Chorzów *Hozh*-uv
Chrzanów *Hzha*-nuv
Ciechanów Che-*ha*-nuv
Cieszyn *Chesh*-yn
Cybina Tsyb-*i*-na
Czarna Hańcza *Char*-na *Han'*-cha
Czechowice- Che-ho-*vi*-tse
Dziedzice Dzhe-*dzhi*-tse
Czeladź *Chel*-adzh
Częstochowa Chen-sto-*hov*-a

D

Darłowo Dar-*wov*-o
Dąbie *Domb*-ye
Dąbrowa Górnicza Dom-*brov*-a Gur-*ni*-cha
Dębe *Dem*-be
Drawa *Dra*-va
Drwęca Dŭr-*ven*-tsa
Dunajec Du-*nay*-ets
Dylewska Góra Dyl-*ev*-ska *Gu*-ra
Dzierżoniów Dzher-*zhon*-yuv

E

Elbląg *El*-blong
Ełk Euk

G

Gdańsk Gŭd-*an'sk*
Gdynia Gŭd-*yn*-ya
Gliwice Gli-*vi*-tse
Głogów *Gwog*-uv
Gniezno Gŭn-*yez*-no
Goczałkowice Goch-au-ko-*vi*-tse
Gołonog Go-*won*-og
Gopło *Gop*-wo
Górnośląski Okręg Gur-nosh-*lon*-ski
Przemysłowy *Ok*-reng
Pshem-ys-*wov*-y
Góry Stołowe *Gu*-ry Sto-*wov*-e
Góry Świętokrzyskie *Gu*-ry Shvyen-tok-*zhysk*-ye
Gorzów Wielkopolski *Gozh*-uv Vyel-ko-*pol*-ski
Grochów *Gro*-huv
Grodziec *Grod*-zhets
Grudziądz *Grud*-zhondz

H

Hajduki Hay-*du*-ki

I

Inowrocław I-no-*vrots*-wav

J

Jarosław Ya-*ros*-wav
Jasło *Yas*-wo
Jasna Góra *Yas*-na-*Gu*-ra
Jaworzno Ya-*vozh*-no
Jelcz Yelch
Jelenia Góra Yel-*en*-ya *Gu*-ra
Jeziorak Ye-*zhor*-ak

K

Kalisz *Kal*-ish
Kamienna Kam-*yen*-na
Karkonosze Kar-ko-*nosh*-e
Katowice Kat-o-*vi*-tse
Kędzierzyn Kend-*zhezh*-yn
Kępa Oksywska *Kem*-pa Ok-*syv*-ska
Kielce *Kyel*-tse
Kłodnica Kwod-*ni*-tsa
Kłodzko *Kwodz*-ko
Knurów *Knur*-uv
Koło *Ko*-wo
Kołobrzeg Ko-*wob*-zheg
Konstantynów Kon-stan-*tyn*-uv
Kostrzyń *Kost*-zhyn'
Koszalin Kosh-*a*-lin
Koźle *Kozh*-le
Kraków *Krak*-uv
Krakowskie Krak-*ovsk*-ye
Przedmieście Pzhed-*myesh*-che
Krapkowice Krap-ko-*vi*-tse
Królewska Huta Kru-*lev*-ska *Hu*-ta
Krzna Kŭzh-*na*
Kujawy Ku-*ya*-vy
Kwidzyn *Kvid*-zyn

L

Legionowo Leg-yon-*ov*-o
Legnica Leg-*ni*-tsa
Leszno *Lesh*-no
Lubaczów Lu-*ba*-chuv
Lubusz *Lu*-bush
Lwów Lŭv-*uv*

Ł

Łabędy Wa-*ben*-dy
Łasztownia Wash-*tov*-nya
Łazienki Wa-*zhen*-ki
Łeba *Web*-a
Łębork *Wem*-bork
Łęczyca Wem-*chyts*-a
Łomża *Wom*-zha
Łódź Wudzh
Łyna *Wyn*-a
Łysogóry Wys-o-*gu*-

M

Majdanek	May-*da*-nek
Mała Panew	*Ma*-wa *Pa*-nev
Małopolska	Ma-wo-*pol*-ska
Marszałkowska	Mar-shau-*kov*-ska
Mazowsze	Maz-*ov*-she
Miedwie	*Myed*-vye
Mielec	*Myel*-ets
Mikołów	Mi-*ko*-wuv
Mikulczyce	Mi-kul-*chyts*-e
Mińsk Mazowiecki	Min'sk Ma-zov-*yet*-ski
Młociny	Mwo-*chi*-ny
Młynów	*Mwyn*-uv
Mokotów	Mok-*ot*-uv
Motława	Mot-*wa*-va
Muchawiec	Mu-*hav*-yets
Muranów	Mu-*ra*-nuv
Myczkowce	Mych-*kov*-tse
Mysłowice	Mys-wo-*vi*-tse

N

Narew	*Na*-rev
Noteć	*Not*-ech
Nowa Huta	*Nov*-a *Hu*-ta
Nowa Sól	*Nov*-a Sul
Nowe Miasto	*Nov*-e *Myas*-to
Nowy Sącz	*Nov*-y Sonch
Nowy Świat	*Nov*-y Shvyat

O

Ochota	O-*hot*-a
Ogród Saski	*Og*-rud *Sas*-ki
Okęcie	Ok-*en*-che
Oleśnica	Ol-esh-*ni*-tsa
Oliwa	Ol-*i*-va
Olkusz	*Ol*-kush
Olsztyn	*Olsh*-tyn
Opole	Op-*ol*-e
Ostrów Wielkopolski	*Ost*-ruv Vyel-ko-*pol*-ski
Ostrowiec Świętokrzyski	Ost-*rov*-yets Shyven-tok-*zhys-ki*
Oświęcim	Osh-*vyen*-chim
Otmuchów	Ot-*mu*-huv
Otwock	*Ot*-votsk
Ożimek	Ozh-*i*-mek

P

Pabianice	Pab-ya-*ni*-tse
Piekary Śląskie	Pye-*ka*-ry *Shlonsk*-ye
Pilica	Pi-*li*-tsa
Piła	*Pi*-wa
Piotrków	*Pyot*-ŭr-kuv
Płock	Pwotsk

Podhale	Pod-*ha*-le
Pojezierze	Poy-ezh-*ezh*-e
Pomorze	Pom-*ozh*-e
Powązki	Pov-*onz*-ki
Poznań	*Poz*-nan'
Pruszcz	Prushch
Pruszków	*Prush*-kuv
Prypeć	*Pryp*-ech
Przemsza, Biała	*Pzhem*-sha, *Bya*-wa
Przemsza, Czarna	*Pzhem*-sha, *Char*-na
Przemyśl	*Pzhem*-ysh-(ŭ)l
Pszczyna	P(ŭ)sh-*chyn*-a
Puławy	Pu-*wa*-vy
Pyskowice	Pys-ko-*vi*-tse

R

Racibórz	Ra-*chi*-buzh
Radzionków	Rad-*zhon*-kuv
Rawa	*Ra*-va
Roztocze	Roz-*toch*-e
Rożnów	*Rozh*-nuv
Ruda Śląska	*Ru*-da *Shlon*-ska
Rzeszów	*Zhesh*-uv

S

Sandomierz	San-*dom*-yezh
Saska Kępa	*Sas*-ka *Kem*-pa
Siedlce	*Shed*-(ŭ)l-tse
Sielce	*Shel*-tse
Siemianowice	Shem-ya-no-*vi*-tse
Skarżysko Kamienna	Skar-*zhys*-ko Kam-*yen*-na
Skawina	Ska-*vi*-na
Skierniewice	Skyer-nye-*vi*-tse
Sławków	*Swav*-kuv
Słupia	*Swu*-pya
Słupsk	Swupsk
Służewiec	Swu-*zhev*-yets
Solina	Sol-*i*-na
Soła	*So*-wa
Sosnowiec	Sos-*nov*-yets
Stalowa Wola	Stal-*ov*-a *Wol*-a
Starachowice	Sta-ra-ho-*vi*-tse
Stare Miasto	*Sta*-re *Myas*-to
Stargard Szczeciński	*Star*-gard Shche-*chin'*-ski
Starogard Gdański	Star-o-gard Gŭd-*an'*-ski
Strzemieszyce	Stzhem-ye-*shyts*-e
Suwałki	Su-*vau*-ki
Szczecin	*Schech*-in
Szczecinek	Shche-*chi*-nek
Szeskie Wzgórza	*Shesk*-ye Vŭz-*gu*-zha
Szopienice	Shop-ye-*ni*-tse

Ś

Śląsk	Shlonsk
Śniardwy	*Shnyard*-vy
Śnieżka	*Shnyezh*-ka
widnica	Shvid-*ni*-tsa
Świdnik	*Shvid*-nik
Świętochłowice	Shvyen-to-hwov-*i*-tse
Świnoujście	Shvi-no-*uy*-shche

T

Targówek	Tar-*gu*-vek
Tarnobrzeg	Tar-*nob*-zheg
Tarnowskie Góry	Tar-*novsk*-ye *Gu*-ry
Tarnów	*Tar*-nuv
Tczew	T(ŭ)ch-*ev*
Tomaszów	Tom-*a*-shuv
Toruń	*Tor*-un'
Trójmiasto	Truy-*myas*-to
Trzebinia	Tzheb-*i*-nya
Trzebnica	Tzheb-*ni*-tsa
Turawa	Tu-*ra*-va
Turoszów	Tu-*rosh*-uv
Tychy	*Ty*-hy

W

Wałbrzych	*Vaub*-zhyh
Wapno	*Vap*-no
Warmia	*Varm*-ya
Warszawa	Var-*sha*-va
Warta	*Var*-ta
Wawel	*Va*-vel
Wejherowo	Vey-her-*ov*-o
Wieliczka	Vye-*lich*-ka
Wielkopolska	Vyel-ko-*pol*-ska
Wieprz	Vyepzh
Wieżyca	Vye-*zhyts*-a
Wilanów	Vi-*la*-nuv
Wilno	*Vil*-no

Wisła, Martwa	*Vis*-wa, *Mart*-va
Wisłok	*Vis*-wok
Wisłoka	Vis-*wok*-a
Wkra	V(ŭ)-*kra*
Władysławowo	Vwa-dys-wa-*vov*-o
Włocławek	Vwots-*wa*-vek
Wola	*Vol*-a
Wolin	*Vol*-in
Wołomin	Vo-*wom*-in
Wrocław	*Vrots*-wav
Wrzeszcz	Vŭzh-*eshch*
Wyżyna Małopolska	Vyzh-*yn*-a Ma-wo-*pol*-ska

Z

Zabrze	*Zab*-zhe
Zakopane	Zak-o-*pa*-ne
Zalew Szczeciński	*Zal*-ev Shche-*chin'*-ski
Zalew Wiślany	*Zal*-ev Vish-*la*-ny
Zamość	*Zam*-oshch
Zatoka Gdańska	Za-*tok*-a Gŭd-*an'*-ska
Zatoka Pomorska	Za-*tok*-a Pom-*or*-ska
Zawiercie	Zav-*yer*-che
Ząbkowice	Zomb-ko-*vi*-tse
Zduńska Wola	*Zdun'*-ska *Wol*-a
Zdzieszowice	Zŭd-zhesh-o-*vi*-tse
Zegrze	*Zeg*-zhe
Zgierz	Zŭg-*yezh*
Zielona Góra	Zhel-*on*-a *Gu*-ra

Ż

Żary	*Zha*-ry
Żerań	*Zhe*-ran'
Żoliborz	Zol-*i*-bozh
Żuławy	Zhu-*wa*-vy
Żyrardów	Zhy-*rar*-duv
Żywiec	*Zhyv*-yets

RUMANIAN

The stress is irregular.

Note:

VOWELS

ă –ŭ (but shown below as a when final)

i –' when final

ii – i when final

î (also â, but rare) – y

DIPHTHONGS

ea – almost like ya (*not* eya) and shown below as this

oa – wa

CONSONANTS

c, except before e or i	} –k
ch, before e or i	
c, before e or i	–ch
g, except before e or i	} –g
gh, before e or i	
g, before e or i	–dzh
j	–zh
ş	–sh
ţ	–ts

A

Alba Iulia	*Al*-ba *Yu*-li-a
Almaş	*Al*-mash
Almăj	*Al*-mŭzh
Andronache	An-dro-*na*-ke
Anina	A-*ni*-na
Arad	A-*rad*
Argeş	*Ar*-dzhesh

B

Bacău	Ba-*kŭu*
Bahlui	Bah-*lu*-i
Bai	Bay
Baia-Mare	*Bay*-a *Ma*-re
Baia-Nouă	*Bay*-a *No*-wa
Baraolt	Ba-ra-*olt*
Bălan	Bŭl-*an*
Băneasa	Bŭn-*ya*-sa
Bărăgan	Bŭr-ŭg-*an*
Beiuş	Bey-*ush*
Berătău	*Be*-rŭt-ŭu
Bicaz	Bi-*kaz*
Bihor	Bi-*hor*
Bistriţa	*Bis*-tri-tsa
Bîrgău	Byr-*gŭu*
Bîrlad	Byr-*lad*
Bîrzava	Byr-*za*-va
Bodoc	Bod-*ok*
Borzeşti	Bor-*zesht'*
Botoşani	Bot-osh-*an'*
Braşov	Bra-*shov*
Brateş	*Bra*-tesh
Brazi	Braz'
Brăila	Brŭ-*i*-la
Bucegi	Bu-*chedzh*
Bucovina	Bu-ko-*vi*-na

Bucureşti	Bu-ku-*resht'*
Buzău	Bu-*zŭu*

C

Calafat	Ka-la-*fat*
Calea Victoriei	*Cal*-ya Vik-*tor*-i-ey
Caracal	Ka-*ra*-kal
Călan	Kŭl-*an*
Călăraşi	Kŭl-ŭr-*ash'*
Căliman	Kŭl-i-*man*
Căpăţîna	Kŭp-ŭts-*yn*-a
Cerna	*Cher*-na
Cernavodă	Cher-na-*vod*-a
Chilia	Ki-*li*-a
Chiscani	Kis-*kan'*
Cindrel	Chin-*drel*
Cioplea	*Chop*-lya
Ciuc	Chuk
Ciucaş	*Chu*-kash
Cîmpia Turzii	Kym-*pi*-a *Tur*-zi
Cîmpina	*Kym*-pi-na
Cîmpulung-Moldovenesc	*Kym*-pu-lung Mol-dov-en-*esk*
Cîmpulung-Muscel	*Kym*-pu-lung-Mus-*chel*
Cluj	Kluzh
Codru-Moma	*Kod*-ru-*Mo*-ma
Colentina	Kol-en-*ti*-na
Colibaşi	Kol-i-*bash'*
Comăneşti	Kom-ŭn-*esht'*
Constanţa	Kon-*stan*-tsa
Copşa-Mică	*Kop*-sha *Mi*-ka
Corabia	Kor-*a*-bi-a
Cotroceni	Kot-ro-*chen'*
Cozia	*Koz*-i-a
Craiova	Kray-*ov*-a

Criş	Krish	Iaşi	Yash'
Crişana	Kri-*sha*-na	Iezer	*Ye*-zer
Curcubăta	Kur-ku-*băt*-a		

J

		Jijia	Zhi-*zhi*-a
D		Jilava	Zhi-*la*-va
Dămăroaia	Dŭm-ŭr-*wa*-ya	Jiu	*Zhi*-u
Dărmăneşti	Dŭr-mŭn-*esht'*		
Dej	Dezh	**L**	
Dîmboviţa	*Dym*-bo-vi-tsa		
Dobreşti	Dob-*resht'*	Lainici	La-i-*nich'*
Dobrogea	*Dob*-rodzh-a	Lăpuş	Lŭp-*ush*
Doman-Secu	*Dom*-an *Sek*-u	Leşul Ursului	*Lesh*-ul *Ur*-su-lu-i
Dudeşti	Du-*desht'*	Lipova	*Li*-po-va
Dunărea	*Du*-nŭr-ya	Lotru	*Lot*-ru
		Lugoj	*Lu*-gozh
E		Lupeni	Lu-*pen'*
Eforie	E-for-*i*-e		

M

F		Mamaia	Mam-*ay*-a
Făgăraş	Fŭg-ŭr-*ash'*	Mangalia	Man-*ga*-li-a
Ferneziu	Fer-nez-*yu*	Maramureş	Ma-ra-*mu*-resh
Feteşti	Fe-*tesht'*	Măcin	Mŭch-*in*
Fieni	Fi-*en'*	Medgidia	Med-dzhi-*di*-ya
Floreasca	Flor-*ya*-ska	Mediaş	*Med*-i-ash
Focşani	Fok-*shan'*	Mehedinţi	Me-he-*dints'*
Fundeni	Fun-*den'*	Merişor	Me-ri-*shor*
		Meseş	*Mes*-esh
G		Moineşti	Moy-*nesht'*
Galaţi	Gal-*ats'*	Moldova	Mol-*dov*-a
Gheorghe	Ge-*or*-ge	Moldova Nouă	Mol-*dov*-a *No*-wa
Gheorghiu-Dej	Ge-or-*gi*-u Dezh	Moldoveanu	Mol-dov-*ya*-nu
Gheorghieni	Ge-or-gi-*en'*	Munţii Apuseni	*Mun*-tsi Ap-u-*sen'*
Ghimeş-Palanca	*Gi*-mesh Pa-*lan*-ka	Mureş	*Mu*-resh
Giurge	*Dzhur*-dzhe		
Giurgeu	Dzhur-*dzheu*	**N**	
Giurgiu	*Dzhur*-dzhu		
Godeanu	God-*ya*-nu	Nădrag	Nŭd-*rag*
Govora	*Gov*-or-a	Năvodari	Nŭv-o-*dar'*
Greaca	*Grya*-ka	Nedeia	Ne-*dey*-a
Griviţa	*Gri*-vi-tsa	Negoi	Ne-*goy*
Gura Văii	*Gu*-ra *Vŭy*-i	Nemira	Ne-*mi*-ra
Gurghiu	Gur-*gyu*		
Gutîi	Gu-*ty*	**O**	
		Oaş	Wash
H		Obcine	*Ob*-chi-ne
		Ocna Mureş	*Ok*-na *Mu*-resh
Harghita	Har-*gi*-ta	Olteniţa	Ol-*te*-ni-tsa
Haţeg	*Hats*-eg	Oneşti	On-*esht'*
Hăghimaş	Hŭg-i-*mash*	Oradea	Or-*a*-dya
Herăstrău	He-rŭst-*rŭu*	Orşova	*Or*-sho-va
Hîrşova	*Hyr*-sho-va	Oţelu Roşu	Ots-*e*-lu *Rosh*-u
Hunedoara	Hu-ned-*wa*-ra		
		P	
I		Parîng	Pa-*ryng*
Iacobeni	Ya-ko-*ben'*	Pădurea Craiului	Pŭd-*u*-rya Kray-u-*lu*-i
Ialomiţa	*Ya*-lo-mi-tsa		

Peleaga	Pel-*ya*-ga	Suceava	Su-*cha*-va
Penteleu	Pen-te-*leu*	Sulina	Su-*li*-na
Perşani	Per-*shan'*		
Petrila	Pet-*ri*-la	**Ş**	
Petroşeni	Pet-ro-*shen'*	Şerban-Vodă	Sher-*ban Vod*-a
Piatra Neamţ	Pi-*at*-ra Nyamts	Şes	Shes
Piaţa Unirii	*Pyat*-sa U-*ni*-ri	Şureanu	Shu-*rya*-nu
Pietros	Pyet-*ros*		
Piteşti	Pi-*tesht'*	**T**	
Ploieşti	Ploy-*esht'*	Tarcău	Tar-*kŭu*
Poiana-Ruscă	Poy-*a*-na *Rus*-ka	Techirghiol	*Tek*-ir-gyol
Popeşti-Leordeni	Pop-*esht'* Le-or-*den'*	Tecuci	Te-*kuch*
Potelu	Pot-*e*-lu	Teleajen	Tel-*ya*-zhen
Prahova	*Pra*-ho-va	Timiş	*Ti*-mish
Predeal	Pred-*yal*	Timişoara	Ti-mish-*wa*-ra
Pricopan	Pri-ko-*pan*	Tîrgovişte	Tyr-*gov*-ish-te
		Tîrgu Jiu	*Tyr*-gu *Zhi*-u
R		Tîrgu Mureş	*Tyr*-gu *Mu*-resh
Razelm	*Raz*-elm	Tîrgu Săcuiesc	*Tyr*-gu Sŭk-u-*yesk*
Reghin	*Reg*-in	Tîrnava	*Tyr*-na-va
Reşiţa	*Resh*-i-tsa	Tîrnăveni	Tyr-nŭv-*en'*
Retezat	Ret-ez-*at*	Trascău	Tras-*kŭu*
Rîmnicu Sărat	*Rym*-ni-ku Sŭr-*at*	Trotuş	*Trot*-ush
— Vîlcea	— *Vyl*-cha	Tulcea	*Tul*-cha
Rîşnov	*Rysh*-nov	Turnu-Măgurele	*Tur*-nu Mŭg-u-*re*-le
Roman	*Rom*-an	Turnu Severin	*Tur*-nu Se-ve-*rin*
România	Rom-yn-*i*-a		
Roznov	*Roz*-nov	**Ţ**	
		Ţara Românească	*Tsa*-ra Rom-yn-*yas*-ka
S		Ţarcu	*Tsar*-ku
Sarmisegetuza	*Sar*-mi-se-ge-*tu*-za	Ţibleş	*Tsi*-blesh
Satu-Mare	*Sat*-u *Ma*-re		
Săcele	Sŭ-*che*-le	**V**	
Săvineşti	Sŭv-i-*nesht'*	Vedea	*Ved*-ya
Schela	*Ske*-la	Victoria	Vik-*tor*-i-a
Semenic	Se-me-*nik*	Vîlcan	Vyl-*kan*
Sibiu	Si-*bi*-u	Vlăhiţa	Vlŭ-*hi*-tsa
Sighet	*Si*-get	Vrancea	*Vran*-cha
Sighişoara	Si-gish-*wa*-ra	Vulcan	Vul-*kan*
Sinoe	Si-*no*-e		
Slatina	*Slat*-i-na	**Z**	
Someş	*Som*-esh	Zarand	Za-*rand*
Stînişoara	Styn-ish-*wa*-ra	Zimnicea	*Zim*-ni-cha

Appendix 3

STATISTICAL TABLES

The following tables have been compiled from the annual statistical year-books published by the United Nations (or League of Nations), with the exception of Table C. They are intended to give a comparative view of trends in the seven countries since 1938. The statistics quoted in the chapters on individual countries have been derived from national sources, however, and certain discrepancies may arise as a result.

A. Population, area and density
B. Birth-rates and death-rates
C. Urbanization and employment in mining and manufacturing
D. Production

Detailed figures of production, etc.:
E. Wheat, maize and rye
F. Barley, oats, rice and potatoes
G. Livestock numbers
H. Meat, cow's milk, sugar and tobacco
I. Coal and coke (metallurgical)
J. Crude petroleum, natural gas and manufactured gas
K. Electricity generation
L. Iron ore, pig-iron and crude steel
M. Leading metal ores
N. Leading non-ferrous metals
O. Lumber, pulp and paper
P. Sulphur, fertilizers, etc.
Q. Salt and soda
R. Yarns and filaments
S. Motor vehicles and radio and television sets
T. Railway traffic and cement

A

POPULATION, AREA AND DENSITY
1938-1963

Country	1938[1]	Population (millions)[2] 1948[2]	1958	1963	Area (sq km)	Area (sq miles)	Persons per sq km (1963)	Persons per sq mile (1963)
Albania	1·04	1·18	1·51	1·76	28,700	11,100	61	158
Bulgaria	6·25	7·13	7·73	8·08	110,700	42,700	73	189
Czechoslovakia	15·24[3,4]	12·34	13·47	13·95	127,900	49,400	109	282
Hungary	9·17	9·16	9·88	10·09	93,000	35,900	108	280
Jugoslavia	15·38	15·90	18·02	19·07	255,800	98,800	75	194
Poland	34·68	23·98	28·77	30·69	312,500	120,700	98	254
Rumania	19·85[5]	15·89	18·06	18·81	237,500	91,700	79	205

[1] Mid-1938 boundaries   [3] 1937 figure   [5] 15·60 in post-war boundaries
[2] Post-war boundaries   [4] 14·60 in post-war boundaries

Sources: Statistical Yearbook of the League of Nations, 1939–40
Demographic Yearbook of the United Nations, 1960
Demographic Yearbook of the United Nations, 1964

B

BIRTH-RATES AND DEATH-RATES
1938–1963
(per thousand) [1]

Country	1938				1948				1958				1963			
	Births	Deaths	Natural increase	Infant deaths	Births	Deaths	Natural increase	Infant deaths	Births	Deaths	Natural increase	Infant deaths	Births	Deaths	Natural increase	Infant deaths
Albania	34·4	17·6	16·8	?	?	?	?	?	41·8	9·3	32·5	68	39·1	10·0	29·1	91
Bulgaria	22·8	13·7	9·1	144	24·6	12·6	12·0	118	17·9	7·9	10·0	52	16·4	8·2	8·2	36
Czechoslovakia	16·8	12·8	4·0	121	23·4	11·5	11·9	84	17·4	9·3	8·1	30	16·9	9·5	7·4	22
Hungary	20·1	14·4	5·7	131	21·0	11·6	9·4	94	16·0	9·9	6·1	58	13·1	9·9	3·2	43
Jugoslavia	26·7	15·6	11·1	144	28·1	13·5	14·6	102[2]	24·0	9·3	14·7	86	21·4	8·9	12·5	78
Poland	24·5	13·8	10·7	140	29·3	11·2	18·1	111	26·3	8·4	17·9	72	19·0	7·5	11·5	49
Rumania	29·6	19·2	10·4	183	23·9	15·6	8·3	143	21·6	8·7	12·9	71	15·7	8·3	7·4	55

[1] Infant death-rate defined as deaths of infants under one year old per 1,000 live births
[2] 1949

Sources: Statistical Yearbook of the League of Nations, 1939–40
Demographic Yearbook of the United Nations, 1958, 1963 and 1964

C

URBANIZATION[1] AND EMPLOYMENT[2] IN MINING AND MANUFACTURING
(millions)

Country	Population in places of over 5,000	Per cent of total population	Urban[3] population	Per cent of total population	Population of capital city	Per cent of urban population	Employment in mining	Employment in manufacturing
Albania	0·33	24·8	0·38	27·5	0·11	28·2		0·07[4]
Bulgaria	2·78	36·5	2·56	33·6	0·64	25·2	0·12	0·71
Czechoslovakia	5·65	41·1	6·55	47·6	1·01	15·4	0·20	2·21
Hungary	5·77	57·8	3·96	39·7	1·81	45·6	0·16	1·07
Jugoslavia	5·40	29·1	5·24	28·3	0·59	11·2	0·15	1·04
Poland	12·88	43·3	14·11	48·1	1·14	8·0	0·43	2·86
Rumania	6·71	38·4	5·47	31·3	1·29	23·6		1·46[5]

[1] 1960 or 1961, except Albania (1955) and Bulgaria and Rumania (1956)
[2] 1963, except Rumania (1962)
[3] As defined by each country on the basis of administrative status, or size or economic functions of communities
[4] From Vjetari Statistikor i R.P.Sh., 1964
[5] From Anuarul Statistic al R.P.R., 1963

Sources: Demographic Yearbook of United Nations, 1962 (some data reworked) and 1964
Statistical Yearbook of United Nations, 1964

D

PRODUCTION
1938–1963
(1958 = 100)

(a) INDEX OF INDUSTRIAL PRODUCTION[1]
(b) INDEX OF PER CAPITA GROSS NATIONAL PRODUCT[2]

Country	1938 (a)	1938 (b)	1948 (a)	1948 (b)	1953 (a)	1953 (b)	1958 (a)	1958 (b)	1963 (a)	1963 (b)
Albania	?	?	?	?	?	?	?	?	?	?
Bulgaria	11[3]	?	22	?	55	82	100	100	188	136[6]
Czechoslovakia	31[4]	?	33	?	64	75	100	100	143	118
Hungary	28	?	28	56[5]	82	84	100	100	159	135
Jugoslavia	29[3]	?	43	?	53	73	100	100	171	144
Poland	16	?	28	54[5]	61	73	100	100	153	121
Rumania	25	?	22	?	63	80	100	100	189	149

[1] Including mining and energy
[2] At constant prices. The index is *not* an index of living standards
[3] 1939   [4] 1937   [5] 1949   [6] 1962

Source: United Nations Statistical Yearbook, 1963 and 1964

E

WHEAT, MAIZE AND RYE

(millions of metric tons)

1938–1962

Country	1934–8 av.[1]			1948–52 av.			1958–62 av.		
	Wheat	Maize	Rye	Wheat	Maize	Rye	Wheat	Maize	Rye
Albania	?	?	?	0·09	0·11	0·01	0·09	0·17	0·01
Bulgaria	1·70	0·91	0·27	1·78	0·78	0·24	2·26	1·38	0·08
Czechoslovakia	1·51	0·23	1·57	1·49	0·31	1·11	1·56	0·50	0·94
Hungary	2·22	2·31	0·70	1·91	2·07	0·73	1·81	3·17	0·34
Jugoslavia	2·47	4·69	0·21	2·17	3·08	0·25	3·37	5·32	0·22
Poland	1·97	—	6·85	1·83	—	6·37	2·52	0·03	7·68
Rumania	2·60	4·06	0·17	2·49	2·37	0·16	3·68	5·10	0·11

[1] Post-war boundaries

Sources: United Nations Statistical Yearbooks, 1958 and 1963

F

BARLEY, OATS, RICE AND POTATOES
(millions of metric tons)
1938–1962

Country	1934–8[1]				1948–52 av.				1958–62 av.			
	Barley	Oats	Rice	Potatoes	Barley	Oats	Rice	Potatoes	Barley	Oats	Rice	Potatoes
Albania	?	?	?	?	0·01	0·02	?	?	0·01	0·01	?	?
Bulgaria	0·37	0·12	?	?	0·33	0·15	0·04	0·24	0·57	0·18	0·04	0·39
Czechoslovakia	1·11	1·21	—	9·64	1·05	0·96	—	7·26	1·55	0·94	—	5·67
Hungary	0·61	0·27	—	2·13	0·65	0·21	0·05	1·72	0·99	0·18	0·05	2·23
Jugoslavia	0·41	0·32	0·004	1·63	0·32	0·29	0·005	1·49	0·52	0·36	0·02	2·79
Poland	1·63	2·83	—	38·04	1·06	2·24	—	29·64	1·24	2·72	—	38·28
Rumania	?	0·53	?	?	0·39	0·37	0·04	1·70	0·41	0·26	0·04	2·85

[1] Post-war boundaries

Sources: United Nations Statistical Yearbooks, 1958 and 1963

G

LIVESTOCK NUMBERS

Pre-war–1963
(millions)

Country	Pre-war[1]				1947/8–1951/2 av.				1958/9[2]				1962/3[3]			
	Cattle	Pigs	Sheep	Horses	Cattle	Pigs	Sheep	Horses	Cattle	Pigs	Sheep	Horses	Cattle	Pigs	Sheep	Horses
Albania	?	?	?	?	0·41	?	1·63	?	0·42	?	1·62	?	0·42	?	1·59	?
Bulgaria	?	?	9·94	?	1·69	1·00	8·38	0·51	1·36	2·05	8·62	0·38	1·58	2·07	10·11	0·28
Czechoslovakia	4·71	3·54	0·53	0·66	3·97	3·61	0·55	0·61	4·18	5·28	0·82	0·46	4·51	5·90	0·52	0·25
Hungary	1·88	5·22	1·87	0·94	2·05	4·13	1·03	0·67	2·00	6·23	2·16	0·72	1·91	5·43	3·04	0·34
Jugoslavia	4·88	5·04	12·29	1·33	4·87	3·96	10·49	1·06	5·04	5·66	11·25	1·27	5·36	5·01	10·06	1·18
Poland	10·55	7·53	3·41	3·92	6·90	7·53	2·21	2·67	8·35	11·21	3·78	2·84	9·84	11·65	3·06	2·62
Rumania	?	?	9·77	?	4·44[4]	2·15	10·64	0·94	4·39	4·01	10·66	1·22	4·57	4·52	12·17	0·78

[1] Various years between 1931 and 1939. Post-war boundaries   [2] Albania 1959/60
[3] Albania 1961/2   [4] Incl. buffaloes

Sources: United Nations Statistical Yearbooks, 1958, 1963 and 1964

H

MEAT, COW'S MILK, SUGAR[1] AND TOBACCO[2]

(millions of metric tons, except tobacco – thousands of metric tons)

Pre-war–1963

Country	Pre-war[3]				1948[4]				1958				1963[5]			
	Meat	Milk	Sugar	Tobacco	Meat	Milk	Sugar	Tobacco	Meat	Milk	Sugar	Tobacco	Meat	Milk	Sugar	Tobacco
Albania	?	?	—	?	?	?	—	?	?	?	0·01	?	?	0·08	0·01	?
Bulgaria	?	0·52	0·02	31	?	0·28	0·07	45	0·26	0·59	0·16	83	0·24	0·78	0·18	105
Czechoslovakia	?	4·84	0·53	11	0·61	3·19	0·63	8	0·71	3·76	0·93	8	0·78	3·54	0·94	8
Hungary	?	1·49	0·11	21	?	1·44	0·25	22	0·18	1·95	0·27	31	0·40	1·80	0·41	27
Jugoslavia	?	1·53	0·04	17	0·28	1·47	0·18	24	0·37	2·19	0·18	39	0·50	2·17	0·34	54
Poland	?	11·70	0·55	9	0·90	8·34	0·68	29	1·61	11·86	1·15	37	1·57	12·64	1·32	49
Rumania	?	2·58	0·16	9	?	1·49	0·10	17	?	2·01	0·20	31	?	2·54	0·31	40

[1] Almost entirely from home-grown sugar beet [2] Tobacco crop, not tobacco products

[3] Sugar–1938, milk and tobacco–various years, or averages of certain years, between 1933 and 1939

[4] Average 1948–52 for meat, milk and tobacco [5] 1961 for Albania

Sources: United Nations Statistical Yearbooks, 1958 and 1964

I

COAL AND COKE (METALLURGICAL)
1938–1963
(millions of metric tons)

Country	1938			1948			1958			1963 (est.)		
	Black coal	Coke	Brown coal and lignite	Black coal	Coke	Brown coal and lignite	Black coal	Coke	Brown coal and lignite	Black coal	Coke	Brown coal and lignite
Albania	—	—	—	—	—	—	—	—	0·26	—	—	0·30
Bulgaria	0·15	?	1·94	0·13	0·01	4·14	0·38	0·01	11·57	0·66	0·13	20·28
Czechoslovakia	15·84	2·77	16·03	16·68	3·68	23·59	23·93	5·84	56·84	28·18	7·74	73·30
Hungary	1·04	—	8·32	1·24	—	9·38	2·63	0·34	21·62	3·71	0·66	26·77
Jugoslavia	0·45	—	5·29	0·95[1]	—	9·69	1·21	1·03	17·78	1·29	1·09	26·14
Poland	38·10	?	0·01	70·26[1]	2·12	5·04[1]	94·98	6·31	7·54	113·15	8·36	15·34
Rumania	0·35	0·08	2·48	2·04[2]	0·08	0·91[2]	3·91	0·56	3·48	5·66	1·14	4·61

[1] Extension of national boundary
[2] Re-categorization of coal (0·22 and 2·72 according to former categories)
Sources: United Nations Statistical Yearbooks, 1958 and 1964

CRUDE PETROLEUM, NATURAL GAS AND MANUFACTURED GAS[1]

(petroleum – thousands of metric tons)

(gas – millions of cubic metres)

1938–1963

Country	1938			1948			1958			1963 (est.)		
	Petroleum	Natural gas	Manu-factured gas	Petroleum	Natural gas	Manu-factured gas	Petroleum	Natural gas	Manu-factured gas	Petroleum	Natural gas	Manu-factured gas
Albania	?	—	—	132[2]	—	—	403	—	—	785[3]	—	—
Bulgaria	—	2	?	—	—	—	222	—	—	173	—	?
Czechoslovakia	19	8	126	31	?	2,064	106	1,246	3,611	180	998	5,358
Hungary	43	8	?	480	320	171	830	379	450	1,756	612	742
Jugoslavia	1	2	?	36	8	25	462	46	26	1,611	101	53
Poland	507	584	?	140[4]	157[4]	2,105	175	385	4,747	212	945	5,788
Rumania	6,594	2,026	?	4,149	2,346	34	11,336	8,506	291	12,233	14,548	530

[1] From cokeries and gasworks   [2] 1950   [3] 1962   [4] Change of boundary

Sources: United Nations Statistical Yearbooks, 1958 and 1964

K

ELECTRICITY GENERATION

1938–1963

(millions of killowatt-hours)

Country	1938 Total	1938 Hydro	1948 Total	1948 Hydro	1958 Total	1958 Hydro	1963 (est.) Total	1963 (est.) Hydro
Albania	2	?	?	?	150	87	242[2]	118
Bulgaria	266[1]	153	550	236	3,024	960	7,184	2,086
Czechoslovakia	4,052	600	7,515	909	19,620	2,616	29,861	2,289
Hungary	1,399	20	2,228	50	6,479	48	9,663	81
Jugoslavia	1,090	470	2,061	1,053	7,356	4,300	13,535	8,028
Poland	3,977	—	7,514	?	23,962	763	36,963	669
Rumania	1,130	148	1,500	130	6,184	281	11,682	537

[1] 1939   [2] 1962

Sources: United Nations Statistical Yearbooks, 1958 and 1964

L

IRON ORE,[1] PIG-IRON AND CRUDE STEEL
1938–1963
(millions of metric tons)

Country	1938			1948			1958			1963 (est.)		
	Fe ore	Pig-iron	Steel	Fe ore	Pig-iron	Steel	Fe ore	Pig-iron	Steel	Fe ore	Pig-iron	Steel
Albania	—	—	—	—	—	—	?	—	—	?	—	—
Bulgaria	0·01	—	—	0·01	0·001	0·005	0·14	0·09	0·21	0·25	0·27	0·46
Czechoslovakia	0·53	1·32	1·87[2]	0·43	1·65	2·62	0·84	3·81	5·51	0·95	5·31	7·60
Hungary	0·07	0·34	0·65	0·08	0·38	0·77	0·11	1·10	1·63	0·18	1·40	2·37
Jugoslavia	0·28	0·12	0·23	0·31	0·18	0·37	0·70	0·78	1·12	0·81	1·06	1·59
Poland	0·32	0·88	1·44	0·22	1·13	1·96	0·58	3·86	5·66	0·72	5·40	8·00
Rumania	0·07	0·13	0·28	0·09	0·19	0·35	0·22	0·74	0·93	0·73	1·71	2·70

[1] By metal content   [2] 2·30 in 1937

Sources: United Nations Statistical Yearbooks, 1958 and 1964

M

LEADING METAL ORES[1]
1938–1963
(thousands of metric tons)[2]

Country	1938					1948					1958					1963 (est.)				
	Bauxite	Copper	Lead	Manganese	Zinc	Bauxite	Copper	Lead	Manganese	Zinc	Bauxite	Copper	Lead	Manganese	Zinc	Bauxite	Copper	Lead	Manganese	Zinc
Albania	—	?	—	—	—	—	?	—	—	—	—	2	—	—	—	—	3	—	—	—
Bulgaria	—	?	1[3]	0·6[3]	1[3]	—	1	13	?	10	—	8	78	7	61	—	21	100	11	74
Czechoslovakia	—	?	?	?	?	—	?	?	17	?	—	?	6	27	?	—	?	14	14	?
Hungary	540	?	?	9	?	478	?	—	20	—	1,049	0·4	1	44	2	1,362	0·4	1	39	3
Jugoslavia	406	45	85	1	45	144	41	63	4	37	733	35	90	3	60	1,285	62	102	3	61
Poland	—	—	?	—	70	—	?	15	—	96	—	8	33	—	123	—	13	39	—	147
Rumania	12	?	6	22	?	—	?	4	18	?	73	?	12	50	?	10	?	13	60	?

[1] Excluding iron   [2] By metal content, except bauxite   [3] 1939

Sources: United Nations Statistical Yearbooks, 1958 and 1964

N

LEADING NON-FERROUS METALS

(thousands of metric tons)

1938–1963

Country	1938				1948[1]				1958[1]				1963 (est.)[1]			
	Al	Cu[2]	Pb[2]	Zn[2]	Al	Cu	Pb	Zn	Al	Cu	Pb	Zn	Al	Cu	Pb	Zn
Albania	—	—	—	—	—	?	—	—	—	1[3]	—	—	—	2[3]	—	—
Bulgaria	—	?	—	—	—	—	2	?	—	6[3]	26	8	—	20	51	56
Czechoslovakia	—	?	5	9	—	?	6?	?	26?	?	9?	30?	60?	?	14?	30?
Hungary	1	?	?	?	9	?	?	?	40	5	1	1	56	12	2	1
Jugoslavia	1	42	9	5	2	14	49	7	22	30	84	31	36	49	104	42
Poland	—	—	20	108	—	1	19	71	22	18	36	163	47	30	39	181
Rumania	—	1	6	?	?	?	4?	?	?	?	12?	?	?	?	13?	?

[1] Including, in some instances, 'secondary' metal recovered from scrap
[2] Smelter production only in most instances   [3] Smelter production

Sources: United Nations Statistical Yearbooks, 1958 and 1964

O

LUMBER,[1] PULP[2] AND PAPER

(lumber – thousands of cubic metres)
(others – thousands of metric tons)
1938–1963

Country	1938				1948				1958				1963 (est.)			
	Lumber	Wood pulp	Newsprint	Other paper	Lumber	Wood pulp	Newsprint	Other paper	Lumber	Wood pulp	Newsprint	Other paper	Lumber	Wood pulp	Newsprint	Other paper
Albania	?	?	?	?	?	?	?	?	?	?	?	?	?	?	?	?
Bulgaria	360	?	?	13	695	?	?	22	1,230	?	?	47	1,580	?	?	60[3]
Czechoslovakia	3,010	?	44	200	3,133	304	29	231	4,251	495	35	369	3,696	593	42	429
Hungary	415	?	16	39	?	19	10	33	509	48	—	80	826	65[3]	—	122[3]
Jugoslavia	3,260	27	?	25	2,458	39	—	50	1,862	148	28	90	2,693	275	32	209
Poland	3,200	194	34	171	3,831	227	53	194	6,837	388	71	361	6,680	490	76	511
Rumania	3,360	?	?	58	2,176	?	20	44	3,540	144	41	78	4,572	205	50	141

[1] Sawn-wood, from both coniferous and deciduous trees   [2] Chemical and mechanical   [3] 1962

Sources: United Nations Statistical Yearbooks, 1958, 1963 and 1964

SULPHUR, FERTILIZERS, etc.
(millions of metric tons)
(nitrogenous fertilizers by nitrogen content)
1938-1963

Country	1938[1]				1948[2]				1958[3]				1963 (est.)[4]			
	Sulphur	Sulphuric acid	Super-phosphates	Nitrogenous fertilizers	Sulphur	Sulphuric acid	Super-phosphates	Nitrogenous fertilizers	Sulphur	Sulphuric acid	Super-phosphates	Nitrogenous fertilizers	Sulphur	Sulphuric acid	Super-phosphates	Nitrogenous fertilizers
Albania	—	—	—	—	—	—	—	—	—	—	—	—	—	—	—	—
Bulgaria	?	?	?	?	?	?	?	18[5]	29[P] } 38	64	?	40	5[P] } 68 [11]	269	?	94[6]
Czechoslovakia	?	165[7]	128	25[7]	?	215	179	35	144[P]	463	408	74	136[P]	725	817	154
Hungary	?	40	52	?	?	33	?	6	?	148	205	33[8]	?	283	513	79
Jugoslavia	63	25	28[9]	8	135[P]	44	52	4	149[P]	125	265	5	160[P]	391	732	63
Poland	36[P][7]	181[7]	228	52	23[P]	222	279	74[10]	77[P]	573	581	201	80[P] } 369[8]	888	1,010	330
Rumania	5[P]	44	?	?	?	?	1	?	82[P]	144	121	6	133[P]	343	623	85

[1] For nitrogenous fertilizers 1938/9
[2] For nitrogenous fertilizers 1948/9-1952/3 average
[3] For nitrogenous fertilizers 1957/8
[4] For nitrogenous fertilizers 1963/4

[5] 1952
[6] 1962/3
[7] 1937
[8] 1958/9

[9] 1939
[10] 1949
[11] 1962

Sources: United Nations Statistical Yearbooks, 1958 and 1964
P–Sulphur content of pyrites
S–Mined sulphur

Q

SALT AND SODA
1938–1963
(thousands of metric tons)

Country	1938			1948			1958			1963 (est.)		
	Salt[1]	Caustic[2] soda	Soda[3] ash	Salt	Caustic soda	Soda ash	Salt	Caustic soda	Soda ash	Salt	Caustic soda	Soda ash
Albania	?	—	—	?	—	—	?	—	—	?	—	—
Bulgaria	77	—	—	67	—	—	112	15	104	105	21	208
Czechoslovakia	181[4]	?	?	140	37	99	162	93	89	187	144	57
Hungary	?	4	?	?	?	?	?	17	?	?	40	?
Jugoslavia	74	11	20	102	19	35	172	42	77	167	70	91
Poland	643	30	?	?	47	98	1,610	151	380	2,132	200	543
Rumania	368	12	24	352	14	27	732	41	82	1,637	166	327

[1] Sodium chloride   [3] Sodium carbonate
[2] Sodium hydroxide
[4] 1937

Sources: United Nations Statistical Yearbooks, 1958 and 1964

R

YARNS[1] AND FILAMENTS
1938–1963
(thousands of metric tons)

Country	1938				1948				1958				1963 (est.)			
	Cotton	Wool	Rayon and acetate	Non-cellulosic	Cotton	Wool	Rayon and acetate	Non-cellulosic	Cotton	Wool	Rayon and acetate	Non-cellulosic	Cotton	Wool	Rayon and acetate	Non-cellulosic
Albania	—	—	—	—	—	—	—	—	1	?	—	—	?	?	—	—
Bulgaria	12[2]	1[2]	—	—	16	5	—	—	36	12	—	—	56	17	—	—
Czechoslovakia	89[3]	27[3]	3	—	68	32	22	—	95	37	53	1	107	41	68	6
Hungary	21	12	—	—	24	8	2	—	46	13	4	—	64	17	4	2
Jugoslavia	19[2]	6[2]	—	—	28	13	—	—	45	17	10	—	75	26	20	—
Poland	64	34[3]	10	—	82	33	18	—	135	57	61	5	160	60	77	11
Rumania	17	7	1	—	21	8	1	—	47	18	3	—	71	23	3	3

[1] Including mixed fibres   [2] 1939   [3] 1937

Sources: United Nations Statistical Yearbooks, 1958 and 1964

S

MOTOR VEHICLES[1] AND RADIO AND TELEVISION SETS
(thousands)
1938–1963

Country	1938			1948			1958			1963 (est.)		
	Vehicles	Radio sets	TV sets	Vehicles	Radio sets	TV sets	Vehicles	Radio sets	TV sets	Vehicles	Radio sets	TV sets
Albania	—	—	—	—	—	—	—	—	—	—	—	—
Bulgaria	—	?	—	—	3	—	—	131	—	—	204	29
Czechoslovakia	13·0	144	—	35·4	268	—	81·9	309	134	100·5	273	235
Hungary	?	?	—	?	?	—	5·2	453	37	6·1	169	251
Jugoslavia	—	—	—	0·5	23	—	7·7	259	—	29·9	377	117
Poland	?	145	—	?	34	—	25·4	790	57	52·5	487	365
Rumania	—	—	—	?	—	—	6·9	139	—	20·2	240	67

[1] Cars, buses and lorries chiefly, and excluding farm tractors. Only Czechoslovakia, Jugoslavia and Poland produce cars (1963).

Sources: United Nations Statistical Yearbooks, 1958 and 1964.

T

RAILWAY TRAFFIC AND CEMENT

(railway traffic – millions of passenger-km or ton-km)

(cement – millions of metric tons)

1938–1963

Country	1938			1948			1958			1963 (est.)		
	Passenger-km	Freight net ton-km	Cement	Passenger-km	Freight net ton-km	Cement	Passenger-km	Freight net ton-km	Cement	Passenger-km	Freight net ton-km	Cement
Albania	—	—	?	?	?	?	?	?	0·08	?	?	0·15
Bulgaria	0·74[1]	1·08	0·19	2·56	1·72	0·38	3·09	5·24	0·93	4·02	8·57	2·21
Czechoslovakia	7·51[2]	11·06[2]	1·18	14·98	14·28	1·66	18·68	42·67	4·11	19·04	51·66	5·18
Hungary	3·11	3·13	0·32	?	4·55[3]	0·55	1·88	10·24	1·30	13·18	15·18	1·80
Jugoslavia	3·02	4·24	0·71	6·10	6·56	1·17	8·72	11·89	1·97	10·67	17·35	2·85
Poland	6·95[4]	22·05[4]	1·72	20·42	28·29	1·82	38·09	57·19	5·06	32·14	74·43	7·67
Rumania	5·30	5·75	0·51	6·48	5·66	0·66	11·62	17·02	2·57	12·84	26·76	4·37

[1] Standard gauge only   [3] 1949

[2] 1937   [4] 1937 figures for pre-war territory

Sources: United Nations Statistical Yearbooks, 1958 and 1964

Appendix 4

BIBLIOGRAPHY

Select references and further reading (small paperback editions marked with an asterisk)

(a) East-Central Europe: General Books

GEOGRAPHY

Ancel, J. *Manuel géographique de politique européenne, 1: L'Europe centrale. 2: L'Europe germanique et ses bornes.* Librairie Delagrave, Paris, 1936, 1940.

Birot, P., and Dresch, J. *La Méditerranée et le Moyen-Orient, 2: La Méditerranée orientale et le Moyen-Orient.* Presses universitaires de France, Paris, 1956.

*Blanc, A. *Géographie des Balkans.* Presses universitaires de France, Paris, 1965.

Bowman, I. *The new world: problems in political geography.* World Book Co., New York, 4th ed., 1928.

Chataigneau, Y., and Sion, J. *Géographie universelle, 7: Méditerranée, péninsules méditerranéennes, 2: Italie, Pays Balkaniques.* Librairie Armand Colin, Paris, 1934.

Cvijić, J. *La péninsule Balkanique: géographie humaine.* Librairie Armand Colin, Paris, 1918.

East, W. G., and Moodie, A. E. (eds.). *The changing world: studies in political geography.* Harrap, London, 1956. (Especially chaps. 1, 2, 4 and 8.)

*George, P. *Géographie de l'Europe centrale slave et danubienne.* Presses universitaires de France, Paris, 1964

George, P., and Tricart, J. *L'Europe centrale,* 2 vols. (Collection 'Orbis'). Presses universitaires de France, Paris, 1954.

*Hoffman, G. W. *The Balkans in transition* (Searchlight Book 20). Van Nostrand, Princeton, N.J., 1963.

Kostrowicki, J. (ed.). *Land utilization in east-central Europe: case studies* (*Geographia Polonica* 5 of Institute of Geography, Polish Academy of Sciences). Wydawnictwa Geologiczne, Warsaw, 1965.

Kubiena, W. L. *The soils of Europe.* Murby, London, 1953.

de Martonne, E. *Géographie universelle, 4: Europe centrale.* 2 parts. Librairie Armand Colin, Paris, 1930–1.

Newbigin, M. L. *Geographical aspects of Balkan problems.* Constable, London, 1915.

Partsch, J. (trans. Black, C.). *Central Europe.* Heinemann, London, 1903.

Pounds, N. J. G. (ed.). *Geographical essays on Eastern Europe* (Russian and East European Series 24). Indiana University, Bloomington, 1961.

Wanklyn, H. G. *The eastern marchlands of Europe*. Geo. Philip, London, 1941.

MARXISM–INTRODUCTORY

*Freedman, R. (ed.). *Marx on economics*. Penguin Books, Harmondsworth, 1962.

*Hunt, R. N. C. *The theory and practice of Communism*. Penguin Books, Harmondsworth, 1963.

*Mills, C. W. *The Marxists*. Penguin Books, Harmondsworth, 1963.

ECONOMICS, HISTORY AND POLITICS

Basch, A. *The Danubian basin and the German economic sphere*. International Library of Sociology and Social Reconstruction. Kegan Paul, London, 1944.

Betts, R. R. (ed.). *Central and south-east Europe, 1945-1948*. Auspices of Royal Institute of International Affairs. Oxford University Press, London, 1950.

Burks, R. V. *The dynamics of communism in eastern Europe*. Princeton University Press, 1961.

Dvornik, F. *The Slavs in European history and civilization*. Rutgers University Press, New Brunswick, N.J., 1962.

*Fischer-Galati, S. (ed.). *Eastern Europe in the sixties* (Praeger publications in Russian history and world communism 137). Praeger, New York and London, 1963.

Hertz, F. *The economic problem of the Danubian states*. Gollancz, London, 1947.

*Ionescu, I. *The break-up of the Soviet empire in eastern Europe*. Penguin Books, Harmondsworth, 1965.

Jelavich, C. and B. (eds.). *The Balkans in transition*. University of California Press, Berkeley and Los Angeles, 1963.

Kaser, M. *Comecon: integration problems of the planned economies*. Auspices of Royal Institute of International Affairs. Oxford University Press, London, 1965.

Macartney, C. A. *Problems of the Danube basin*. Cambridge University Press, 1942.

Macartney, C. A., and Palmer, A.W. *Independent eastern Europe*. Macmillan, London, 1962.

McNeill, W. H. *Europe's steppe frontier, 1500–1800*. Chicago University Press, 1964.

Moore, W. E. *Economic demography of eastern and southern Europe*. League of Nations, Geneva, 1945.

PEP (Political and Economic Planning). *Economic development in S.E. Europe*. PEP and Oxford University Press, London, 1945.

Pounds, N. J. G., and Spulber, N. (eds.). *Resources and planning in eastern*

Europe (Slavic and East European Series 4). Indiana University, Bloomington, 1957.

Proudfoot, M. J. *European refugees, 1939-1952: a study in forced population movements.* Faber, London, 1957.

Roucek, J. S., *et al. Central-eastern Europe: crucible of world wars.* Prentice-Hall, New York, 1946.

Royal Institute of International Affairs. *South-eastern Europe: a political and economic survey.* Oxford University Press, London, 1939.

Sanders, I. T. (ed.). *Collectivization of agriculture in eastern Europe.* University of Kentucky Press, Lexington, 1958.

Schechtman, J. B. *European population transfers, 1939-1945.* Oxford University Press, London, 1946.

Schechtman, J. B. *Post-war population transfers in Europe, 1945-1955.* Oxford University Press, London, 1962.

Seton-Watson, H. *Eastern Europe between the wars, 1918-1941.* Cambridge University Press, 2nd ed., 1946. Archon Books, Hamden, Connecticut, 3rd ed., 1962.

Seton-Watson, H. *The East European revolution.* Methuen, London, 3rd ed., 1956.

Seton-Watson, H. *The pattern of communist revolution: a historical analysis.* Methuen, London, 1960 (rev. ed.).

Spulber, N. *The economics of communist eastern Europe.* Wiley, New York, 1957.

Stavrianos, L. S. *The Balkans since 1453.* Rinehart, New York, 1958.

*Stavrianos, L. S. *The Balkans, 1815-1914* (Berkshire Studies in European History). Holt, Rinehart & Winston, New York, 1963.

*Taylor, A. J. P. *The Habsburg Monarchy, 1809-1918.* Hamish Hamilton, London, 1948. Penguin Books, Harmondsworth, 1964.

United Nations, Economic Commission for Europe. *Economic survey of Europe.* United Nations, Geneva (annual).

Warriner, D. *Economics of peasant farming.* Oxford University Press, London, 1939.

Warriner, D. *Revolution in eastern Europe.* Turnstile Press, London, 1950

Wiskemann, E. *Germany's eastern neighbours: problems relating to the Oder–Neisse line and the Czech frontier regions.* Auspices of Royal Institute of International Affairs. Oxford University Press, London, 1956.

Wolff, R. L. *The Balkans in our time.* Harvard University Press, Cambridge, Mass., 1956.

Zagoroff, S. D., Végh, J., and Bilimovich, A. D. *The agricultural economy of the Danubian countries, 1935-1945.* Food Research Institute, Stanford University. Stanford University Press, 1955.

Zauberman, A. *Industrial progress in Poland, Czechoslovakia and East Germany, 1937-1962.* Auspices of Royal Institute of International Affairs. Oxford University Press, London, 1964.

Zeman, Z. A. B. *The break-up of the Habsburg Empire, 1914-1918.* Oxford University Press, London, 1961.

(b) General Geographical Articles

Kiss, G. TVA on the Danube? *Geographical Review* 37 (1947) 274–302.

Kosiński, L. Les problèmes démographiques dans les territoires occidentaux de la Pologne et les régions frontières de la Tchécoslovaquie. *Annales de Géographie* 71 (1962) 79–98.

de Martonne, E. The Carpathians: physiographic features controlling human geography. *Geographical Review* 3 (1917) 417–37.

Mellor, R. E. H. The German refugee problem: ten years retrospect. *Scottish Geographical Magazine* 73 (1957) 1–18.

Ormsby, H. The Danube as a waterway. *Scottish Geographical Magazine* 39 (1923) 103–12.

Popper, O. The international régime of the Danube. *Geographical Journal* 102 (1943) 240–53.

Pounds, N. J. G. The spread of mining in the coal basin of Upper Silesia and Northern Moravia. *Annals of the Association of American Geographers* 48 (1958) 149-63.

Revue Géographique de l'Est. 'Chronique d'Europe Orientale' is an annual feature from 1963.

Sinnhuber, K. A. Central Europe–Mitteleuropa–Europe Centrale: an analysis of a geographical term. *Transactions and Papers, 1954, Institute of British Geographers* 20 (1954) 15–39.

Wallis, B. C. The peoples of Austria. *Geographical Review* 6 (1918) 52–65.

Wallis, B. C. The Rumanians in Hungary. Ibid., 156–71.

Wallis, B. C. The Slavs of northern Hungary. Ibid., 268–81.

Wallis, B. C. The Slavs of southern Hungary. Ibid., 341–53.

(c) Individual Countries. Geographical Books and Others of Interest, also Geographical Articles, in English, French or German

ALBANIA

BOOKS

Great Britain: Naval Intelligence Division. *Albania* (Geographical Handbook Series B.R. 542). 1945.

Hamm, H. (trans. Andersen, V.). *Albania: China's beachhead in Europe.* Weidenfeld & Nicolson, London, 1963.

Skendi, S. (ed.). *Albania* (East-central Europe under the Communists, ed. Byrnes, R. F.). Mid-European Studies Center of the Free Europe Committee Inc. and Atlantic Books, New York and London, 1957.

ARTICLE

Blanc, A. Naissance et évolution des paysages agraires en Albanie. *Geografiska Annaler* 43 (1961) 8–16.

BULGARIA

BOOKS

Beškov, A. (trans. Georgieva, B.). *Volksrepublik Bulgarien: Natur und Wirtschaft.* Verlag die Wirtschaft, E. Berlin, 1960.

Dellin, L. A. D. (ed.). *Bulgaria* (East-central Europe under the Communists, ed. Byrnes, R. F.). Mid-European Studies Center of the Free Europe Committee Inc. and Atlantic Books, New York and London, 1957.

Kossev, D. *et al. A short history of Bulgaria.* Sofia, 1963.

Macdermott, M. *A history of Bulgaria, 1393–1885.* Allen & Unwin, London, 1962.

ARTICLES

Batakliev, I. Viticulture in Bulgaria. *Geography* 24 (1939) 85–94.

Beaver, S. H. Bulgaria: a summary. *Geography* 25 (1940) 159–69.

Beshkov, A. The Upper Thracian Plain in Bulgarian agriculture. *Economic Geography* 15 (1939) 179–84.

Beshkov, A. Tobacco in Bulgaria. *Economic Geography* 16 (1940) 188–94.

Billaut, M. La collectivisation agraire en Bulgarie: l'exemple du village de Petartch. *Annales de géographie* 69 (1960) 484–92.

Bruman, H. J. The Bulgarian rose industry. *Economic Geography* 12 (1936) 273–8.

Doukas, K. A. Bulgaria's modes of transport. *Economic Geography* 19 (1943) 337–46.

Hoffman, G. W. Transformation of rural settlement in Bulgaria. *Geographical Review* 54 (1964) 45–64.

Osborne, R. H. Economic regionalization in Bulgaria. *Geography* 45 (1960) 291–4.

Penkoff, I. Die Siedlungen Bulgariens, ihre Entwicklung, Veränderungen und Klassifizierung. *Geographische Berichte* 5 (1960) 211–27.

Roucek, J. A. Economic geography of Bulgaria. *Economic Geography* 11 (1935) 307–23.

CZECHOSLOVAKIA

BOOKS

Blažek, M. (trans. Langer, H.). *Ökonomische Geographie der Tschechoslowakischen Republik.* Verlag die Wirtschaft, E. Berlin, 1959.

Busek, V., and Spulber, N. (eds.). *Czechoslovakia* (East-central Europe under the Communists, ed. Byrnes, R. F.). Mid-European Studies Center of the Free Europe Committee Inc. and Atlantic Books, New York and London, 1957.

Luža, R. *The transfer of the Sudeten Germans: a study of Czech-German relations, 1933–1962.* Routledge & Kegan Paul, London, 1964.

Seton-Watson, R. W. *A history of the Czechs and Slovaks.* Hutchinson, London, 1943. Archon Books, Hamden, Conn., 1965.

Taborsky, E. *Communism in Czechoslovakia 1948–60.* Princeton University Press, 1961.

Thomson, S. H. *Czechoslovakia in European history.* Oxford University Press, London, 1944.

Wanklyn, H. (Mrs J. A. Steers). *Czechoslovakia: a geographical and historical study.* Geo. Philip, London, 1954.

ARTICLES

George, P., *et al.* 'Études et recherches' section of *Revue géographique de l'Est* 3 (1963) 113–65 has six articles.

Kahoun, F. Geographische Aspekte des 3.Fünfjahrplans der ČSSR. *Geographische Berichte* 7 (1962) 170–93.

Moscheles, J. The natural regions of Czechoslovakia. *Geographical Review* 14 (1924) 561–75.

Moscheles, J. Demographic, social and economic regions of Greater Prague. *Geographical Review* 27 (1937) 414–29.

Shute, J. Czechoslovakia's territorial and population changes. *Economic Geography* 24 (1948) 35–44.

Steers, Mrs J. A. The middle people: resettlement in Czechoslovakia. *Geographical Journal* 112 (1948) 28–42.

Střída, M. Les méthodes de détermination des régions économiques en Tchécoslovaquie. *Annales de géographie* 70 (1961) 137–44.

HUNGARY

BOOKS

Helmreich, E. C. (ed.) *Hungary* (East-central Europe under the Communists, ed. Byrnes, R. F.). Mid-European Studies Center of the Free Europe Committee Inc. and Atlantic Books, New York and London, 1957.

Macartney, C. A. *Hungary and her successors: the Treaty of Trianon and its consequences, 1919–1937.* Oxford University Press, London, 1937.

Macartney, C. A. *October 15th: a history of modern Hungary, 1929–1945.* Edinburgh University Press, 2nd ed., 1961.

Macartney, C. A. *Hungary: a short history.* Edinburgh University Press, 1962.

Miklós, Gy. *Studies in Hungarian geographical sciences.* Akadémiai Kiadó, Budapest, 1960.

Pécsi, M. (ed.). *Ten years of physico-geographic research in Hungary (Studies in Geography 1* of Geographical Research Institute of Hungarian Academy of Sciences). Akadémiai Kiadó, Budapest, 1964.

Pécsi, M., and Sárfalvi, B. *The geography of Hungary.* Corvina, Budapest, and Collet's, London, 1964.

Radó, S. (ed.). *Ökonomische Geographie der Ungarischen Volksrepublik.* Verlag die Wirtschaft, E. Berlin, 1962.

Sárfalvi, B. (ed.). *Applied geography in Hungary (Studies in Geography 2* of Geographical Research Institute of Hungarian Academy of Sciences). Akadémiai Kiadó, Budapest, 1964.

Sárfalvi, B. (ed.). *Geographical types of Hungarian agriculture (Studies in Geography 3* of Geographical Research Institute of Hungarian Academy of Sciences). Akadémiai Kiadó, Budapest, 1966.

Sinor, D. *History of Hungary.* Allen & Unwin, London, 1959.

ARTICLES

Beynon, E. D. Budapest: an ecological study. *Geographical Review* 33 (1943) 256–75.

Compton, P. A. The new socialist town of Dunaújváros. *Geography* 50 (1965) 288–91.

Enyedi, G. Le village hongrois et la grande exploitation agricole. *Annales de Géographie* 73 (1964) 687–700.

Wallis, B. C. Central Hungary: Magyars and Germans. *Geographical Review* 6 (1918) 421–35.

Wanklyn, H. The rôle of peasant Hungary in Europe. *Geographical Journal* 97 (1941) 18–35.

JUGOSLAVIA

BOOKS

Barker, E. *Macedonia: its place in Balkan power politics.* Royal Institute of International Affairs, London, 1950.

Byrnes, R. F. (ed.). *Yugoslavia* (East-central Europe under the Communists). Mid-European Studies Center of the Free Europe Committee Inc. and Atlantic Books, New York and London, 1957.

Great Britain: Naval Intelligence Division. *Jugoslavia* (Geographical Handbook Series B.R. 493). 3 vols. 1944–5.

Hoffman, G. W., and Neal, F. W. *Yugoslavia and the new communism.* Twentieth Century Fund, New York, 1962.

Mellen, M., and Winston, V. H. *The coal resources of Yugoslavia.* Praeger, New York, 1956.

Moodie, A. E. F. *The Italo-Yugoslav boundary: a study in political geography.* Geo. Philip, London, 1945.

Sugar, P. F. *Industrialization of Bosnia-Hercegovina, 1878–1918.* University of Washington Press, Seattle, 1964.

Tomasevich, J. *Peasants, politics and economic change in Yugoslavia.* Stanford University Press, 1955.

Trouton, R. *Peasant renaissance in Yugoslavia, 1900–1950.* International Library of Sociology and Social Reconstruction. Routledge & Kegan Paul, London, 1952.

Wilkinson, H. R. *Maps and politics: a review of the ethnographic cartography of Macedonia.* Liverpool University Press, 1951.

ARTICLES

Caesar, A. A. L. Yugoslavia: geography and post-war planning. *Transactions and Papers 1962,* Institute of British Geographers 30 (1962) 33–43.

Fisher, J. C. Urban analysis: a case study of Zagreb, Yugoslavia. *Annals of the Association of American Geographers* 53 (1963) 266–84.

Hamilton, F. E. I. Yugoslavia's hydro-electric power industry. *Geography* 48 (1963) 70–3.

Hamilton, F. E. I. The changing pattern of Yugoslavia's manufacturing industry, 1938–1961. *Tijdschrift voor economische en sociale geografie* 54 (1963) 96–106.

Hamilton, F. E. I. Location factors in the Yugoslav iron and steel industry. *Economic Geography* 40 (1964) 46–64.

Hoffman, G. W. Yugoslavia in transition: industrial expansion and resource bases. *Economic Geography* 32 (1956) 294–315.

Johnston, W. B. and Crkvenčić, I. Changing peasant agriculture in North-western Hrvatsko Primorje, Yugoslavia. *Geographical Review* 44 (1954) 352–72.

Milojević, B. Ž. The kingdom of the Serbs, Croats and Slovenes: administrative divisions in relation to natural regions. *Geographical Review* 15 (1925) 70–83.

Wilkinson, H. R. Jugoslav Macedonia in transition. *Geographical Journal* 118 (1952) 389–405.

Wilkinson, H. R. Jugoslav Kosmet: the evolution of a frontier province and its landscape. *Transactions and Papers 1955*, Institute of British Geographers 21 (1955) 171–93.

POLAND

BOOKS

Barbag, J., and Berezowski, S. *Ökonomische Geographie der Volksrepublik Polen*. Deutsche Verlag der Wissenschaften, E. Berlin, 1956.

Beaver, S. H., and Kosiński, L. (eds.). *Problems of applied geography 2* (*Geographia Polonica 3*) (Institute of British Geographers and Institute of Geography, Polish Academy of Sciences). Państwowe Wydawnictwo Naukowe, Warsaw, 1964. (Proceedings of Second Anglo-Polish Geographical Seminar.)

Dziewoński, K., *et al.* (eds.). *Problems of applied geography* (*Geographical Studies 25*, Institute of Geography, Polish Academy of Sciences). Państwowe Wydawnictwo Naukowe, Warsaw, 1961. (Proceedings of First Anglo-Polish Geographical Seminar.)

Francastel, P. (ed.). *Les origines des villes polonaises* (École pratique des hautes études, Sorbonne: 6-ème section, sciences économiques et sociales: congrès et colloques 2). Mouton, Paris and The Hague, 1960.

Halecki, O. (ed.). *Poland* (East-central Europe under the Communists, ed. Byrnes, R. F.). Mid-European Studies Center of the Free Europe Committee Inc. and Atlantic Books, New York and London, 1957.

Halecki, O. *A history of Poland*. Dent, London. Rev. ed., 1961.

Hiscocks, R. *Poland: bridge for the abyss?* Oxford University Press, London, 1963.

*Leslie, R. F. *The Polish question: Poland's place in modern history*. Historical Association, London, 1964.

Leszczycki, S., *et al.* (eds.). *Geographia Polonica 2* (Institute of Geography, Polish Academy of Sciences). Państwowe Wydawnictwo Naukowe, Warsaw, 1964. (Papers for the 20th International Geographical Congress, London.)

Leszczycki, S., *et al.* (eds.). *Geographia Polonica* 7 (Institute of Geography, Polish Academy of Sciences). Państwowe Wydawnictwo Naukowe, Warsaw, 1965. (Papers on economic geography.)

Pounds, N. J. G. *The Upper Silesian Industrial Region* (Indiana University Publications, Slavic and East European Series 11). Bloomington, Indiana, 1958.

*Pounds, N. J. G. *Poland between East and West* (Searchlight Book 22). Van Nostrand, Princeton, N.J., and London, 1964.

Reddaway, W. F., *et al.* (eds.). *The Cambridge history of Poland.* 2 vols. Cambridge University Press, 1941 and 1950.

Taylor, J. *The economic development of Poland, 1919–50.* Cornell University Press, Ithaca, N.Y., 1952.

ARTICLES

Brown, E. H. Glacial and periglacial landscapes in Poland. *Geography* 50 (1965) 31–44.

Cleef, E. van. Danzig and Gdynia. *Geographical Review* 23 (1933) 101–7.

Dobrowolska, M. The morphogenesis of the agrarian landscape of southern Poland. *Geografiska Annaler* 43 (1961) 26–45.

Hamilton, F. E. I. Geological research, planning and economic development in Poland. *Tijdschrift voor economische en sociale geografie* 55 (1964) 252–3.

Hartshorne, R. Geographic and political boundaries in Upper Silesia. *Annals of the Association of American Geographers* 23 (1933) 195–228.

Hartshorne, R. The Upper Silesian Industrial District. *Geographical Review* 24 (1934) 423–38.

Kosiński, L. Warschau. *Geographische Rundschau* 17 (1965) 259–69.

North, G. Poland's population and changing economy. *Geographical Journal* 124 (1958) 517–27.

Osborne, R. H. Changes in the urban population of Poland. *Geography* 44 (1959) 201–4.

Pounds, N. J. G. Nowa Huta: a new Polish iron and steel plant. *Geography* 43 (1958) 54–6.

Pounds, N. J. G. The industrial geography of modern Poland. *Economic Geography* 36 (1960) 231–53.

de Réparaz, G. A. Notes sur les campagnes et la vie rurale du Nord-est polonais. *Revue géographique de l'Est* 5 (1965) 41–75.

Romer, E. Poland: the land and the state. *Geographical Review* 4 (1917) 6–25.

Wrzosek, A., and Kortus, B. Krakau. *Geographische Rundschau* 17 (1965) 270–7.

Zaleska, M. K. Various trends of transformation of Polish rural settlements. *Geografiska Annaler* 43 (1961) 321–8.

RUMANIA

BOOKS

Fischer-Galati, S. (ed.). *Romania* (East-central Europe under the Communists, ed. Byrnes, R. F.). Mid-European Studies Center of the Free

Europe Committee Inc. and Atlantic Books, New York and London, 1957.

Ionescu, G. *Communism in Rumania, 1944–1962.* Auspices of the Royal Institute of International Affairs. Oxford University Press, London, 1965.

Jordan, C. N. *The Romanian oil industry.* New York University Press, 1955.

Morariu, T., *et al.* (eds.). *Receuil d'études géographiques concernant le territoire de la République Populaire Roumaine* (publiées a l'occasion du XIXe Congrès International de Géographie). Academy of the R.P.R., Institute of Geology, Geophysics and Geography, Bucharest, 1960.

Roberts, H. L. *Rumania: political problems of an agrarian state.* Yale University Press, New Haven, 1951.

Seton-Watson, R. W. *A history of the Roumanians from Roman times to the completion of unity.* Cambridge University Press, 1934.

ARTICLES

Poncet, J. Les transformations de l'agriculture roumaine. *Annales de Géographie* 73 (1964) 540–67.

Roubitschek, W. Zur Bevölkerungs- und Agrar-struktur Rumäniens. *Petermanns Geographische Mitteilungen* 104 (1960) 23–32.

Spulber, N. The Danube–Black Sea canal and the Russian control over the Danube. *Economic Geography* 30 (1954) 236–45.

Şandru, I., *et al.* Contribution géographique à la classification des villes de la République Populaire Roumaine. *Annales de Géographie* 72 (1963) 162–85.

(d) Some Recent Geographical Works in the Languages of East-Central Europe

ALBANIA

Geço, P. *Gjeografia ekonomike e Shqipërisë.* Universiteti Shtetëror i Tiranës, Tirana. 2nd ed., 1964.

Geço, P. *Gjeografia fizike e Shqipërisë.* Universiteti Shtetëror i Tiranës, Tirana, 1963.

BULGARIA

Beshkov, A. S., and Valev, E. B. (eds.). *Geografiya na Bŭlgariya, Vol. 2 – Ikonomicheska Geografiya.* Bulgarian Academy of Sciences, Sofia, 1961.

Khristov, T. *Geografiya na promishlenostta v Bŭlgariya.* Nauka i izkustvo, Sofia, 1962. (Industrial geography.)

Penkov, I., and Khristov, T. *Ikonomicheska geografiya na Bŭlgariya.* Nauka i izkustvo, Sofia. 2nd ed., 1964.

CZECHOSLOVAKIA

Blažek, M. *Hospodářský zeměpis Československa.* Orbis, Prague, 1958. (Economic geography.)

Häufler, V., Korčák, J., and Král, V. *Zeměpis Československa.* Czechoslovak Academy of Sciences, Prague, 1960.

Střída, M. (ed.). *Oblasti Československa*. Státní Pedagogické Nakladatelství, Prague, 1963. (Regions.)

Ústřední Správa Geodézie a Kartografie. *Československo* (Series 'Poznáváme svět'). 2nd ed., 1962.

HUNGARY

Bernát, T., and Enyedi, G. *A Magyar mezőgazdaság termelési körzetei. 1–A szántóföldi növénytermelés körzetei.* Mezőgazd asági Kiadó, Budapest, 1961. (Hungarian agricultural regions. 1–Arable regions.)

Bulla, B. *Magyarország természeti földrajza.* Tankönyvkiadó, Budapest, 1962. (Physical geography.)

Radó, S. (ed.). *Magyarország gazdasági földrajza.* Gondolat, Budapest, 1963. (Economic geography.)

JUGOSLAVIA

Blašković, V. *Ekonomska geografija Jugoslavije.* Birozavod, Zagreb, 1962.

Mardešić, P., and Dugački, Z. *Geografski atlas Jugoslavije.* Znanje, Zagreb, 1961.

Melik, A. *Jugoslavija : zemljopisni pregled.* Školska Knjiga, Zagreb, 1952.

Melik, A. *Slovenija : geografski opis, 1.* Izdala Slovenska Matica, Ljubljana, 1963.

POLAND

Kostrowicki, J. *Środowisko geograficzne Polski.* Państwowe Wydawnictwo Naukowe, Warsaw. 2nd ed., 1961. (Geographical environment.)

Lencewicz, S., and Kondracki, J. *Geografia fizyczna Polski.* Państwowe Wydawnictwo Naukowe, Warsaw, 1959.

Loth, J., and Petrażycka, Z. *Geografia gospodarcza Polski.* Polskie Wydawnictwa Gospodarcze, Warsaw, 1960. (Economic geography.)

RUMANIA

Gherasimov, I. P., Herbst, C., *et al.* (eds.). *Monografia geografica a Republicii Populare Romîne.* 2 vols. and 2 map supplements. Academy of R.P.R., Bucharest, 1960.

Haşeganu, M. (ed.). *Geografia economică a R.P.R.* Editura Stiintifică, Bucharest, 1957.

Morariu, T., *et al. Republica Populară Romînă: Noua Geografie a Patriei.* Editura Ştiinţifică, Bucharest, 1964.

(e) **Geographical and Other Scientific Periodicals with either Articles, Summaries or Occasional Issues in English, French or German. Published in East-Central Europe**

BULGARIA

Godishnik na Sofiyskiya Universitet, Biologo-geologo-geografski Fakultet (Annual of Sofia University, Biology-geology-geography Faculty). Sofia.

Izvestiya na Bŭlgarskoto Geografsko Druzhestvo (Bulletin of Bulgarian Geographical Society). Sofia.

Izvestiya na Geografskiya Institut, Bŭlgarska Akademiya na Naukite (Bulletin of Geographical Institute, Bulgarian Academy of Sciences, Section of Geology and Geography). Sofia.

CZECHOSLOVAKIA

Acta Geologica et Geographica Universitatis Comenianae: Geographica (Geological and Geographical Transactions, Comenius University: Geography). Bratislava.

Geografický Časopis (Geographical Review, Geographical Institute of Slovak Academy of Sciences). Bratislava.

Sborník Československé Společnosti Zeměpisné (Journal of Czechoslovak Geographical Society). Prague.

Zprávy geografického ústavu ČSAV (Reports of Geographical Institute of Czechoslovak Academy of Sciences). Opava.

HUNGARY

Acta Geographica Debrecina: Series Geographica, Geologica et Meteorologica (Geographical Transactions, University of Debrecen). Debrecen.

Acta Geographica: Acta Universitatis Szegediensis: Pars Geographica, Scientiarum Naturalium (Geographical Transactions, University of Szeged). Szeged.

Földrajzi Értesítö (Geographical Journal, Geographical Research Institute, Hungarian Academy of Sciences). Budapest.

Földrajzi Közlemények (Geographical Review, Hungarian Geographical Society). Budapest.

Studies in Geography (Geographical Research Institute, Hungarian Academy of Sciences). Budapest. *In English.*

JUGOSLAVIA

Geografski Glasnik (Geographical Bulletin, Geographical Society of Croatia and University of Zagreb). Zagreb.

Geografski Pregled (Geographical Review, Geographical Society of Bosnia and Hercegovina). Sarajevo.

Geografski Razgledi (Geographical Review, Faculty of Natural Sciences, University of Skopje, Geography and Geology Series). Skopje.

Geografski Vestnik (Geographical Bulletin, Geographical Society of Ljubljana). Ljubljana.

Geografski Zbornik—Acta Geographica: Slovenska Akademija Znanosti in Umetnosti, Institut za Geografijo (Geographical Transactions, Institute of Geography, Slovenian Academy of Sciences and Arts). Ljublana. Also Monographs (*Dela*).

Glasnik Srpskog Geografskog Društva (Bulletin of Serbian Geographical Society). Belgrade. Also *Éditions spéciales* and *Mémoires*.

Radovi Geografskog Instituta (Transactions, Institute of Geography, University of Zagreb). Zagreb.

Receuil de Travaux: l'Institut de Géographie 'Jovan Cvijić' (Transactions of Jovan Cvijić Institute of Geography, University of Belgrade). Belgrade. Also Monographs (*Posebna Izdanja*).

Zbornik na Prirodne Nauke of *Matica Srpska* (Proceedings for Natural Sciences of *Matica Srpska*). Novi Sad.

Zbornik Radova (Proceedings of Institute of Geography, Serbian Academy of Sciences and Arts). Belgrade. Also Monographs (*Posebna Izdanja*).

POLAND

Acta Geographica Lodziensia (Łódź Geographical Transactions, Łódź Scientific Society and University of Łódź). Łódź.

Annales Universitatis Mariae Curie-Skłodowska: Sectio Geographia, Geologia, Mineralogia et Petrographia (Annals of Marie Curie-Skłodowska University, Geography . . . Section). Lublin.

Badania Fizjograficzne nad Polską Zachodnią (Physiographical Researches on Western Poland, Poznań Society of Friends of Science, Mathematics and Natural Sciences Section). Poznań.

Czasopismo Geograficzne (Geographical Journal, Polish Geographical Society). Wrocław.

Geographia Polonica (Institute of Geography, Polish Academy of Sciences). Warsaw. *In English.*

Prace Geograficzne (Geographical Studies, Institute of Geography, Polish Academy of Sciences). Warsaw. *Some numbers in English.*

Prace Geograficzne: Zeszyty Naukowe Uniwersytetu Jagiellońskiego (Geographical Studies, Scientific Transactions of Jagiellonian University). Kraków.

Przegląd Geograficzny (Geographical Review, Institute of Geography, Polish Academy of Sciences). Warsaw.

Zeszyty Geograficzne: Wyższa Szkoła Pedagogiczna w Gdańsku (Geographical Transactions, Pedagogical Higher School of Gdańsk). Gdańsk.

Zeszyty Naukowe: Nauki matematyczno-przyrodnicze, Uniwersytet M. Kopernika w Toruniu (Scientific Transactions: Mathematical and Natural Sciences, Copernicus University). Toruń.

RUMANIA

Analele Ştiinţifice ale Universităţii 'Al. I. Cuza': Ştiinţe Naturale, Geologie-Geografie (Scientific Annals of Cuza University: Natural Sciences, Geology-Geography). Iaşi.

Analele Universităţii Bucureşti: Seria Ştiinţele Naturii, Geologie-Geografie (Annals of University of Bucharest, Natural Sciences Series, Geology-Geography). Bucharest.

Comunicări de Geografie (Geographical Communications, Rumanian Society of Natural Sciences and Geography). Bucharest.

Natura: Geografie-Geologie (Rumanian Society of Natural Sciences and Geography). Bucharest.

Revue Roumaine de Géologie, Géophysique et Géographie: Série de Géographie (Institute of Geology, Geophysics and Geography, Rumanian Academy). Bucharest. *In English and French.*

Studia Universitatis Babeş-Bolyai: Series Geologia-Geographia (Studies of Babeş-Bolyai University, Series Geology-Geography). Cluj.

Studii şi Cercetări de Geologie, Geofizică şi Geografie: Seria Geografie – formerly *Probleme de Geografie* (Studies and Researches of Geology, Geophysics and Geography: Geography Series, Institute of Geology, Geophysics and Geography, Rumanian Academy). Bucharest.

(f) Other Periodicals sometimes containing Articles of Geographical Interest

Czechoslovak Economic Papers (Czechoslovak Academy of Sciences, Prague).

East Europe: a review of East European affairs (Free Europe Committee Inc., New York).

Eastern European Economics (International Arts and Sciences Press, New York).

Études Rurales: revue d'histoire, géographie, sociologie et économie des campagnes (Sorbonne, Paris).

International Affairs (Royal Institute of International Affairs, London).

Journal of Central European Affairs (University of Colorado, Boulder).

Journal of International Affairs (Columbia University, New York).

New Hungarian Quarterly (Budapest).

Osteuropa: Zeitschrift für Gegenwartsfragen des Ostens (Stuttgart).

Population (Institut National d'Études Démographiques, Paris).

Problems of Communism (United States Information Agency).

Slavic Review: American Quarterly of Soviet and East European Studies (formerly *American Slavic and East European Review*) (American Association for the Advancement of Slavic Studies Inc., USA).

Slavonic and East European Review (Athlone Press, London, for University of London, School of Slavonic and East European Studies).

Survey: a Journal of Soviet and East European Studies (London).

The World Today (Royal Institute of International Affairs, London).

Yugoslav Survey (Belgrade).

Zeitschrift für Ostforschung: Länder und Völker im Östlicher Mitteleuropa (Marburg).

INDEX

Personal and geographical names have generally been omitted, with the leading exception of those cities and towns mentioned in detail in the text. Figures are indicated by italic page-numbers.

A

Albania:
Bibliography 369, 375
Chief cities and towns *83*, 87-8
Climate 80-2
Dimensions and limits 71
Distribution of population 86-7
Drainage *79*
Energy supplies 85-6
Historical background 73-7
Industry and mining 84-5
Lakes 80
Land-use and farming 82-4
Land-use regions *83*
Metallurgy 86
Mineral exploitation *83*
Minorities 72-3
Physiographic regions *79*
Pronunciation of geographical names 326-8
Relief *78*
Religion 72
Soils 82
The land 77-80
Trade 89-90
Transport 88-9
Vegetation 82
Albanian (language) 26, 71-2, 323
Albanian minorities 50, 185-6
Arad 314
Ausgleich 40, 124, 162, 292

B

Balkan Wars 38, 44, 75, 96, 192, 291
Belgrade *219*, 219-21
Bessarabia *42 et seq.*, 284, 287-9, 292-3
Białystok 269
Brăila 314
Braşov 314-15
Bratislava 153
Brno 153
Bucharest *312*, 312-14
Bucovina 41, 47, 49, 284, 288, 292

Budapest 178-81, *179*
Bulgaria:
Bibliography 369, 375, 376-7
Chemicals 108
Chief cities and towns *112*, 112-15
Climate 103-4
Dimensions and limits 91-2
Distribution of population 111-12
Drainage *100*
Energy supplies 109-10
Engineering 108
Historical background 93-8
Industry and mining 107-11
Land-use and farming 104-7
Land-use regions *105*
Metallurgy 111
Mineral exploitation *109*
Minorities 92
Physiographic regions *100*
Pronunciation of geographical names 328-9
Relief *99*
Soils 104
Textiles 108
The land 98-103
Transport 115-16
Vegetation 104-5
Bulgarian (language) 24, 93, 323
Bydgoszcz 269-70
Bytom 275-6

C

Carpathian Ukraine 45, 48, 120, 127
Chorzów 275-6
Cluj 315
Constanţa 315
Council for Mutual Economic Assistance ('Comecon') 18, 69
Craiova 315
Curzon Line 43, 48, 235
Czech and Slovak (languages) 24, 118, 323

Czechoslovakia:
  Bibliography 370–1, 375–7
  Chemicals 148–9
  Chief cities and towns *151*, 151–4
  Climate 137–8
  Dimensions and limits 118–20,
    131–3, 135–6
  Dissolution (1938–9) *126*
  Distribution of population 150–1
  Drainage *134*
  Energy supplies 143–5
  Engineering 147–8
  Glass 150
  Historical background 120–9
  Industry and mining 143–50
  Land-use and farming 139–42
  Land-use regions *140*
  Metallurgy 145–7
  Mineral exploitation *143*
  Minorities 118–20, 124–5
  Physiographic regions *132*
  Pronunciation of geographical
    names 329–32
  Relief *130*
  Soils 138–9
  Textiles etc. 149–50
  The land 129–37, Bohemia:
    131–5, Moravia: 135,
    Slovakia: 135–7
  Trade 156
  Transport 154–6
  Vegetation 139
Częstochowa 270

D
Danzig (Gdańsk) (Free City) 42
  et seq., 234–5
Debrecen 181
Durrës 88

E
East Prussia 43, 48, 228, 235–7
East-central Europe:
  Administrative-economic regions
    63
  Agriculture 59–61
  Area and population 19
  Boundaries, 1914 and 1938 *39*
  Boundaries, 1941–2 and post 1945
    46
  Chemicals 62–3
  Climate 55
  Coasts 51
  Cretaceous/Tertiary platforms 53
  Cultural background 20–3
  Definition 17–20

Drainage 54–5
Economic geography 56–63
Energy resources 61
Engineering 63
Geographical background 38–70
Glacial deposits 53–4
Hercynian areas 51–2
Industry 61–3
Iron and steel 62
Languages 24–6, 322–4
Mineral resources 61–2
Minorities 25–6, 50–1
Motor vehicles 63
Non-ferrous metals 62
Peoples 17–37
Physical geography 51–5
Political geography 38–51
Population 63–5
Pronunciation of geographical
  names 325–44
Religions 25–9
Socialism 30–7
Statistical tables (see separate
  heading)
Tertiary fold-mountains 52
Tertiary lowlands 53
Trade 68–70
Transport 67–8
Urbanization 65–7
Elbasan 88

F
First World War 40–1
Fiume (Rijeka) 44, 195

G
Galaţi 315–16
Gdańsk (see also Danzig) 274–5
Gdynia 274–5
German (language) 322
German minorities 25–6, 49,
  118–20, 159–60, 162, 185, 286–7
Gliwice 275–6
Gypsies 25–6, 73, 92, 120, 159,
  287

H
Hungarian (Magyar) (language) 26,
  160, 324
Hungarian (Magyar) minorities 28,
  50, 119–20, 158–9, 186, 286–7
Hungary:
  Bibliography 371–2, 376–7
  Boundaries (before and after First
    World War) *158*
  Chemicals 176

Hungary—*continued*
Chief cities and towns *178*,
178–82
Climate 168–9
Dimensions and limits 157–9
Distribution of population 177–8
Drainage *166*
Energy supplies 173–4
Engineering 176
Historical background 159–64
Industry and mining 172–7
Land-use and farming 170–2
Land-use regions *170*
Metallurgy 174–5
Mineral exploitation *173*
Minorities 159
Physiographic regions *165*
Pronunciation of geographical
names 332–4
Relief *165*
Soils 169
Textiles etc. 176
The land 164–8
Trade 183
Transport 182–3
Vegetation 170

I
Iaşi 316

J
Jews 25, 50, 92, 120, 159, 186, 229,
287–8
Jugoslav languages 24, 185–6, 323
Jugoslavia:
Bibliography 372–3, 376–8
Chemicals 216
Chief cities and towns *218*,
219–23
Climate 205–7
Coast 203
Constituent Republics *187*, 188
Dimensions and limits 184
Distribution of population 216–19
Drainage *202*
Energy supplies 211–14
Engineering 215–16
Historical background 189–97
Bosnia and Hercegovina 194–5
Croatia 193–4
Macedonia 190, 192
Montenegro 193
Serbia 190–2
Slovenia 193
Industry and mining 210–16
Karstic features 201–2

Land-use and farming 207–10
Land-use regions *209*
Metallurgy 214–15
Mineral exploitation *212*
Minorities 185–6
Physiographic regions *200*
Pronunciation of geographica
names 335–7
Relief *198*
Religion 25, 186
Soils 206–7
Territorial growth: Jugoslavia,
Montenegro, Serbia *187*
Textiles etc. 216
The land 197–205
Trade 225–6
Transport 223–5
Vegetation 207, 209

K
Katowice 275–6
Korçë 88
Košice 153
Kraków 270–1

L
Ljubljana 221
Łódź 271–2
Lublin 272

M
Marxism 23, 30–7
'Military Frontier' 191, 194
Miskolc 181

N
Novi Sad 221

O
Oder–Neisse line 48–9, 236–7
Oradea 316
Ostrava 154

P
Pécs 181–2
Petroşeni 316
Ploieşti 316
Plovdiv 114–15
Plzeň 154
Poland:
Bibliography 373–4, 376, 378
Boundaries: Partitions and
'Congress' Kingdom *228*
After two World Wars *229*
Central Industrial Region (inter-
war) 235, 250

Poland—*continued*
  Chemicals 262–3
  Chief cities and towns *265*,
    265–78
  Climate 244–5
  Coal output (table) 257
  Coast 244
  'Congress' Kingdom *228*, 233–4
  Dimensions and limits 227–9
  Distribution of population 263–5
  Drainage *241*
  Energy supplies 251–8
  Engineering 261–2
  Foreign trade (table) 281
  Glaciation 242–4
  Historical background 230–8
  Industry and mining 249–63
  Land-use and farming 246–9
  Land-use regions *246*
  Metallurgy 258–61
  Mineral exploitation *251*
  Minorities 229–30
  Partitions 42, *228*, 233
  Physiographic regions *240*
  Pronunciation of geographical
    names 338–41
  Recovered Territories 48, *229*,
    237
  Relief *239*
  Soils 245–6
  Textiles etc. 261
  The land 238–44
  Trade 280–2
  Transport 278–80
  Vegetation 246–7
Polish (language) 24, 229–30, 323
Polish Corridor 43, 45, 235
Pomaks 92
Poznań 272
Prague 151–3, *152*

R
Radom 273
Rijeka (see also Fiume) 221–2
Ruda Śląska 275–6
Rumania:
  Bibliography 374–6, 378–9
  Boundary changes since 1913 *284*
  Chemicals 309
  Chief cities and towns 312–16
  Climate 300–1
  Dimensions and limits 283–5
  Distribution of population
    310–11, *311*
  Drainage *296*
  Energy supplies **305**–7

  Engineering 309
  Historical background 288–94
  Industry and mining 305–10
  Land-use and farming 302–4
  Land-use regions *302*
  Metallurgy 307–8
  Mineral exploitation *306*
  Minorities 286–7
  Physiographic regions *295*
  Pronunciation of geographical
    names 341–4
  Relief *294*
  Soils 301–2
  Textiles etc. 309
  The land 294–300
  Trade 320–1
  Transport 317–20
  Vegetation 302–3
Rumanian (language) 24–6, 285–6,
  322
Ruse 115

S
Sarajevo 222
'Saxons' 287
Second World War 45–7
Shkodër 88
Sibiu 316
Skopje 222
Socialism 30–7
Sofia 112–14, *113*
Sosnowiec 275–6
Soviet Union 17, 19, 20, 23, 31–6
Split 222–3
Statistical tables (data by
    countries):
  Area 346
  Barley 351
  Birth rates 347
  Cement 365
  Coal 354
  Coke 354
  Death rates 347
  Electricity generation 356
  Employment (mining and
    manufacturing) 348
  Fertilizers 361
  Gas, manufactured 355
  Gas, natural 355
  Iron ore 357
  Livestock 352
  Lumber 360
  Maize 350
  Meat 353
  Metal ores 358
  Milk 353

Statistical tables—*continued*
  Motor vehicles 364
  Non-ferrous metals 359
  Oats 351
  Paper 360
  Petroleum 355
  Pig iron 357
  Population 346
  Population density 346
  Potatoes 351
  Production indices 349
  Radio and TV sets 364
  Railway traffic 365
  Rice 351
  Rye 350
  Salt 362
  Soda 362
  Steel (crude) 357
  Sugar 353
  Sulphur 361
  Tobacco 353
  Urbanization 348
  Wheat 350
  Wood-pulp 360
  Yarns and filaments 363
Sudetenland 44–5, 50, 118–19, 128
'Swabians' 287
Szczecin 273
Szeged 182
Szeklers 158, 160, 286–7

T
Timişoara 316
Tirana 87–8
Toruń 273–4
Treaties, agreements, pacts, etc.
  Adrianople 290
  'Anti-Comintern' 32
  'Balkan Entente' 196
  Berlin 38, 75, 96, 192–3, 195, 290
  Brest-Litovsk 41–2
  Craiova 97
  German-Soviet (1939) 32, 45
  Karlovci (Karlowitz) 161, 191, 194

  Kuchuk Kainardzhi 289
  'Little Entente' 43, 125, 163, 196
  Munich 45, 119–20, 126
  Neuilly 97, 196
  North Atlantic 19, 34
  Potsdam 48–9, 119, 236–7
  Požarevac (Passarowitz) 161, 191
  Rapallo 195
  Riga 235
  San Stefano 74–5, 95, 192
  St Germain 195
  Tilsit 233
  Toruń 232
  Trianon 43, 158, 195
  Tripartite 47
  Warsaw 18
  Yalta 48, 236
Trieste 49, 197
Trójmiasto 274–5
Turkish (language) 26, 324
Turkish minorities 25–6, 92, 186

U
Upper Silesia:
  Coalfield *252*, 252–7, *253*, 262
  Conurbation *253*, 275–7

V
Varna 115
Vlachs 72–3, 186, 189, 285
Vlorë 88

W
Wałbrzych 277
Warsaw 265–9, *266*
Western Europe 18–19
World Wars:
  First 40–1
  Second 45–7
Wrocław 277–8

Z
Zabrze 275–6
Zagreb 223